Inside Generic CADD 6, 2nd Edition

Randall S. Newton

Inside Generic CADD 6, 2nd Edition

By Randall S. Newton

Published by:
New Riders Publishing
11711 N. College Ave., Suite 140
Carmel, IN 46032
USA

Copyright © 1992 by New Riders Publishing

Printed in the United States of America 1 2 3 4 5 6 7 8 9 0

Library of Congress Cataloging-in-Publication Data

```
Newton, Randall S., 1955-
    Inside Generic CADD 6, 2nd Edition / Randall S. Newton.
       p.      cm.
    Includes index.
    ISBN 1-56205-067-2 : $29.95
    1. Computer graphics. 2. Generic CADD (Computer program)
  I. Title.
T385.N49    1992                                    92-8551
                                                        CIP
```

Publisher
David P. Ewing

Product Director
B. Rustin Gesner

Acquisitions Editor
Brad Koch

Managing Editor
Tim Huddleston

Editors
Gail S. Burlakoff
Rob Lawson
Rob Tidrow

Technical Editor
Ralph Ferrin

Editorial Secretary
Karen Opal

Book Design
Scott Cook

Production
Brad Chinn
Christine Cook
Laurie Lee
Cindy L. Phipps
Joe Ramon
Kevin Spear
Lisa Wilson

Proofreaders
Paula Carroll
Keith Davenport
Mark Enochs
Audra Hershman
Carrie Keesling
Betty Kish
Laurie Lee
Anne Owen
Linda Seifert
Caroline Roop
Sandra Shay
Kevin Spear
Suzanne Tully
Phil Worthington

Indexed by
Loren Malloy

About the Author

Randall S. Newton is publications manager for Autodesk Retail Products, formerly Generic Software, Inc. Mr. Newton is editor of the award-winning *Autodesk Retail Software News* and has written three other books on the use of Generic CADD. His writing has appeared in many other publications, including *Computer Graphics Report, Plot and Print, San Francisco Chronicle,* and *Columbiana.* Mr. Newton also has served as director of Academic Computing for Heritage College. He and his wife Teresa have six children.

D. FORSYTH

BOX 349

MARTENSVILLE

SOK T20

931-2018

Acknowledgments

New Riders Publishing would like to express its sincere thanks to the following people, for their contributions to this book:

Bob Davison and Gary Kerr, of Autodesk Retail Products, whose invaluable assistance made this project possible.

Ralph Ferrin, of Autodesk Retail Products, for technical editing.

Rusty Gesner, for initial development.

Gail Burlakoff, for taking charge of the many pieces of this project, and for her usual masterful editing.

Rob Lawson and Rob Tidrow, for their assistance in preparing the book for production.

Tim Huddleston, for managing us all.

Randall Newton would like to thank his wife Teresa and his children for their patience and understanding.

Cover illustration appears through the courtesy of Autodesk Retail Products, Bothell, WA.

Trademark Acknowledgments

New Riders Publishing has made every attempt to supply trademark information about company names, products, and services mentioned in this book. Trademarks indicated below were derived from various sources. New Riders Publishing cannot attest to the accuracy of this information.

Trademarks of other products mentioned in this book are held by the companies producing them.

Warning and Disclaimer

This book is designed to provide information about the Generic CADD computer-aided drafting and design program. Every effort has been made to make this book as complete and as accurate as possible, but no warranty or fitness is implied.

The information is provided on an "as is" basis. The author and New Riders Publishing shall have neither liability nor responsibility to any person or entity with respect to any loss or damages arising from the information contained in this book or from the use of the disks or programs that may accompany it.

Contents

3 Graphic Entities 73

6 Labeling and Explaining the Drawing 163

9 Editing Individual Objects 267

20 Macro Programming Language Fundamentals 621

Introduction

ince it began in 1985 as a trim and relatively simple $99 computer-aided drafting program, Generic CADD has grown into a robust, powerful $495 two-dimensional drafting and design tool. With all the program's power and features, users now need more than an afternoon to learn to use Generic CADD. As software complexity increases, so does the task of mastery. *Inside Generic CADD 6*, 2nd Edition, is written with one goal in mind: to enable you to master Generic CADD as easily as possible.

How Inside Generic CADD Is Organized

This book is organized to reveal the features of Generic CADD in a natural sequence. The text starts by showing you how to set up the program to match your needs and the task at hand. Next come introductions to the basics of drawing and editing. (In CADD, "editing" means modifying the objects you have drawn. Editing is as important as drawing in the creation of the final product.)

Explanations of the more powerful features follow, such as dimensioning (placing measurements on the drawing) and the use of attributes (database-type information that you can attach to the objects in a drawing). This book ends by teaching you how to customize Generic CADD to further automate your drafting and design work.

Inside Generic CADD 6, 2nd Edition does not teach you the fundamentals of drafting. Nor does the book show you how to become a contractor, architect, engineer, facilities manager, or designer. In other words, to take full advantage of both Generic CADD and *Inside Generic CADD 6*, 2nd Edition, you need to have an application in mind, and you need to know what end result you are trying to achieve. After all, CADD stands for "Computer-Aided Drafting and Design," not "Computers replAce Drafters and Designers."

Each chapter follows the same format. First, the chapter's topic is introduced so that you can become familiar with new concepts and program features. Each aspect of the topic is covered with an explanation and then an exercise.

The Explanations

Each command or feature covered in *Inside Generic CADD 6*, 2nd Edition, has its own explanation. This section gives you a framework for using the command in the context of your drawing and editing. Many Generic CADD commands share a common logic, which is discussed in the explanation, making it easier for you to learn the new feature by comparing it to one you already have covered.

The Exercises

An exercise follows the introductory explanation, so that you can apply the knowledge gained from the discussion of the command or feature. It would be an unusual person who could simply read a software manual and then immediately be productive. Most users need to work through commands and procedures, so that they can become comfortable gradually. It is one thing for your brain to understand a software command, but quite another for your fingers to become equally knowledgeable. The exercises in *Inside Generic CADD 6*, 2nd Edition, are designed to bridge that gap.

Some of the exercises are progressive. In such exercises, you start a task in the beginning of the chapter and build on it as the chapter progresses. Other chapters contain a series of separate, unique exercises, which concentrate on only one or two commands.

Additional explanations may sometimes follow the exercise, adding new insights that should make more sense once you have finished the exercise.

The exercises consist of three columns. The first column shows the Generic CADD prompt in a special typeface. The middle column tells you how to respond to each prompt. In the second column (as in the normal text), characters you type are shown in **boldface**. If you need only to type something and then press Enter, the exercises just show the input you need to type in bold; you must remember to press Enter after typing the input. The third column describes the results of the actions you take.

When the exercise tells you to click somewhere in the drawing window, press the first mouse button. If you do not have a mouse or digitizer, press Enter to achieve the same effect. Sometimes you are asked to "click" in the menu. Always use the second mouse button to choose items from the menu; use the keyboard's Home key if you do not have a pointing device.

Where the exercise shows Command:, you should see the prompt Enter a command > just below your drawing window. If you see an ellipsis (three periods) in the leftmost column, it means that the book is showing only part of a prompt that displays more than one option. The option listed is the one you need to choose. For example, the Text Spacing command displays six options after you first invoke the command. In an exercise, therefore, you see ...Justification (left) in the exercise if you are going to select justification.

Exercise Format

Prompt	Input	Description
Command	**RE**	Starts the Rectangle command
Enter one corner of rectangle	Click	Starts drawing first corner of rectangle
Enter opposite corner	Move cursor to the opposite corner, then click	Draws the rectangle

The Optional Inside Generic CADD Disk

An optional disk is available from New Riders Publishing to accompany this book. The *Inside Generic CADD Disk* contains finished versions of all the drawings and exercises in this book. If you are not sure whether your work matches the description in the book, or if you want to skip some exercises to concentrate on more difficult material, the completed drawing files can make it easier to follow the exercises in the book. You do not need the disk, however, to benefit from using *Inside Generic CADD*.

How To Use This Book

Just as no two individuals learn in the same way, no two readers of *Inside Generic CADD 6,* 2nd Edition, will use this book in the same way. For this reason, you can use this book in one of two ways.

Using the Book as a Tutorial

Most Generic CADD users who buy this book do so because they want detailed help in learning to use the program. To make sure that as many people as possible benefit, computer jargon is kept to an absolute minimum, and CADD jargon (a necessary evil) is defined on first usage. For example, notice that the terms "editing," "dimensions," and "attributes" already have been defined as they apply to Generic CADD. These definitions will be repeated and expanded later because some people do not read introductions.

Using the Book as a Reference

Some Generic CADD users will buy *Inside Generic CADD 6 ,* 2nd Edition, as a supplementary reference work. To help them, in addition to the Table of Contents and the Index, there is a glossary of CADD vocabulary and two complete listings of Generic CADD commands—one as organized in the Generic CADD menus, and a second one following the organization of this book. If you want to use this book as a supplementary reference, you may need only the explanations and the guides to be successful.

Learning To Use Generic CADD— Two Important Tips

Reading this book and following the exercises are important, but true mastery of Generic CADD requires a little more bravery on your part. To really benefit from *Inside Generic CADD 6*, 2nd Edition, take the following two tips.

1. Learn to use Generic CADD's two-letter commands.

   You can enter Generic CADD commands by using the on-screen menu, and then by typing additional information as needed. But Generic CADD's real power comes from its two-letter commands, such as ZA for Zoom All, RE for Rectangle, and CP for Component Place. Most of the two-letter commands are mnemonic and are easy to remember after you have used them only once or twice.

2. Play with the commands.

   After you work through the exercises in each chapter, erase your work and start fresh on a drawing of your own. The verb "play" is not used here by accident. "Play" implies that you are doing the activity for fun and enjoyment, without pressure or obligation. Play with the commands until you are familiar with them: then put them to work.

What You Need

This book makes a few assumptions about the program in use, the reader's knowledge, and the computer equipment available.

Generic CADD Version 6.0

Inside Generic CADD 6, 2nd Edition, is based on version 6.0 of Generic CADD, published by Autodesk, Inc. This book also works well with Generic CADD version 5.0, which was sold between September 1990 and January 1992. With version 5.0, the Generic CADD developers substantially reworked the basic logic of how the program should be used; version 6.0 adds many new features but leaves the basic structure of the program untouched.

This book is not intended to be used with Generic CADD Level 3 or Generic CADD version 3.0. Because the differences between those versions and the current product are so great, one book cannot cover them all. If you own one of these early versions of Generic CADD, you should consider purchasing an update directly from Autodesk Retail Products (the new name of Generic Software, Inc.).

MS-DOS

Whereas this book assumes no prior knowledge of Generic CADD or a specific method of drafting, you need a basic working knowledge of DOS, the computer's operating system. In particular, you should know the following:

- What directories and subdirectories are, and how to move between them

- What files are, and how to copy or delete them

- How to start programs from the DOS prompt

In addition, you need to know how to use a word processor or text editor to create ASCII text files. This book also refers to database-management programs and spreadsheets, but you do not need to know how to use a particular database or spreadsheet program.

Hardware

Generic CADD requires a computer with a minimum 640K (kilo-bytes) of RAM, a hard disk, and a video display device capable of showing graphics. Unlike most powerful CADD programs, Generic CADD still runs on a PC or an XT that otherwise meets these requirements. (As of this writing, for example, the DOS version of AutoCAD Release 11 requires an AT-compatible computer with a 80386 processor. Autodesk has developed a version of AutoCAD Release 11 that supports 80286 processors, but Autodesk does not plan to support the use of AutoCAD on PC- and XT-level computers.)

In addition to the hardware required by Generic CADD, this book assumes that you have a mouse or a digitizer for use as a pointing device. Although you can use Generic CADD without a pointing device, it is not a productive use of one's time. The most efficient way to use Generic CADD is to combine the two-letter commands with a pointing device. (If you just bought Generic CADD and you need to buy a mouse, be sure to get one with three buttons.)

Summary

If you are standing in the aisle of a bookstore reading this introduction, it's decision time. This book will help you become comfortable and productive with Generic CADD version 6. It offers explanations in real English and exercises that are practical, yet easy to follow. This book will serve you now as you learn Generic CADD, and later when you need to review a command or feature.

Getting Started

This chapter covers the basics of getting Generic CADD up and running on your computer. It discusses the computer hardware you need and the pitfalls of hardware incompatibility. The installation of Generic CADD on your computer also is covered. Then the chapter introduces the Generic CADD display screen and explains how to execute commands. The number one question of new users—"What if I make a mistake?"—is answered. (The quick answer, of course, is "Do not worry about it.") The basics of loading and saving drawings are explained.

Just as you use Generic CADD to design things, the way Generic CADD operates is by design. From the start, the book refers to the logic behind the operation of Generic CADD. This "open architecture" approach makes it easier for you to understand commands as they are presented and even to anticipate correctly how new features work.

Setting Up Generic CADD

If you have not already done so, take the time right now to install your copy of Generic CADD on your computer. If you have purchased additional hardware for your system to use with Generic CADD, such as a mouse, a hard drive, or a new video display system, install it first and make sure it is working properly.

Although installation of Generic CADD is straightforward, the program has to work with literally hundreds of possible combinations of *peripheral devices* (the pieces of equipment one connects to the computer). Despite the fact that the IBM clone is an industry "standard," incompatibility between devices sometimes happens.

Generic CADD has an uncanny capability for rooting out the otherwise hidden incompatibilities between devices. One of the computers used to write this book is an example. By CADD standards, the machine was modest: a 12-MHz AT-compatible with a 40M hard drive, one 1.2M floppy drive, 640K of RAM memory on the motherboard, and another 2M of RAM memory on an add-in board. The system also sported one serial port, one parallel printing port on a separate card, a 16-bit VGA video adapter board, a fax/modem board, and a math coprocessor. The version of MS-DOS used was 3.3.

The system was assembled and seemed to work fine for word processing and telecommunications; then Generic CADD was installed. At first Generic CADD could not complete the installation process. Several hours of analysis later, it turned out that the file COMMAND.COM, part of MS-DOS 3.3, had been tampered with. (The tip-off was the size of the file; it did not match that of other versions of MS-DOS or PC-DOS 3.3.) After the DOS was replaced, the Generic CADD installation program ran through to completion.

Next, the CADD program itself would not run. An error message appeared when **CADD** was typed at the DOS prompt. Pressing any key returned the computer to the DOS prompt. Several additional hours of analysis revealed that the fax/modem board, the parallel printer port card, the serial port/RAM card, and the math coprocessor were all stepping on each other's toes. (The problem involved IRQ interrupts and other internal entanglements.) Remove any one of the devices, and CADD would operate just fine. But with all of the devices installed, CADD balked. Because telecommunications and use of the printer were essential, and the mouse was connected to the serial port, the math coprocessor was sacrificed for the cause of IRQ-interrupt peace. Now CADD runs without a hitch, albeit a little slowly without the math coprocessor.

No bug in Generic CADD caused this unfortunate string of events—the problems lay elsewhere. Generic CADD was just the messenger of bad tidings. If the conflict had not been rooted out by Generic CADD, sooner or later this problem would have erupted, probably in the middle of some crucial task.

 Buying a new computer? Make sure that it runs Generic CADD with all devices installed before you buy it.

Hardware conflicts are not the only problems Generic CADD has brought to the surface. Several Generic CADD users have called to thank the publisher because the program helped them discover viruses lurking in their computers. In each case, CADD had stopped working; investigating why led to discovery of the viruses. Although such timely discoveries may have saved each user hundreds of dollars, Autodesk has no plans to advertise Generic CADD as a virus catcher.

Installing Generic CADD

The minimum hardware requirements for Generic CADD are a 100 percent IBM-compatible computer with 640K of RAM memory, one hard drive and one floppy drive, DOS version 3.0 or later, and a video graphics display adapter. These items should be considered absolute minimums; CADD performance improves dramatically when using better hardware. When faster, more current hardware is used, a word processor receives a modest gain. CADD, on the other hand, looks and behaves like a completely new program. If you want to boost performance by buying new equipment, do so in the following order (the higher on the list, the more benefit to CADD performance):

1. Math coprocessor

2. Faster CPU with matching math coprocessor

3. Faster, larger hard drive

4. Faster high-resolution video display adapter

5. More RAM

Despite the power-user advantages of better hardware, one of the beauties of Generic CADD is that it runs on a very modest computer. An XT-compatible computer with 640K of RAM, a 20M hard drive, one floppy drive, a math coprocessor, and a monochrome graphics display adapter and monitor can be purchased new for less than $700 (a used system for half that). Add $495 (suggested retail price) for Generic CADD, and you have a great introductory drafting station, ideal for students, moonlighters, or anyone on a budget who wants to use a professional CADD program.

 By the way, an XT with a math coprocessor runs Generic CADD faster than an AT without a math coprocessor.

Whether your computer system is state-of-the-art or state-of-the-budget, installation of Generic CADD should go smoothly. Before you begin, make sure you know what devices are installed in the computer, how much RAM you have, and whether any of that memory is being used as EMS memory. For safety's sake, make backup copies of the Generic CADD disks before you start, and use the backups for installation.

Also, before you start, fill out and mail the registration card. Registering your purchase of Generic CADD makes you eligible for unrestricted, free technical support (you pay for the phone call). Autodesk Retail's technical support staff members are extremely knowledgeable and helpful. You can rely on them (but they are popular and hard to reach). The best times to get through are between 4 and 6 p.m. Pacific time (weekdays) and between 9 a.m. and noon Pacific time on Saturdays. Registering your purchase of Generic CADD also puts you on the mailing list to receive *Autodesk Retail Software News*, an award-winning 16-page bimonthly tabloid filled with technical tips, user profiles, new product announcements, CADD upgrade notices, and letters from users.

For now, follow the program's recommendations for the creation of directories on the hard drive. If you are installing Generic CADD on the C drive, the installation program creates a directory called CADD6 and five subdirectories: CMP, for components; GCD, for drawing files; FNT, for fonts; HCH, for hatch pattern files; and MCR, for macros (see fig. 1.1).

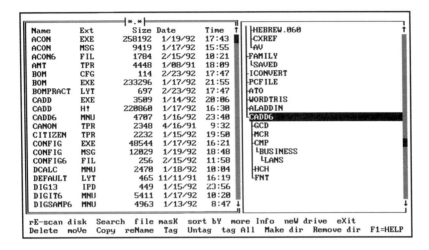

Figure 1.1:

A typical DOS directory with Generic CADD installed.

After you approve or change the choices for hard drives, a screen appears that enables you to choose which parts of the program you want to copy. If room on your hard drive is limited, you may prefer not to copy most of the components onto your hard drive. To be able to follow the discussions in this book, you should install the following parts of the program:

- Core files (This is CADD—you cannot do anything without these.)

- AutoCAD Import/Export

- Bill of Material Program

- Fillable outline fonts

- AutoCAD style fonts

- Business components

- Sample drawings and template drawings

If your system has enough room for all parts of Generic CADD, just select Yes for the top item—all files. If you plan to install selected parts only, use the arrow keys to move the white bar up and down, and press the spacebar to switch from Yes to No. Press Enter when you are ready for CADD to act on your choices.

If you have used older versions of Generic CADD, you notice that the directory for drawings has a new name. Because version 6.0 of Generic CADD can import AutoCAD drawings directly, Generic CADD drawings are now saved with the extension GCD (for Generic CADD Drawing). Before version 6.0, both programs used DWG as the extension name for drawings.

After the installation process is complete, the first screen you see (the Current Configuration screen) lists your video adapter and mouse. Even if these seem incorrect, press Enter. (If you exit at this point, you have to start all over again.) The next screen lists four configuration options (see fig. 1.2).

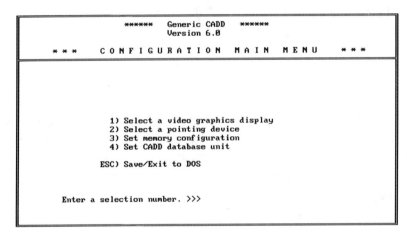

Figure 1.2:

The configuration main menu screen.

You must respond to the first two options to complete installation of Generic CADD. Press the number of the option you want to set, and then press Enter.

For the video graphics display option, press 1, and then Enter. You are asked if you want to enable the Image Save/Load feature. The text on the screen mentions only that images can be saved in GX2 format, but the Image Save/Load feature also is used to save CADD drawings in a variety of formats popular in desktop publishing and paint-and-draw software. If you intend to save drawings as PCX or TIF files, for example, you need to enable this option. Type **Y** or **N**, according to your needs. Enabling this option reduces by 10K the RAM available for your drawings.

After you choose the Image Save/Load feature, a list of video boards supported by Generic CADD is displayed on-screen. The entire list is several screens long; if you do not see your video card on the first screen, press Enter to move screen by screen until you find your card.

For most standard VGA cards, the IBM VGA option is the best choice.

CADD programs are extremely demanding of a video board's capabilities, and the mark of a conscientious video board manu-facturer is the distribution of specialty video drivers for various CADD programs, including Generic CADD. (A *video driver* is a software program that acts as the go-between for the program and the video board.)

If your video display device is CGA-compatible or MCGA-compatible, you do not have color when you use Generic CADD. This is not a bug in CADD, but a limitation of the video display device. Unless CGA and MCGA systems are used in monochrome mode, they cannot access enough memory to display CADD adequately.

If you have an EGA monitor and adapter card, you may be able to achieve higher resolution with Generic CADD than you can with most programs. Refer to the index of your *Generic CADD 6.0 User's Guide* for the location of information about achieving higher resolution for EGA devices.

Depending on the video device you select, you may be asked additional questions—strictly a matter of personal preference—about the display.

After selecting the video display option that best matches your hardware, you need to select a pointing device; press 2, and then Enter, at the configuration screen.

If you have a mouse, it has either two or three buttons. (If you have yet to buy a mouse, be sure to get one with three buttons. Generic CADD can take advantage of all three buttons, even though most programs on the market use only two.) If you have a two-button mouse, you still can do all the things you could with the third button, by holding down Shift and pressing the first button (the one on the left).

The MOUSE.COM driver option that matches your mouse is the best option to select in most cases. For this selection to work, you must use the MOUSE.COM program that came with your mouse. It must be loaded before you use Generic CADD. The best approach is to have your AUTOEXEC.BAT file load MOUSE.COM into memory when your computer starts up. Refer to your DOS manual if you need help in creating an AUTOEXEC.BAT file.

Option 3 enables you to customize Generic CADD's use of the memory in your computer. The seven memory-related options are shown in figure 1.3.

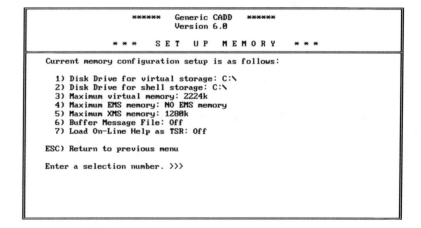

Figure 1.3:

The memory configuration screen.

The first option enables you to set which drive you want Generic CADD's virtual-memory capability to use. Virtual memory is a "trick" that lets CADD use a portion of the hard drive as if it were random-access memory (RAM). When virtual memory is in operation, your drawings can take more memory than the amount of RAM in your computer. (This one feature, introduced in version 5.0, was reason enough for many hard-core Generic CADD users to upgrade.) If you do not change the setting, CADD uses the ROOT directory as the location of the virtual memory file. If you have another hard drive (D, for example) that has more room available than your C drive, you may want to have the virtual memory file created on that drive. The file created by the virtual memory function is temporary; it is erased when you exit CADD.

The second option sets the drive in which Generic CADD stores a "placeholder" file when you shell out of CADD. (When you *shell out*, you freeze the execution of CADD and run another program. After you finish using the other program, you can return to CADD and continue as though you had never left.) Unless you have more room on another drive, it is best to leave this option as-is. Like the virtual memory file, the file created by the shell routine is temporary; it is erased when you close Generic CADD.

Option 3 enables you to stipulate how much room to devote to virtual memory. When CADD starts up, it scans the hard drive and determines how much room is available for virtual memory. As you can see from figure 1.4, you may choose to use all or only a percentage of the amount of room available.

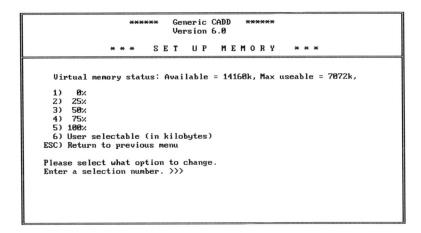

Figure 1.4:

Virtual memory size options.

Options 4 and 5 (refer to fig. 1.3) need to be considered together. Option 4 controls the amount of EMS (expanded) memory used by Generic CADD, and option 5 controls the amount of XMS (extended) memory used by CADD. If your computer has more than 640K of RAM, one or both of these memory-management systems may be in operation.

EMS also is known as the *LIM specification*. (LIM stands for Lotus Intel Microsoft, the three companies that developed the EMS standard.) If EMS is in operation in your computer, either an EMS memory board is installed in your computer or you are running a special program that converts RAM above 640K to EMS. The only way a PC-class or XT-class computer can use more than 640K of memory is with EMS.

Extended memory (XMS) is any memory beyond 640K in an 80286-, 80386-, or 80486-based computer. Most programs that use conventional memory are unable to recognize any memory higher than 640K; special instructions are required to access this memory because the early versions of DOS did not make allowance for any memory above 640K. Generic CADD can use extended memory if you have an extended-memory manager running when you install CADD. Common extended-memory managers are HIMEM.SYS, which ships with DOS 5.0 and Windows 3, and QEMM.SYS, which ships with DesqView. Other commercial and shareware extended-memory managers also are available.

If you have a choice, devote your memory resources to XMS. Generic CADD runs faster in XMS than in EMS, and the XMS memory manager requires less memory to operate. With XMS, as with virtual memory, you may choose to use a percentage of the available memory or set a specific size in kilobytes.

If you have both EMS and XMS running in your computer, and CONFIG reports no available XMS memory, the problem is that CADD looks first for EMS, then looks to see whether there is any XMS memory. Some memory managers (including QEMM.SYS) control both EMS and XMS. When CADD makes a query to the management program for EMS, the memory manager responds by providing all available memory as EMS. Then when CADD queries the memory manager for XMS, the response is that none is available. To overcome this (since EMS is slower than XMS), use the CADD configuration program to set EMS memory to zero.

Looking for EMS first is not an example of poor design on the part of Generic CADD's programmers. Because some dual memory managers cannot allocate EMS properly after you ask for XMS, CADD asks for EMS first (even though it is slower) to prevent memory allocation errors.

Installing a disk cache program is a good way to increase Generic CADD's operating speed. You should allocate between 750K and 1024K of memory for best results. Make sure that the disk cache program is current with the technology of the version of SMARTDRV.SYS that ships with DOS 5; older disk cache programs have been known to misbehave occasionally.

If you used an EMS simulation program with earlier versions of Generic CADD, it may be accessing the hard drive to create the extra memory. In this case, disable the EMS simulator and devote those resources to CADD's virtual memory, which is much faster than any EMS simulator on the market for use with Generic CADD.

The last option is a toggle that controls whether Generic CADD's on-line help is loaded into the computer's memory as a TSR (terminate-and-stay-resident) program. If left off, the program is loaded from the hard drive when requested. Most CADD users should not operate the Help program as a TSR. It takes up 51K of RAM, a rather large amount. Running as a TSR, the Help program can create a memory-shortage problem for CADD. You should not consider running Help as a TSR unless you have more than 600K of free RAM in conventional memory before you start Generic CADD. (Depending on which version of DOS you have, you can use CHKDSK or MEM to see how much conventional memory is available on your system.) Even then, consider utilizing Help in TSR mode only if your hard drive is really slow, and you plan to use the Help program often. Having a disk cache gives you most of the speed you gain by having Help loaded as a TSR, but without the loss of conventional memory for Generic CADD.

After you finish installing Generic CADD, but before you use it for the first time, be sure to read the contents of two text files in the \CADD6 directory: READ.ME (or possibly README.1ST or README.DOC) and HARDWARE.DOC. These two files describe changes made to the program after the manual was written; these files are updated regularly. Much of the material, especially in HARDWARE.DOC, is highly technical and applies to only a few CADD users; nevertheless, skim the material in case any of the information is relevant to your situation.

After you finish setting all the memory configurations, press the Escape key until you reach the main configuration screen again. The last item (number 4 in fig. 1.2) concerns the units used by the CADD database. This setting controls how Generic CADD stores data in files. Unless you need to work in metric units, or your work is in a field such as surveying, it is best to leave the Units setting in Inches, the default setting. If you switch back and forth between various units using this setting, CADD must recalculate all units used in the drawing file, and round-off errors are sure to occur. As you will see, setting the units for the database does not affect the display of distances on-screen.

After all the configuration options have been set, press the Escape key (referred to from now on as Esc). A prompt that asks Do you wish to keep the changes? (Y,N) >> is displayed. If you are satisfied, press **Y**; if you need to make a change or double-check a setting, press **N** and go back to the item you want to review. You do not need to press Enter after pressing **Y** or **N**.

After you press **Y**, the configuration program asks whether you want Generic CADD to update your AUTOEXEC.BAT file. If you say yes, it adds to your AUTOEXEC.BAT file two lines that help the program use your video display to best advantage. If you say no, you need to add these lines yourself. Although protecting your AUTOEXEC.BAT file zealously is wise, letting Generic CADD change this file is safe. Just as a precaution, the existing AUTOEXEC.BAT file is automatically renamed as AUTOEXEC.BAK and saved separately before a new AUTOEXEC.BAT is created.

Creating a Subdirectory for Exercises

After completing the installation and configuration of Generic CADD, you need to create a subdirectory on your hard drive, one in which you will save the drawings you create while using *Inside Generic CADD 6*, 2nd Edition.

After the configuration program ends, the DOS prompt should show that you are in the CADD6 directory (C:\CADD6>). Type the following line:

```
md IGC-GCD
```

DOS creates a new subdirectory, called IGC-GCD, in the CADD6 directory (see fig. 1.5).

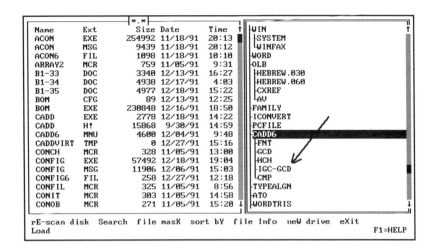

Installing the Optional Inside Generic CADD 6, 2nd Edition Disk

If you purchased the optional disk that accompanies this book, copy its contents to this new directory. From the C:\CADD6\ IGC-GCD directory prompt, enter the following:

```
COPY A:*.*
```

If you placed the floppy in your B drive, substitute B: for A: in the preceding line.

Communicating with Generic CADD

You are ready to start Generic CADD and take a look at how it operates. At the DOS prompt of the \CADD6 directory, type:

```
CADD
```

The first time you use CADD, default settings for the plotter and printer are in effect. You must configure for your particular output devices from within Generic CADD. Chapter 8 covers configuring for your printer or plotter.

If all the settings are fine, press Enter to continue.

Understanding Informational Screen Displays

Although some CADD programs start off with a full screen of menus, Generic CADD takes you straight to the drawing screen, which is home base for everything you do in Generic CADD. You can leave this screen to print or plot, or to search the hard drive for files, but you always return to this screen. Figure 1.6 shows the following parts of the drawing screen:

1. The drawing window
2. The drawing cursor
3. The coordinate display
4. The ROOT menu
5. The menu bar
6. The prompt line
7. The status lines

The largest portion of the screen is the drawing window, where you create and edit your drawings. The crossed lines in the drawing window form the drawing cursor, which responds when you move the pointing device or the arrow keys. (From now on, the drawing cursor is referred to as the cursor.)

At the top of the screen is the coordinate display, item 3 in figure 1.6. Using a Cartesian coordinate grid as a frame of reference, the coordinate display gives a continuous readout of the cursor's location. You learn more about the coordinate display when the concept of real scale is discussed, a little later in this chapter.

Using Generic CADD's Menus

Along the right side of the screen is the ROOT menu, item 4 in figure 1.6. Each item on this menu is the topic of one or more

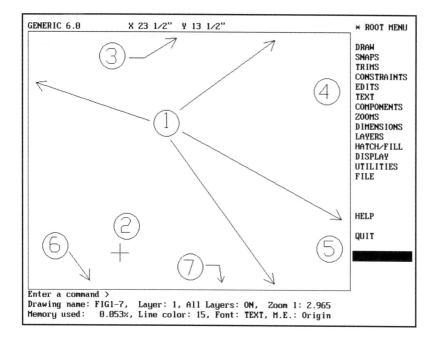

Figure 1.6:

The Generic CADD drawing screen.

submenus. To select an item from the ROOT menu, move the pointing device or press an up-arrow or down-arrow key. The menu bar (item 5 in fig. 1.6) moves as the cursor moves. When the menu bar is on the item you want, press the second pointer button or the Home key on the keyboard. To return to this menu from any submenu, select the ROOT MENU option, always found at the bottom of any submenu. If you just want to look at the different submenus without selecting commands, press PgUp or PgDn on the keyboard. The Generic CADD menu is like a belt on rollers: if you move through it far enough, you return to the beginning.

When configuring Generic CADD, you had the option of increasing the amount of memory reserved for the menu. Now, you do not need any more memory than is already allocated. If you customize the menu or add symbol library menus later, however, you may need to increase the memory allocated to the menu. You learn more about this topic in the discussion of menu customization, in Chapter 19.

The menu that appears when you first start Generic CADD is one of several available for the program. Some of the others are for specific tasks and are discussed in other chapters. On one menu, the command names are abbreviated so that the two-letter commands are visible on-screen. If you want to change the on-screen menu to the one that lists the two-letter commands, follow these steps:

1. With the ROOT menu visible on-screen, move the menu bar to FILE.

2. Press the second mouse button (or Home).

3. Move the menu bar onto MENUS.

4. Press the second mouse button (or Home).

5. Move the menu bar onto New Menu.

6. Press the second mouse button (or Home).

7. Move the menu bar onto HELP6.

8. Press the second mouse button (or Home).

9. Move the menu bar onto ROOT MENU.

10. Press the second mouse button (or Home).

You can now see the two-letter abbreviation for each command as you use the menus.

Using Two-Letter Drawing Commands

Although it is possible to execute most commands in Generic CADD by using the menu, experienced CADD users often find that using Generic CADD's two-letter commands is faster. When you type a two-letter command, it appears on the prompt line. As you can see from figure 1.6, the prompt line and the status lines (items 6 and 7, respectively) are at the bottom of the screen. If Generic CADD requires any additional information from you to complete the command, the prompt and status lines display the request.

Almost all of the two-letter commands are mnemonic (LI for Line, ZP for Zoom Previous), which makes them easy to learn. As new features are described, the book gives you the two-letter commands. And they are now listed in the CADD menu if you loaded the HELP6 menu, following the steps listed earlier.

Below the prompt line are the two status lines. When you are not in the middle of executing a command, these lines display the status of a variety of settings. If you have given a name to the drawing you are working on or if you have loaded a drawing from disk, the name appears after Drawing Name. The number after Layer refers to the drawing layer in use. Think of layers as sheets of clear plastic that you can draw on, adding or removing sheets at will. Generic CADD drawings can be divided into as many as 256 layers (numbered 0 through 255). The efficient use of layers is discussed in Chapter 2 and elsewhere.

The next item in the first status line shows the status of the All Layers Edit command. If All Layers is on, you can edit any item that appears on-screen. If All Layers is off, only items on the current layer can be edited; items on other visible layers may not be edited. As a new Generic CADD user, you may have difficulty imagining when you would need such a feature, but it comes in handy quite often.

After All Layers is the status display of the scale of the drawing, listed as the Zoom. For a description of the Zoom Status, see the discussion of real scale, later in this chapter.

The second status line starts with a display of the amount of memory used. Unless you have very little virtual memory available, you do not need to worry about the amount of memory available until you start to develop complicated drawings. Even then, the virtual memory feature of CADD generally ensures plenty of space for even the most complicated drawings.

Depending on your video display hardware, you have either 16 or 256 colors available. (On monochrome displays, you may select from the 16 basic line colors, but they all look the same on your screen.) The Line Color status shows you the number of the currently selected line color, displaying the number in the color it represents. The next item, Font, shows what style of font has been selected. The color of the font name is the color that is used to place text in the drawing. It can be adjusted to any available color and does not have to be the same as the line color.

The last item, the cryptic M.E., shows the method of manual entry in effect. In manual entry, you use the keyboard to enter coordinates, distances, and angles instead of drawing them with the pointing device. Three Manual Entry settings are possible: Origin, Relative, and Basepoint. Chapter 2 introduces you to these settings, and a full discussion of these options is presented in Chapter 5. Mice and digitizers are wonderfully useful drawing tools, but sometimes it is more efficient to enter the length, location, or angle of an object from the keyboard.

Drawing in Real Scale

If you have been trained in drafting procedure, you are at home with the concept of drawing scale, and you know its importance when you draft manually. But CADD changes the rules, making drawing scale a seldom-considered aspect of the drawing process. To understand why, consider the following example.

A football field is 100 yards long and 50 yards wide. If you want to draw it on a piece of paper, you need to calculate at what scale to draw it so that it is an accurate representation. If you choose to draw so that 1" on the paper represents 12" of real football field, you need a piece of paper 300" wide. Setting 1" on paper equal to 36" (one yard) requires a page 100" wide. Setting the scale at 1" on paper equal to 360" (10 yards) of real football field requires a page 10" wide. Finally—a manageable size to work with. To draw the first side line, you calculate the scale (100 yards divided by 10 equals 10 inches on paper) and draw the line.

Now consider the same project, done in Generic CADD. Because the sidelines are 100 yards long, in real life, the first thing to do in CADD is to draw a line 100 yards long—no calculating scale, no worrying about making it fit. Just draw the line.

No—a step was not skipped. When drawing in CADD, you always draw the real-world size of an object. The drawing window is not a fixed size like the sheet of paper: it is a viewport, a window into a flat, two-dimensional universe that can be as big or as small as anything in our three-dimensional world.

Take a moment to look out the nearest window. Can you see things larger than the pane of glass in front of you? Of course you can, because of the distances involved. CADD, being limited to two dimensions, does not have distance, but it offers a good substitute: the Zoom factor. If you are drawing the drain in a sink, you can set the screen to have the drain fill the screen. You can then adjust the view and have the sink, the kitchen, or even the entire house fill the screen just as easily as the drain filled the screen. Like a television camera at a baseball game that provides a close-up view of the batter even though the camera sits in center field, Generic CADD can easily "zoom" to any required viewpoint.

Throughout the book, exercises have the following format. The first column shows the Generic CADD prompt or message. (Note that the on-screen prompt Enter a command > is shortened here to Command.) The center column, labeled Input, is what you type or otherwise execute, and the third column describes what happens. Follow these steps to draw the outline of a football field at real scale, using manual (keyboard) entry. Figure 1.7 shows the drawing after entering the first corner of the rectangle.

Drawing a Football Field

Prompt	Input	Description
Command	**MO**	Sets Manual Entry to Origin
Command	**RE**	Invokes Rectangle command
Enter one corner of the rectangle	**0,0**	Starts one corner of the rectangle at coordinate location X 0" Y 0" (see fig. 1.7)
Enter opposite corner	**300',162'**	Sets the opposite corner of rectangle at X 300", Y 162", and draws four lines of the rectangle (see fig. 1.8)
Command	**ZA**	Zoom All command redraws the screen to view rectangle (see fig. 1.9)

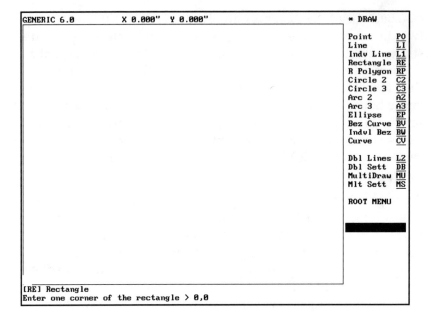

Figure 1.7:

Entering the first corner of the rectangle.

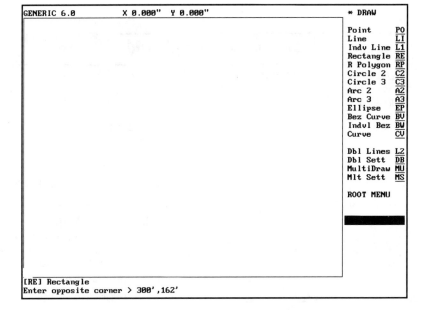

Figure 1.8:

Entering the opposite corner of the rectangle.

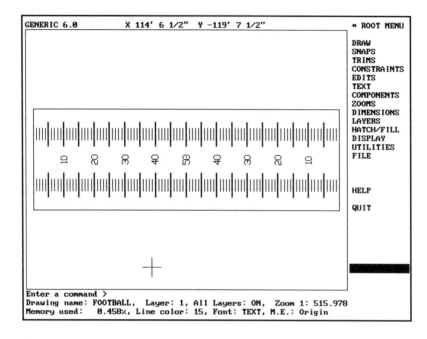

```
GENERIC 6.0        X 114' 6 1/2"  Y -119' 7 1/2"        * ROOT MENU

                                                       DRAW
                                                       SNAPS
                                                       TRIMS
                                                       CONSTRAINTS
                                                       EDITS
                                                       TEXT
                                                       COMPONENTS
                                                       ZOOMS
                                                       DIMENSIONS
                                                       LAYERS
                                                       HATCH/FILL
                                                       DISPLAY
                                                       UTILITIES
                                                       FILE


                                                       HELP

                                                       QUIT


        +

Enter a command >
Drawing name: FOOTBALL,  Layer: 1, All Layers: ON,  Zoom 1: 515.978
Memory used:    0.458%, Line color: 15, Font: TEXT, M.E.: Origin
```

Figure 1.9:

The completed rectangle, with field marks added.

In the preceding exercise, you drew two lines that for all practical purposes are each 100 yards long and two more lines that are 53 1/3 yards long to represent the dimensions of a football field. In the database CADD creates for storing drawing data, these lines are listed as being those dimensions. No consideration is given to scale. When you type **ZA** for Zoom All, Generic CADD automatically adjusts the view on the monitor so that you can see the entire football field.

If you are in the habit of drawing everything to scale from years of manual drafting, try to relax and enjoy the new freedom of drawing to real scale. But do not worry that scale has been completely forgotten. You return to it when you print your drawings because the drawings you create in Generic CADD often need to be placed on paper at specific scales.

Handling Errors

Now that you have broken the ice and have actually drawn something in Generic CADD, feel free to put your hand on the mouse or the arrow keys (the poor man's mouse, they say) and doodle. Move the cursor and press the first button on the mouse (or the Enter key) to start a line automatically. Move the cursor again and press the first button (or Enter) again to finish the line. Note that CADD continues, drawing another line. If you want to disconnect from the last point you placed on-screen, press Esc or move the menu bar to a blank menu line and press the second mouse button. Try drawing lines all over the football field.

All you need for this risk-free exercise is a willingness to draw, but now is a good time to become familiar with four commands that get you out of a jam if you make a mistake in future exercises.

Undo (OO)

Typing **OO** at the prompt summons the Undo command (often called the Oops! command). This command does not erase but actually restores the drawing as it was before your last action. If you draw a line and then type **OO**, Generic CADD removes the line. This seems simple enough, but Undo is much more powerful than just simple line removal. You could execute a complicated sequence of commands that had been saved as a macro on a function key, only to realize that you started the command at the wrong location. Type **OO** (repeating it for each step of the macro, up to 25 steps) and you are back where you started before the macro was executed. Generic CADD remembers your actions as if they were placed on a list, keystroke by keystroke, mouse click by mouse click. When you undo something, CADD refers to the list, removes the last step from the drawing, and restores the drawing to its status before the command was executed originally.

Redo (UU)

Yes, sometimes even using the Undo command can be a mistake. That is why Generic CADD offers its opposite, Redo. If you type **OO**, only to say "Oops!" because of it, type **UU** and breathe a sigh of relief.

Although Undo and Redo are not infinitely powerful, each can reach back a total of 25 actions, which can represent a great deal of drawing and editing. If you use the Pack Data, Definition Unload, Window Text, or Drawing Remove commands, Generic CADD's undo/redo list is wiped clean.

Erase Last (EL)

Less powerful than Undo, Erase Last is handy nonetheless. By typing **EL** at the prompt (or selecting it from the EDITS menu), you erase the last object drawn on the screen. If you use RE to draw a rectangle, and then type **EL**, only the fourth line of the rectangle is erased because the rectangle is made of four objects (straight lines, in this case).

UnErase (UE)

Used Erase Last by mistake, did you? Do not fret. Just type **UE** or select UnErase from the EDITS menu, and all is forgiven. Erase Last and UnErase can be used repeatedly to "undraw" or redraw your work. They are limited to removing or replacing simple objects. If you perform a more complicated editing command, and need to reverse the action, use Undo or Redo.

Using On-line Help (Alt-H)

New to version 6 of Generic CADD is an on-line help program called, appropriately enough, Help. It may be summoned whenever you are using Generic CADD; just press the Alt key and type **H**. If you press Alt-H when CADD is waiting for a command, the Help program opens at an alphabetical menu screen (see fig. 1.10), which you may scroll through to find information on any command. If you press Alt-H while in the middle of executing a CADD command, Help opens at a description of the task you are currently trying to perform.

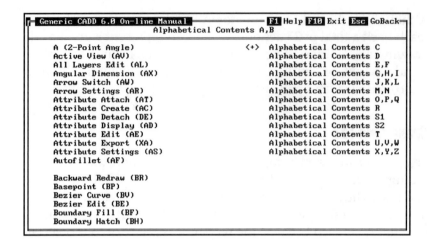

Figure 1.10:

The first screen of Help's topic list.

Figure 1.11 shows the help screen for Rectangle, which was requested while drawing the outline of the football field.

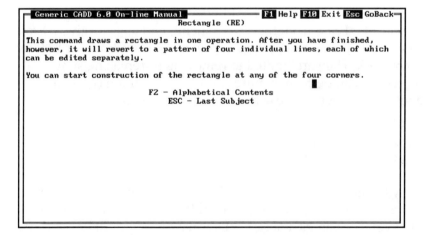

Figure 1.11:

The on-line help description of the Rectangle (RE) command.

You may use the arrow keys or the mouse to select topics or functions while using Help. When scrolling through the alphabetical list of commands, the plus (+) key moves the list down one screen, and the minus (–) key moves the list up one screen. Some topic descriptions have highlighted words or phrases. If you want a description of any of these highlighted words, move the cursor onto the word, and then press Enter or click with the first mouse button. After you finish using Help, press the F10 function key to return to CADD.

Saving and Loading Drawings

If you want to quit for now but return later to your doodled-on football field, you need to know how to save the drawing on disk and how to retrieve it. There are several options for each action.

Options for Saving a Drawing

When you save a drawing to disk, you can choose to save the entire drawing or only a portion of it. The commands are described in the following sections.

Save (SA)

Save is an all-purpose command found in the FILE menu. When you type **SA** or click on it in the menu, you can choose to save a drawing file as well as several other file types (see fig. 1.12). Each of these save options is discussed with the relevant material (Save as DXF, for example, is discussed in Chapter 17).

To save your doodling, follow these steps.

Saving Your Drawing

Prompt	Input	Description
Command	**SA**	Initiates Save command
Save	**D**	Saves a drawing file
Save file as>>	**C:\CADD6 \IGC-GCD\ FOOTBALL**	Expects name of drive, directory, and file
Saving file		
Save is complete		

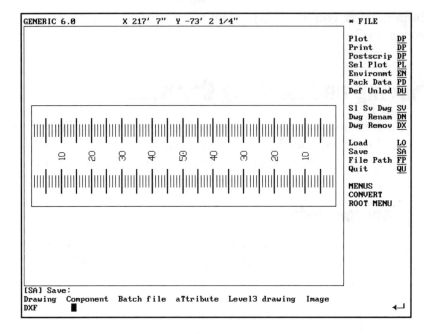

Figure 1.12:

Options available using the Save command.

Drawing Save (DS)

Save can be used to save files other than standard drawing files. Since it is a good habit to save often, no matter what software application you use, Generic CADD offers a shortcut to bypass the steps involved in using Save. When you type **DS** for Drawing Save, Generic CADD immediately knows that you want to save the current drawing file and displays the name of the file. If the name is correct (you can choose to rename the file at this point), press Enter. If a version of the drawing is already on disk, CADD asks whether you want to overwrite the version on disk or to rename the version on disk to filename.BAK; just type **O** or **R**, depending on what you want to do, and the drawing is saved.

Even though using the Rename command means taking up more room on the hard drive, it is a good idea to have a version saved as a backup file (filename.BAK). Should Generic CADD crash (rare but possible, and sometimes not CADD's fault), the current drawing file could be corrupted or lost, but the version renamed filename.BAK would be safe.

Selection Save (SV)

If you ever want to save certain objects in a drawing file of their own, use the Selection Save (SV) command. This command enables you to pick and choose the objects to be saved; all others do not become part of the new file being recorded on disk (see fig. 1.13). To understand completely the options in the Selection Save Drawing command, you need to read Chapter 10's detailed coverage of the selection process. Generic CADD uses the selection process extensively; you will be thoroughly familiar with it by the time you finish this book.

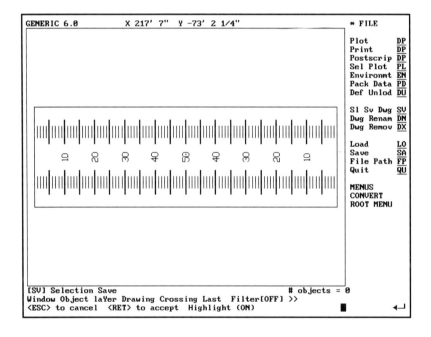

Figure 1.13:

Options available with Selection Save (SV) command.

Layer Save (YS)

If you have divided a drawing into several layers, you can save the contents of an individual layer as a separate drawing file, using Layer Save (YS), found in the LAYERS menu. Selection Save Drawing also enables you to save the contents of a layer, but the two are not redundant commands. Layer Save saves only one layer, whereas Selection Save Drawing enables you to choose several layers and select objects in other ways. When you use Layer Save, the command automatically names the drawing, using either the number of the layer or the name (if you have named the layer). You learn more about Layer Save in Chapter 10, which discusses layers in detail.

Options for Loading a Drawing

Having saved a drawing to disk, sooner or later you will probably want to print it or retrieve it and make changes. To do so, use one of the following Load commands.

Load (LO) and File Selector

The FILE menu's Load command is the all-purpose opposite of Save. Using Load, you can load from disk all the file types that can be saved to disk with Save. If you look near the bottom of the menu in figure 1.14, you see the words File Selector. When you select this item from the menu, Generic CADD switches away from the drawing screen to the File Selector.

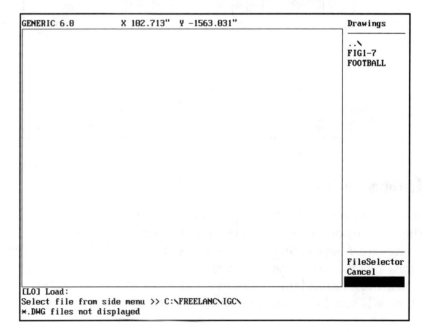

Figure 1.14:

Options available using the Load command.

You can use File Selector to view the contents of any directory on your hard drive, making it easier to search for files. Individual files in each directory can be highlighted with information on the file displayed at the bottom of the screen. When you find the file you want, File Selector can retrieve it for you. File Selector, shown in figure 1.15, is available in the menu during any file-loading operation. (There is no two-letter command for switching to File Selector.) As you progress, you will find other uses for File Selector, returning to it often.

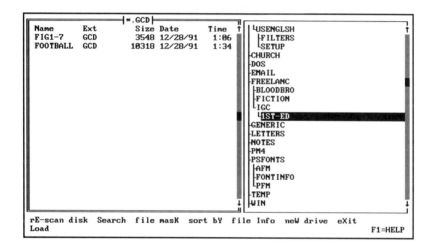

Figure 1.15:

The File Selector screen.

Drawing Load (DL)

Just as Save has an all-purpose opposite in Load, Drawing Save has a function-specific opposite in Drawing Load. If you know the name of the file you need to retrieve from disk, type **DL**, the name of the file (and the directory, if it is different from the one listed), and press Enter. If you type **DL** and then forget the name of the file, look in the menu. All drawing files in the current directory are listed. To select one, move the menu bar onto it and press the second mouse button or the Home key, just as if it were a command. (If you prefer, you may summon File Selector.)

Layer Load (YL)

A good way to add material to an existing drawing is to use the Layer Load command on the LAYERS menu. When you select Layer Load, Generic CADD asks you for a drawing file and then asks what layer of the current drawing this new drawing should be written to. Use the menu to select an unused layer, or type a layer number at the prompt line.

Moving from One Drawing to the Next

With Generic CADD, you frequently may work on one drawing for a while, and then switch and work on another. Two commands (Remove Drawing and Drawing Rename) speed up this process.

Remove Drawing (DX)

To eliminate quickly and completely whatever is on-screen, use Remove Drawing, found in the FILE menu. But be absolutely sure that you want to say good-bye forever to this material. When you type **Y** to say yes to CADD's warning (Do you really want to remove the current drawing? (Y/N) >), the drawing is deleted from RAM and gone forever unless you have saved it to disk.

A common sequence of events for the experienced Generic CADD user can be summarized like this: Draw some, save with DS, draw some more, DS again, draw some more, DS then DX, load a new drawing, and repeat the cycle.

Drawing Rename (DN)

If you are working on a drawing and want to create a second version of it, use the Drawing Rename command, found in the FILE menu. When you use this command, it does not change the name of the drawing on disk, but the next time you save the drawing on the screen, it is saved with the new name. If you are extremely concerned about protecting your work, use Drawing Rename to save several versions of the file under several different names.

Quit (QU)

If you want to end your Generic CADD session for the time being, use the Quit command. Type **QU**. CADD asks whether you want to save the current drawing. If you press **Y** for Yes, the prompt line will display the drawing's current name. If the name is correct, press Enter. Then CADD will prompt you to press **Q** to quit or **C** to continue.

Summary

The consistent logic behind the way Generic CADD commands operate was mentioned early in this chapter. Now that you have been exposed to several commands, perhaps a bit of that logic is evident. Generally, the two-letter commands correspond directly to the name of the command or to a description of what it does. All-purpose commands (such as Load and Save) provide a broad range of services, and function-specific commands complement the general-purpose commands. (Drawing Load, Drawing Save, Layer Load, and Layer Save all focus on particular aspects of the Load/Save process.) This division of labor between all-purpose and function-specific commands is common in Generic CADD, providing users a great deal of flexibility.

Few fishermen enjoy digging for worms before going fishing, but the task is necessary. Some of the settings and operations in Chapter 2 are the CADD equivalent of digging for worms. After you become familiar with these settings and operations and find the best way to use them, you quickly move on to catching the big ones.

2

Getting Ready To Draw

This chapter covers the commands and functions that have everything to do with how the drawing looks and how you organize your work, even though they do not actually create a drawing. By learning to use these commands before moving on to the actual tools of drawing, you can save some time when you start to draw.

Wise Generic CADD users take advantage of the program's layer structure, which allows a drawing to be divided into as many as 256 separate layers. Using layers to organize the information in a drawing makes it easier to prepare custom versions of the drawing and speeds up editing.

Generic CADD offers a myriad of display options that affect color, size, visibility, and response to user input. The best use of each of these is explained here. This chapter also discusses the commands that set the units of measurement and other construction settings. Before you reach for the headache medicine, you should know that Generic CADD offers an easy way to maintain the settings you like so that they may be repeated easily from project to project. This feature is known as the CADD environment, and becoming familiar with it makes your CADD work easier.

Many of the commands in this chapter function as toggle commands. Selecting the command sets its status to the opposite of what it was. To turn All Layers off, for example, enter **AL** or select the command from the Layers menu; enter **AL** again to turn All Layers back on.

If you are familiar with manual drafting, you know that steps need to be taken and decisions need to be made before you draw. Choosing a sheet size, selecting the pen widths, and choosing a drawing scale are three typical decisions. Preparing to draw with Generic CADD, although similar in some ways to preparing to draw manually, is different in others. You do not select a sheet size, for example, but you do set the screen limits. Instead of pen widths, you choose the line color and width and decide if you need to set the line type and line scale. And, as mentioned in Chapter 1, you do not need to be concerned now about drawing scale. You also must consider other aspects that have no counter-part in manual drafting. The best use of layers is one of these areas. Such things as setting elements of the screen display also have no equivalent in manual drafting.

Setting the Screen Limits (LS)

When you start a new drawing project, you generally have a good idea of the real-world size of what you are going to draw. Whether it is a house plan or a gasket, you know how big it is before you start. Generic CADD has a setting called Set Limits in the UTILITIES menu, which sets the size of the on-screen view. The default setting is 24" wide x 36" long (see fig. 2.1). When you start Generic CADD, a rectangle drawn to those dimensions bumps against the left and right sides of the screen and has some room at the top and bottom. If you need to draw a small object, change the limits to match. Figure 2.2 shows the limits set at 12" x 18".

If you are drawing something small that will fit inside a 24" x 36" area, you do not need to adjust the limits unless the object is extremely small. But if you are drawing a house plan, you may want to adjust the screen limits to a multiple of 24" x 36" that will fit your entire drawing on the screen at one time. In figure 2.3, a 20' x 20' cabin fits inside a Limits setting of 240" x 360", leaving room for notations and dimensioning.

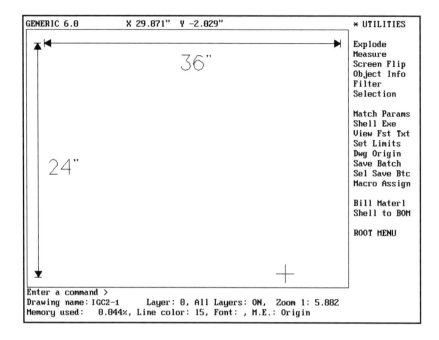

Figure 2.1:

The default screen limits are 24" x 36".

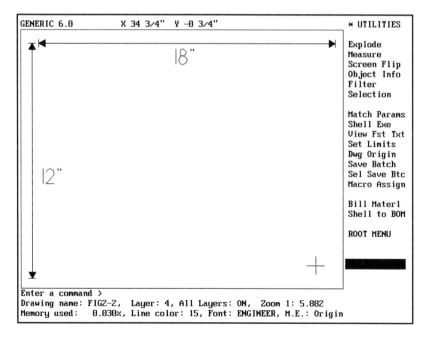

Figure 2.2:

Changing the screen limits to 12" x 18" for a small item.

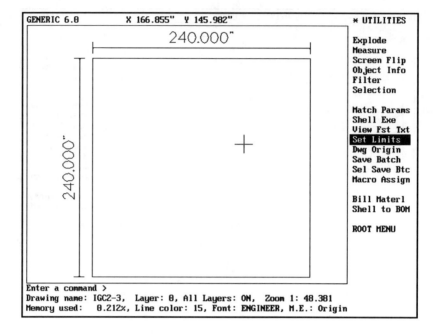

Figure 2.3:

Changing the screen limits to 240" x 360".

Setting the Limits provides a quick way to gain a zoomed view of the entire drawing. Generic CADD executes the Zoom Limits command faster than the Zoom All command. With Zoom Limits, CADD knows to set the screen so that it matches the size you defined with the Limits command. With Zoom All, the program must take the time to calculate the size of everything in the drawing and where it lies on the coordinate plane, and then draw the screen at a scale that shows everything. Beyond this, Set Limits does not limit you in any way. You can still draw anywhere on the coordinate plane, regardless of whether or not the location appears on-screen when you do a Zoom Limits.

Some Generic CADD users combine the knowledge of the size of the object to be drawn with the size of the sheet onto which the final drawing is printed or plotted, and they set the Limits to a ratio of the sheet size that also fits the object.

Organizing by Layers

One of the big advantages computer-aided drafting offers over manual is the use of layers. As you may recall, you can think of layers as sheets of clear plastic. In Generic CADD, you can give each "sheet" a name, which makes it easy to divide a drawing project logically.

When you work on complicated drawings, layers are useful because you can choose to display all layers or to select which ones should be visible. Additionally, you can choose to edit all visible layers or only the layer currently in use. The objects on a layer can be loaded or saved individually. A total of 256 layers is available.

Set Current Layer (YC)

Even if you pay no attention to layers, you are always drawing on some particular layer. CADD always starts with the default Layer 0. If you want to change to a different layer, type **YC** or select Current Layer from the LAYERS menu. Type the number of the layer you want to switch to, and press Enter. Any drawing you do now is on the newly selected layer.

When you type **YC**, the menu changes to show a list of all the layers available in CADD (see fig. 2.4). This list is several screens long. Instead of typing the number of the layer to which you want to switch, you can select it from the menu by moving the menu bar onto it and pressing the Home key or the second button on your mouse. Relying on the video menu to see which layers are in use works best when combined with the use of Name Layer (YN). (The Name Layer (YN) command is explained a little later in this chapter.)

Because you probably do not need to see all 256 layers, you can switch the menu display to the Short List by selecting it from the menu. Only the layers that have been drawn on or named, plus the current layer, appear in this list (see fig. 2.5).

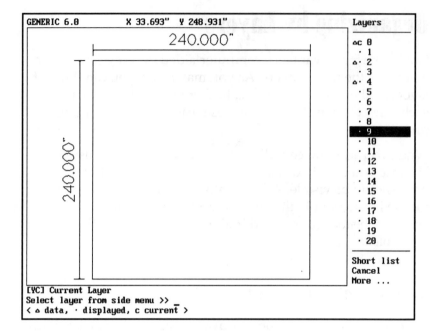

Figure 2.4:

The list of available layers.

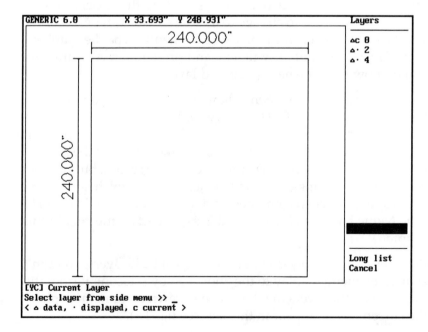

Figure 2.5:

The short version of the menu list.

Generic CADD uses a kind of shorthand in the layer list to provide you with additional information. The layer preceded by "c" is the current layer. Any layer that holds information is preceded by a delta mark (Δ). Any layer visible on-screen is preceded by a raised dot. If you choose to use the short list, CADD ignores visible layers that lack data.

All Layers Edit (AL)

As your drawing becomes more complex, data is placed on a variety of layers. (What you think of as drawings and objects is data to the computer, which is why the terms often are used interchangeably in this book.) You may want to see several layers but not edit them or have to worry about affecting them as you draw. When you start Generic CADD, the All Layers Edit (**AL**) command is set to on; you can see that in the status lines. The items you draw go on the current layer, but if you draw on several layers, you can edit anything visible. When All Layers is off, you can still see every visible layer, but you are limited to editing objects on the current layer.

All Layers is one of the many toggle commands in Generic CADD. To turn All Layers off, type **AL** or select the command from the Layers menu. To turn All Layers on again, just type **AL** again.

One of the important new features in Generic CADD 6.0 is its capability of loading AutoCAD drawings directly. Many people need to review plans created in AutoCAD but do not need its many powerful features regularly. The Layer commands can be used to make Generic CADD a "red-lining" tool for AutoCAD drawings. A supervising engineer, for example, can load an AutoCAD drawing, mark changes on an unused layer, and return the drawing to the drafting department. The person doing the review can even use existing geometry in the red-lining, by drawing on an unused layer with All Layers Edit set to on. The supervisor can snap to existing end points, add new lines to extend old ones, and so on, without compromising the original drawing.

Name Layer (YN)

Both Generic CADD and AutoCAD have the capability of naming layers. This feature makes organizing complicated drawings much easier. Instead of drawing the plumbing on Layer 5, for example, you can put it on the PLUMBING layer. If a layer has been named, the name rather than the number shows in the menu list when the menu switches to display layers (see fig. 2.6). If a named layer is the current layer, the name rather than the number appears in the status lines at the bottom of the screen.

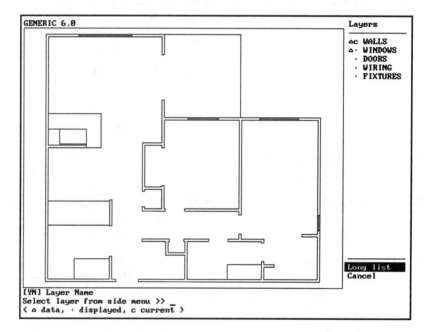

Figure 2.6:

The name of the layer appears instead of the number.

To name a layer, type **YN** or select Name Layer from the LAYERS menu (see fig. 2.6). At the prompt asking you to select a layer to be named, type the number or select it from the menu. Next you are prompted to type a name for the layer. After you type the name, which must not exceed eight characters, press Enter.

AutoCAD layers can have names up to 31 characters long, but only the first 8 characters are displayed on the AutoCAD drawing screen. If you know ahead of time that a drawing will be used in both Generic CADD and AutoCAD, take time to plan the names of the layers to be used.

If AutoCAD is already in use, you should continue using the layer names used there. The original layer names are used when the drawing is loaded into Generic CADD, but the layer names are truncated to 8 characters. This process presents a problem if the AutoCAD layer names follow a convention like "FOUNDA-TION1, FOUNDATION2," and so on. In this case, both layers would be stored in Generic CADD as "FOUNDATI," forcing AutoCONVERT (the AutoCAD-Generic CADD conversion program) to rename them as "FOUNDAT1" and "FOUNDAT2." Generic CADD automatically creates a report that lists all changes made during the translation process between AutoCAD and Generic CADD, but a little advance planning prevents problems later.

If you plan to divide a drawing into several separate layers, name them ahead of time. That way, you can preorganize the layer structure to match your needs.

Setting Entity Display Options

After choosing a plan for the use of layers in CADD, turn to the more visible aspects of work in CADD—how lines and other objects are displayed.

Line Color (LC)

Unless you are using a monochrome monitor, the most obvious display setting is the line color. Most color monitors have 16 colors available; some have 256 colors available. To select a line color, type **LC** or select Line Color from the DISPLAY menu. A chart of the available colors, with the number of each color, appears in the menu. Type the number of the color you want and press Enter or select it from the menu. All lines drawn after you set the Line Color command are in the new color; lines previously drawn in a different color remain the same. To change the color of lines already on the screen, you must use one of the Change commands (Object Change, Change, Layer Change, Window Change, or Drawing Change).

Setting the Line Color to 0 is not a good idea because that is the color of the screen background you are drawing on. Any lines you draw in Line Color 0 are invisible on-screen, but they can print to paper.

Line Width (LW)

Color is not the only way to distinguish lines visually. The width of lines can be adjusted with the DISPLAY menu's Line Width command. Figure 2.7 shows a few of the 256 possible line widths available in Generic CADD. Each number corresponds to an on-screen width in pixels, the points of light that make up the display. Setting the Line Width to 20, for example, creates a line 20 pixels wide. Line Width 0 and 1 are both one pixel wide.

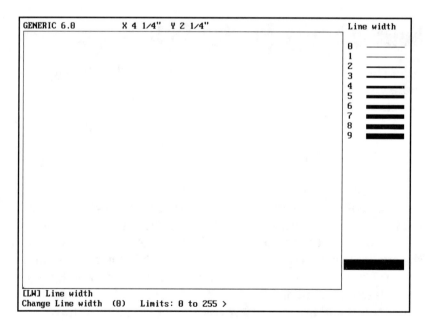

Figure 2.7:

Several possible line widths in Generic CADD.

For most work, you want to use Line Width 0, but sometimes other widths are of value. Extremely wide lines (beyond Line Width 9 or 10) are not very appealing to look at on-screen. The ends do not connect smoothly. Illustrators who use Generic CADD seem to have more use for very wide lines than contractors, architects, and most engineers.

When lines are printed or plotted, their exact width depends on the hardware being used. This topic is covered in detail in Chapter 8, "Printing and Plotting."

Line Type (LT)

The thin solid line is the most commonly used line in CADD, but many other choices are available. The Line Type command, available in the DISPLAY menu, controls the setting of line types. Available line types are numbered 0 through 255. The default is Line Type 0, the ubiquitous thin solid line. When you select the Line Type command, the patterns of Line Types 0 through 9 appear in the menu, as shown in figure 2.8.

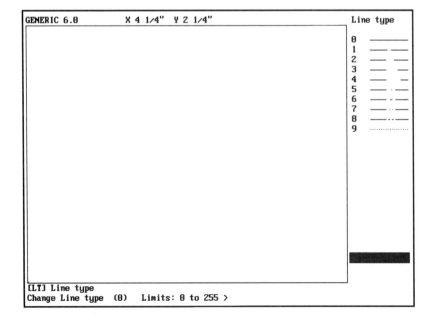

Figure 2.8:

Line Types 0 through 9, as displayed in the menu.

Although 256 line types are available when you use the LT command, there are not really 256 different types of lines. In addition to Line Type 0, a solid continuous line, there are 9 distinct line patterns. Each pattern is a specific combination of lines and spaces. When you use Line Types 1 through 9, you can make your lines long or short—no matter how long you make the lines, Generic CADD scales them so that they look just like the ones in the menu.

Starting with Line Type 10, each pattern is repeated, but the frequency with which each pattern is repeated along the length of the line changes. The degree of change depends on two factors: the line-type number chosen, and the setting of the Line Scale command. This nature of line types can get confusing. Just be patient and work through the remainder of this section, and it will make sense.

Line Scale (LZ)

The Line Type command controls the pattern used for a line. The Line Scale command controls the interval at which the pattern repeats. To help you understand how this all works together and beginning with figure 2.9, look at what happens to Line Type 5 and some of its multiples as the settings change.

Line Type 5 is a pattern of long dashes with a dot centered between each pair of dashes. Line Type 15 is the same pattern, except that each repetition of the pattern (the dash-dot) measures one "unit" (an inch, in this example). To understand the meaning of line-type numbers higher than 9, multiply the 10s-place number by the basic Line Type. Line Type 15, for example, repeats its pattern every 1 unit (1"). Line Type 25 repeats the pattern every 2 units (2")—two times Line Type 5. Line Type 55 repeats the pattern every 5 units (5")—five times Line Type 5. Use the ruler in figure 2.9 to compare the repetition patterns for the various line types. The arrows are for reference, as you compare the lines in figure 2.9 to the lines in figures 2.10 and 2.11.

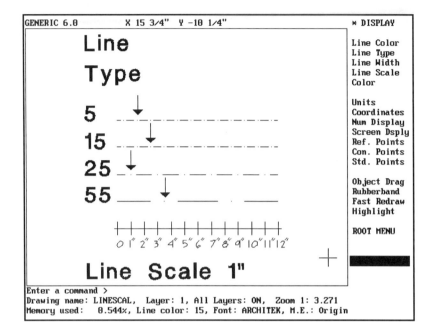

Figure 2.9:

Line types drawn using the default Line Scale setting of 1".

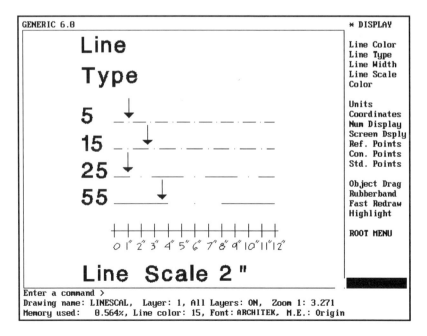

Figure 2.10:

Line types drawn using a Line Scale setting of 2".

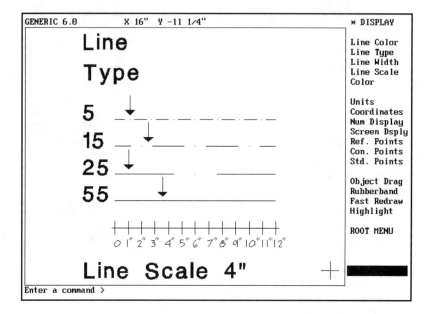

Figure 2.11:

Line types drawn using a Line Scale setting of 4".

The next step is to add Line Scale. When a Line Type is selected, it looks to the Line Scale setting to determine what a "unit" is, so that it knows how often to repeat the pattern. The unit in figure 2.9 is the default Line Scale of 1". In figure 2.10, the Line Scale has been changed to 2". The arrows pointing to the dots have not moved, but look how the change of Line Scale affected the lines.

With a Line Scale setting of 2", each unit of repetition has doubled. Line Type 15 now repeats the dot-dash pattern once every two inches, not once every inch as it did when Line Scale was 1". Line Type 55 now repeats the pattern once every 10" instead of 5" (5 times Line Type 5 times 2"). For one more example, take a look at figure 2.11, which shows the same lines as they appear under the influence of a Line Scale setting of 4".

Even if you do not understand the relationship between line type and line scale yet, you can remember the following important facts about the use of line type and line scale:

- Line Types 0 through 9 are unaffected by the Line Scale command.

- When Line Scale is changed, the line scale setting affects *all* lines in the drawing created using Line Types 11 and up.

One comforting thought is this: line type numbers that are a multiple of 10 are the same as Line Type 0 and are unaffected by line type and line scale factors.

Other Color Settings (CS)

Now for something a little easier. You already have been introduced to the Line Color command, but lines are not the only things in CADD that require a color setting. The Color Settings (CS) command, on the DISPLAY menu, is an all-purpose control device for color. Use it to set the color of text, dimensions, attributes, hatches, and fills (as well as lines) if you like.

Setting Program Display Options

Certain commands enable you to customize the "look and feel" of Generic CADD. Some commands are valuable drawing aids; others appeal to personal style preferences. Because the real use of some of these settings requires an application, their purpose is explained briefly now. You learn more about them as you work through the book.

Screen Display (DI)

The Screen Display command, in the DISPLAY menu, controls the appearance and function of the cursor and the color of the status lines (see fig. 2.12). When you type **DI** or select Display from the menu, you are presented with several choices in the prompt lines. Press the highlighted letter to adjust a setting.

Cursor size may be set to any number between 0 and the number that displays on your screen when you use this command. (It varies depending on your video display hardware.) The numbers refer to pixels; a cursor size of 1 creates a cursor one pixel high and one pixel wide—in other words, barely visible. Setting the cursor size to 0 creates a cursor that stretches from top to bottom and from side to side, as shown in figure 2.13.

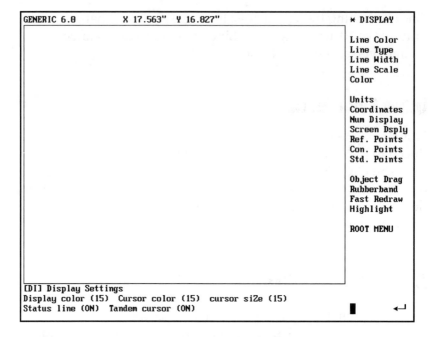

Figure 2.12:

Command options available with Screen Display (DI).

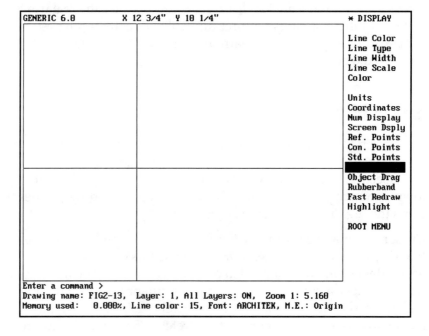

Figure 2.13:

Cursor size set to zero.

The status-line control is a toggle: when it is on, the status lines are visible; when it is off, the status lines disappear.

Tandem Cursor controls the relationship between the drawing cursor (the crosshairs or crosshair cursor) and the menu bar. If Tandem Cursor is set on, both cursors appear all the time, and their movement is linked. If Tandem Cursor is set off, only one cursor is visible at any one time. Most of the time the drawing cursor is the one you can see, but if you move it off the screen to the right, it disappears, and the menu bar appears.

In versions of Generic CADD earlier than version 6.0, Tandem Cursor had to be set on: there was no choice. One potential benefit to switching Tandem Cursor to off, however, is that when the cursors are not linked, the first mouse button can be used with both cursors. When the crosshair cursor is active, the first mouse button identifies points and executes commands, as usual. When the menu bar is active, the first mouse button selects the high-lighted command. If Tandem Cursor is on, you must use the second mouse button to select items from the menu.

Multiple Viewports (VP)

New in version 6.0 is the option to divide the drawing window into sections (viewports). You can organize the viewports so that each one shows a different portion of the drawing you are work-ing on. This is extremely helpful when you are working on large, complex drawings. The use of Multiple Viewports is explored further in later chapters, including Chapter 7, which covers adjust-ing the screen displays in greater detail.

Multiple Viewport (VP) is listed as MultiView in the ZOOMS menu. When the command is selected, the 12 possible viewport options are displayed (see fig. 2.14). Although 6 viewports can be displayed simultaneously (by selecting option 12), displaying 3 or 4 viewports is adequate in most cases. To select a viewport, type the number below your choice, or move the crosshair cursor onto it and click with the first mouse button.

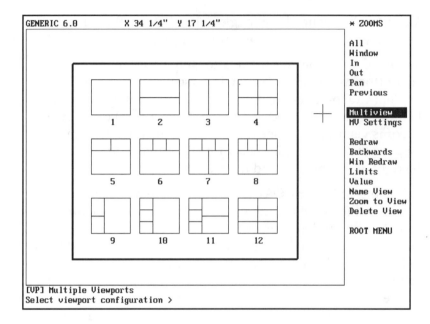

Figure 2.14:

Twelve multiple viewport options are available.

Dividing the drawing window into viewports does not change the drawing. Only one version of the drawing exists—but now several views of it are available. All viewports may be used for drawing, which is especially useful when you need to connect distant portions of a drawing. If you start the line in one viewport, move the cursor to another view, and place the end of the line in that viewport, the line connects the two locations.

Active View (AV)

Sometimes, as you draw or edit with multiple viewports on, you need to change one of the views (to get a close-up of a fitting, for example). If you just type a zoom command, all the views are affected unless you choose to limit zooms and redraws to only one view, using the Active View (AV) command. When in use, only the viewport you select responds to the redraw commands: Pan (PA), Redraw (RD), and all the zoom commands. The active viewport has a red border on color monitors. On monochrome monitors, the border of the active viewport is drawn with a thicker line than the borders of the other viewports. In figure 2.15, the upper right view is active.

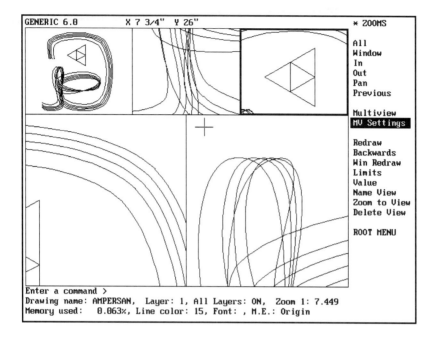

Figure 2.15:

The upper right viewport is active.

Even if an active view has been selected, drawing and editing commands can be used in any viewport. Active View affects only redraws and zooms. To select another viewport as active, you can use the Tab key instead of typing AV again. Each time you press Tab, the active view moves clockwise to the next viewport.

Active View has a two-letter shortcut, but it is not a separate command on the menu. Rather, it is part of the Viewport Settings command, described in the following section.

Viewport Settings (VS)

If you are using the Multiple Viewports option, you can adjust the way the option operates by using the Viewport Settings (VS) command, listed in the ZOOMS menu.

Viewport Settings has three toggle options (see fig. 2.16). The first, Multiple Views, controls whether the screen shows one drawing window or the multiple viewport previously selected. Press **M** to switch between the options. The second, Active View, works in relationship with the Active View (AV) command, explained earlier. When Active View is set to on, the previously selected active view is in use; when set to off, all viewports are affected by redraw commands. Press **A** to switch back and forth. The third toggle is Layer Management, which controls whether Layer Hide (YH) and Layer Display (YD) apply to an active viewport or to all viewports. Press **L** to switch between the choices. Because use of this third option is linked to the use of layers (and because the choices get tricky), a more detailed explanation of its use is given in Chapter 7, with the discussion of layer management.

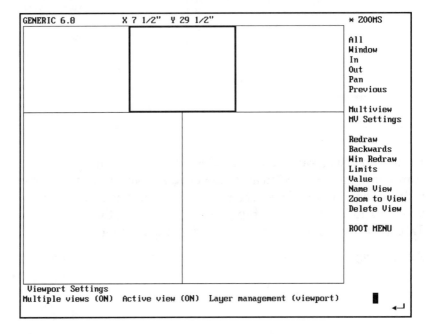

Figure 2.16:

Viewport Settings has three toggle options.

Units (UN)

The Units command, in the DISPLAY menu, sets the unit of measurement used for coordinate display and the placement of dimensions. There are six choices: inches, feet/inches, feet, millimeters, centimeters, and meters. If you want fractions instead of decimals, use the Numeric Display Format command (NF), which is described in the next section of this chapter.

You should match the units of measurement set with this command to the choice of units you made when you configured Generic CADD. If you selected inches or another English unit of measurement during configuration, select only English units with the Units command. If you selected a metric unit, stick to metrics now. Although it is possible to select a metric measurement for the coordinate display when an English measurement has been specified during installation, doing so can lead to roundoff errors when CADD converts between the two. The amount of error will be in the range of 1/100,000th of a unit. If your work depends on extreme accuracy, try to avoid mixing the two unit systems.

Do not confuse the Units command with the setting of database units, which you established when you configured Generic CADD on installation. The Units command controls the display of coordinates; the database units setting provides CADD with a mathematical foundation to build the coordinate grid. With version 5.0 of Generic CADD, you could not load a drawing created with metric database units into an English units database, or vice versa. But version 6.0 enables you to load English drawings into a metric system, and vice versa. If you are mixing files in this way, be patient. A complete recalculation of every coordinate location in the drawing is done as it is loaded into the program.

Numeric Display Format (NF)

Numeric Display Format (NF) controls the way numbers and angles are displayed in the coordinate-display and status lines, as well as the appearance of numbers placed when you use CADD's dimensioning commands. The command is listed in the DISPLAY menu as Num Display.

The available options, as listed in the status lines when the command is activated, are as follows:

Angular: Degrees or Deg:Min:Sec. Press **A** to switch between the two.

Linear: Decimal or Fractional display. Press **L** to switch between the two.

Decimal Value (available only if `Linear` is set to `Decimal`): This option sets the number of decimal places displayed, from 0 to 6. Press **D** and type the number, and then press Enter.

Fractional Value (available only if `Linear` is set to `Fractional`): This option sets the choice of fractional values from 1/2" to 1/64". Press **F**, type the number corresponding to the denominator of the fractional value you need, and then press Enter.

`Leading Zeros`: This is a toggle. 0.112" is Leading Zeros on; .112" is Leading Zeros off. Press **Z** to switch between the two choices.

`Show Units`: This is a toggle that controls the display of the units sign, such as the double quotation mark (") for inches. Press **U** to switch between the two choices.

No matter what NF is set to, metric values always are displayed in decimal format.

Coordinate Display (DC)

The DISPLAY menu's Coordinate Display command controls the setting of the coordinate display. Two types of display and three possible reference points for either display are available.

When you first start Generic CADD, the coordinate display shows X,Y coordinates. As the cursor moves, the coordinate display changes to show its position along the Cartesian coordinate grid: X shows the horizontal value from the 0,0 center of the grid, and Y shows the vertical value.

The center of the Cartesian coordinate grid is known in Generic CADD as the *Origin Point*. Normally, the 0,0 point on the grid refers to the Origin Point, but at times you want the 0,0 to be somewhere else on the grid. CADD provides the following three possibilities:

Absolute mode: The coordinate display shows how far the cursor is from the absolute center of the coordinate grid, the Origin Point.

Relative mode: the coordinate display shows how far the cursor is from the last point placed on the screen. This mode is useful if you are drawing from a set of notes, where one line starts from the end of the previous line.

Basepoint mode: the coordinate display shows how far the cursor is from a point on the grid which you have designated as the basepoint. This is useful when you are drawing objects based on a number of measurements from a common location. The basepoint itself is set using the Basepoint command (BP) in the UTILITIES menu.

In addition to showing the location of the cursor as an X,Y position (based on one of the three reference modes listed above), the coordinate display also may be set to polar coordinate display. Polar coordinates show the distance and angle of the cursor from the origin. As with X,Y coordinates, polar coordinates may be in absolute, relative, or basepoint mode.

For now, leave the coordinate display as it is, set to X,Y display in absolute mode. You take advantage of the other options later.

Reference Points (PR)

Points in Generic CADD are made from small lines. Three styles of points, each with a different meaning, are found in the DISPLAY menu (see fig. 2.17). The command for each is a toggle: display of the point type is either on or off.

Reference points identify text, components, solid color fills, hatches, attributes, dimensions, and the absolute 0,0 point of the screen. If Reference Points are on, any of these items is identified by an asterisk-type marker on the screen. You can erase, copy, scale, move, or change any item marked by a reference point by simply including the reference point in the command—the entire item does not have to be located first.

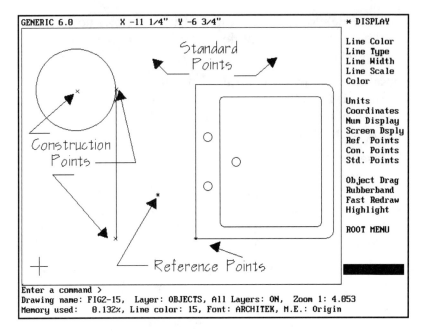

Figure 2.17:

The three styles of points in Generic CADD.

Construction Points (PC)

If Construction Points are on, little x-shaped symbols show up on the screen as you draw. These symbols identify the end points of lines, the end and midpoints of arcs, the center and radius of circles, and various construction parts in curves and ellipses. Turning on Construction Points when you are editing is useful because you often want to connect to these points to carry out various commands. But because these little symbols quickly become distracting, leave them off unless you need them.

Standard Points (PS)

Standard Points are cross-shaped symbols you can place any-where. They are useful for marking temporary locations you may need while drawing. Of the three styles of points, standard points are the only ones that appear if the drawing is printed or plotted. If Standard Points are off, however, they stay hidden.

When any of the three points are changed from off to on or vice versa, the screen must be redrawn for the change to take effect. Use Redraw (RD), located in the DISPLAY menu.

Object Drag (OD)

Object Drag (OD) occurs when objects are being moved from one location to another. Object Drag is found in the DISPLAY menu. If this toggle command is on, a dotted-line outline of the object moves with the cursor while the object's new location is being identified (see fig. 2.18). If Object Drag is off, no separate image is drawn. Although Object Drag is a helpful command that makes the use of Generic CADD more visual and intuitive, generating the outline takes time. (This is especially noticeable on slower computers.) Whether or not CADD takes too much time to do this depends on your hardware and your patience.

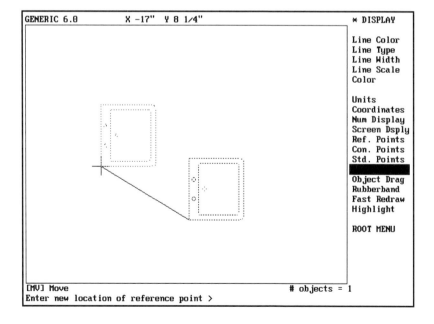

Figure 2.18:
Object Drag in use.

Rubber-Banding (RB)

Rubber-banding occurs as you draw with the cursor. If Rubber-banding is on, a line is attached to the cursor whenever you are drawing. This line helps you preview the placement of a line before you finish placing it on-screen. Because Generic CADD's default operation is drawing a line, having Rubber-banding on shows you if a line will be drawn if you click the first mouse button or press Enter to place a point. Most CADD users leave Rubber-banding on at all times, except while running elaborate macros or batch files. Rubber-banding, a toggle, is found in the DISPLAY menu.

Highlight (HI)

Highlighting occurs when objects are being selected for an editing function. If Highlight is on, all selected items appear with dotted lines instead of their normal line type. As with Object Drag and Rubber-banding, Highlight makes using CADD more visual and intuitive but can slow down the system. Unless it bothers you, leave Highlight on. Highlight, a toggle, is found in the DISPLAY menu; it also is available in the status line whenever the Selection process is in use.

Deleting the Menu

If you ever feel that you do not need the menu, you can remove it from the screen. Because there are times when even the most experienced CADD users rely on menus, you may never want to remove the menu. (But you should know how.) Both menu commands mentioned next are listed in the MENUS menu, which is not available from the ROOT Menu. To reach the MENUS menu, first go to the FILE menu, and then select MENUS.

Display Menu (VM)

Display Menu is a toggle command. If the menu is visible, typing **VM** causes it to disappear; if it is invisible when you type **VM**, the menu reappears.

Remove Menu (VX)

The difference between this command and Display Menu (VM) is that Remove Menu deletes the menu from memory. After this command is used, you must use the Load Menu (LV) command to bring it back. Generally, Remove Menu is used when you switch from one of CADD's standard menus to a custom menu. First, you remove the standard menu with Remove Menu, and then load the new one. For a more detailed treatment of menus, see Chapter 16, "Tailoring the Menu System."

Introducing File Management

Sooner or later, computer users learn the importance of keeping track of the various types of files created and used by their software. Generic CADD has a variety of user-created file types, as well as file types created by the software.

The File Paths (FP) command, found in the FILE menu, is used to set or adjust the DOS path used by each file type. Most of these file paths are established when you install the program. Some you may never need to change, and some you may change daily.

To use File Path, type **FP** at the command prompt or select the command from the FILE menu. To change the DOS path for a file type, press the letter associated with that file type.

As table 2.1 shows, file types have DOS filename extensions and associated letter commands:

Table 2.1
File Type Extensions and Single-letter Commands

File type	Extension	Command
Generic CADD drawings	GCD	G
Components	CMP	C
Fonts	FNT	F
Batch files	MCR	B
Hatch files	HCH	H
Menu files	MNU	M
Destination directory for Shell command		S
Miscellaneous files (including images)		I
AutoCAD drawings	DWG	A
DXF files	DXF	X
Lock file paths		L

For a discussion of locking file paths, see Appendix D.

Integrating CADD Environment Settings

If you are wondering whether or not you must adjust all of the settings in table 2.1 every time you draw, the answer is a reassuring no. If, on the other hand, you know that you want to change some of these settings from their defaults, you may do so, comfortable in the knowledge that they will stay set for you. A feature of Generic CADD known as the *environment* is the key to your peace of mind.

What Is the CADD Environment?

The CADD environment is the sum total of all settings in a drawing (not including the objects in the drawing). When you save a drawing on disk, all the settings in effect at that time are saved with it. When you bring this drawing back into CADD again, the settings in effect when you saved the drawing are again the settings in use, even if you had previously set some of them to something else.

An exception to this rule occurs if you are loading a drawing and a drawing is already on-screen. Generic CADD does not replace one active environment with another. This is true even if a font is loaded into memory or erased objects are in CADD's memory available to be redrawn with the Undo or Unerase commands.

System settings, like file paths and the setting for printing and plotting, are not saved with the display and drawing control settings. They are saved in a separate file (ENVIRON.FIL) on disk.

Environment Save (EN)

If you want the settings you have specified to be active whenever you start a new drawing, use the Environment Save command, located on the FILE menu. This command saves all display and drawing control settings to a file (ENVIRON.GCD) on disk. Whenever you start Generic CADD without specifying a drawing to be loaded, CADD looks to ENVIRON.GCD GCADD.DWG to know which settings should be in effect.

Environment Save when Quitting

In addition to saving the current environment with the Environment Save command, it is possible to save the environment when quitting CADD. After you type **QU** for Quit and you have answered **Yes** or **No** to saving the current drawing, Generic CADD asks you either to type **Q** to quit the program and return to DOS or to type **C** to continue to use CADD. A third option (not shown on the screen) is to type **E**; CADD asks if you want to save the current environment. By typing **Y** for yes, you not only save the environment as part of the current drawing but also update the ENVIRON.GCD file. You may then proceed to exit CADD.

Using Multiple Environments

As your knowledge of CADD increases, if you regularly switch between two or more distinct environments, creating a dummy drawing file for each environment saves you time. Draw one line on the screen, and then establish all the settings just the way you want. Save the drawing, and the settings become part of it. Create a dummy drawing file for each distinct style of environment you need. When you need a particular environment for a project, load the correct dummy file, erase the one line, and go to work on your drawing. Use the Drawing Rename (DN) command to change the name of the dummy file to the new name.

Consider the following example. Joe Caduser makes a living as a consulting engineer and a technical illustrator. He is called upon regularly to audit drawings created in AutoCAD, to see if the designs follow appropriate engineering standards. He picks up an occasional job illustrating maintenance manuals, and he regularly designs tools for a nearby manufacturing firm. Joe uses Generic CADD for each of these tasks, but each task is markedly different from the other two. Joe has a dummy file set up for each application. When he starts a job, he loads the appropriate file. Using the dummy file saves the time and trouble of choosing layers, line colors, fonts, and components, as well as the trouble of establishing a variety of toggles and settings.

Summary

Although a variety of settings controls the way Generic CADD looks and how it responds to your input, all of these settings are linked in what is known as the CADD environment. After you determine your needs and preferences, you can use the CADD environment to transfer this look and feel to every project. You do not have to set each possible display and response command before you start to use Generic CADD. The defaults provided usually are acceptable.

Now you are through the preliminaries. Starting with the next chapter, you begin to draw. Understanding these preliminary steps before you draw gives you a feeling for the context of the drawings you will create.

Graphic Entities

Enough of display settings and multiple environments. You bought Generic CADD for drawing, and it is time to draw. In this chapter, you become familiar with the basic commands that draw all the objects you will use in Generic CADD. Later chapters teach you to edit, embellish, and annotate, but it all starts here.

Manual drafting can be considered the stepchild of formal geometry. The building blocks of drafting are primitive objects defined by their geometric characteristics: lines, arcs, circles, ellipses, rectangles, regular polygons, and curves. Using the computer's capability to calculate rapidly, CADD programs automate the construction of these primitive objects. In Generic CADD, the name of the object and the name of the command are the same, although in some cases there is more than one way to draw the objects (Two-point Arc or Circle and Three-point Arc or Circle are examples). Commands to draw straight lines, arcs, circles, ellipses, polygons, Bézier curves, and complex curves are all available in Generic CADD.

This chapter is relatively short because the usefulness of the basic drawing commands is limited unless you understand Generic CADD's many drawing aids. A few drawing aids are introduced in this chapter, but many more are waiting. Nonetheless, a firm understanding of drawing tools in Generic CADD is the key to your success. These commands, all located on the DRAW menu, are the essence of Generic CADD.

Drawing Points

In the last chapter, you saw that Generic CADD uses three kinds of points on-screen: construction points, reference points, and standard points. Construction and reference points are by-products of the objects with which they associate, but standard points exist in a drawing only because you place them there. They can be used as markers to locate a position you need to identify, to draw something else, or perhaps to show the corners of a sheet.

Standard points are primarily for your benefit, but construction points and reference points are as much for CADD's benefit as for yours. Every object you draw using the draw tools is stored by CADD in a database (think of it as the drawing file). When you draw a line, CADD records the type of object and the coordinate locations of each end of the line. The construction points that gleam at each end of the line (if the display of construction points is turned on) mark the position of the points CADD needs to know in order to save the position and nature of the object in the drawing database. For circles, CADD records the location of the center and the end point of the radius, again needing only two points to create the object. For arcs, CADD needs three points: the center of the arc and the beginning and end points of the portion of the circumference that makes up the arc.

Reference points, which identify objects and drawing elements discussed in later chapters, also are stored in the database to identify the location of the object on the coordinate grid.

Drawing Lines

If you have not already done so, start up Generic CADD. When you get to the drawing screen, move the cursor to about the center of the screen and press Enter or the first mouse button. Generic CADD places a construction point at that spot (you do not see it unless Construction Points [PC] are on). Keep moving the cursor and notice that a line trails behind the cursor, connected to that first construction point (the rubber banding described in the last chapter). Type **RB** to turn this rubber-banding feature on or off.

Now press Enter again. You have just drawn a line. Whenever two points are located on the screen, and Generic CADD is given no additional information, the program places a line between them. Thus, the Line command is Generic CADD's default operation.

Line (LI)

If you want to tell Generic CADD specifically to draw a line, you can do so by using the Line command. Despite the fact that most of the objects in nearly every CADD drawing are straight lines, this command is seldom invoked in Generic CADD. (Using the default line-drawing mode, moving the cursor and pressing Enter or the first mouse button is much easier.)

After Line is invoked, it continues to operate until you specifically stop it or execute another command. Again, that is because it is the default command. To end Generic CADD's automatic line-drawing mode, press Esc or click the second mouse button on a blank line in the menu (sending a Pen Up command that stops the action). If you like using two-letter commands, you can type **PU** at the keyboard at any time to end automatic line-drawing mode.

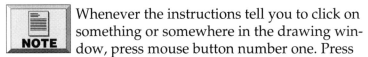

Whenever the instructions tell you to click on something or somewhere in the drawing window, press mouse button number one. Press Enter to achieve the same effect if you do not have a mouse or digitizer. Sometimes you are asked to click in the menu. Always use the second mouse button to select items in the menu; use the Home key if you lack a pointing device.

Individual Line (LI)

You can draw a straight line in Generic CADD without having to turn off the command when finished. Individual Line draws just one straight line—no continued rubber band after the second point is placed and no need to press Esc or type **PU**. Individual

Line is useful when you are selecting commands from the draw menu using the mouse, and you need to draw just one line. It is fast to click on the command name in the menu, place the points, and move on to the next task without having to turn off the Line command.

As you go through the introductions to the draw commands, take time to experiment with these commands. A few tricks also are presented to help as you develop your drawing techniques.

The Individual Line Command (L1)

Prompt	Input	Description
Command	**DXY**	Erases all objects on-screen
Command	Click on DRAW in ROOT menu	Moves to DRAW menu
Command	Click on Individual Line	Selects the command
Starting point	Move cursor to left side of screen and click	Places first point of line
Enter next point on line	Move cursor to top right portion of screen and click	Places end point of line

Watch what happens when you draw a line this time, taking advantage of a Generic CADD drawing technique. The results are shown in figure 3.1.

Command	Press spacebar command (L1)	Repeats the last
Starting point	Move cursor a little below the start of first line and click	Places first point of new line

Prompt	Input	Description
Enter next point on line	Hold down Ctrl as you move cursor to right side of screen and click	Places end point of second line

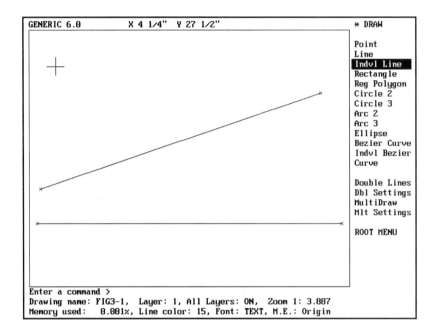

Figure 3.1:

Two lines drawn using the Individual Line (L1) command.

Holding down the Control key (Ctrl) is a way to constrain the cursor temporarily. When Ctrl is down, the cursor can move at right angles only. This useful function is part of Generic CADD's ortho mode features, described in detail later.

Generic CADD is designed to take advantage of three-button mice. So far, you have used the first button to place points on the drawing, and the second button to select items from the menu. Now you are going to use the third button. What, your mouse has only two buttons? Do not worry. Generic CADD is sensitive to the needs of handicapped mice. You can compensate for the missing third button by holding down the Shift key and clicking the first mouse button whenever the exercises call for the use of the third mouse button.

The rest of this book relies on the third mouse button to issue the Snap to Nearest Point (NP) command. Depending on the mouse driver you select during the installation of Generic CADD, your third button may or may not be programmed to issue the NP command when the third mouse button is clicked. If your three-button mouse does not now issue the NP command, follow these steps:

1. At the CADD prompt, type **MA** for Macro Assign.

2. At the next prompt, press the third mouse button.

3. Type **NP**, and then press Enter.

To make this change permanent, at the prompt type **EN** (for Environment Update) and press **Y** to agree to update the CADD environment.

Now draw a line to connect the start points of the two lines on the screen. To create clean connections, try using Snap to Nearest Point (NP), now available on the third mouse button (or press Shift and the second button on a two-button mouse). A Snap is a type of command that causes the cursor to seek and connect to a specific place. In this case, you are telling the cursor to connect to the nearest construction point. Doing this when you are drawing a line has the same effect as pressing the first button: it causes the line to start or end at that point.

If you do not have a pointing device, type **NP** for Snap to Nearest Point.

Drawing a Line

Prompt	Input	Description
Command	Press spacebar	Repeats the last command (L1)
Starting point	Move cursor close to starting point of first line and press third mouse button	Starts the new line by snapping to the left end of the first line drawn

Prompt	Input	Description
`Enter next point on line`	Move cursor down to the starting point of second line and press third mouse button	Finishes this line by snapping to the bottom line on the screen (see fig. 3.2)

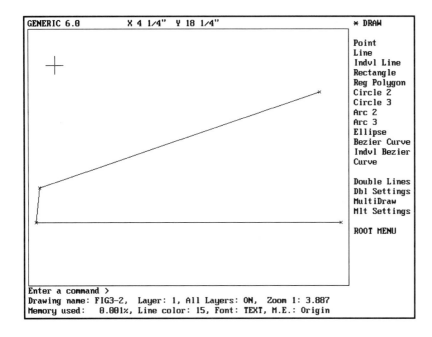

Figure 3.2:

Using Snap to connect the first two lines with a third.

Drawing Arcs and Circles

A straight line, you may remember from geometry classes, is the shortest distance between two points. Another way to connect two points is by placing them on the path of a circle. Such a line, if it does not form a complete circle, is known as an *arc*.

Generic CADD offers three ways to draw an arc. One of them, the Four-point Arc command, is not documented in the *Generic CADD Reference Manual* or listed in the DRAW menu.

Two-point Arc (A2)

The Two-point Arc command is used to draw an arc when you know the length of the arc's radius. To use this command, you start by selecting the center of the radius (Snap to Nearest Point is often used for this). Next, move the cursor to the location where the arc is to begin, and click to set the start of the arc. To finish the arc, move the cursor to the point where you want the arc to end, and click to select the end point.

Now try placing an arc on the screen, using the Two-point Arc command. You also will learn another drawing technique, one you can use in a variety of situations.

Using the Two-point Arc Command

Prompt	Input	Description
Command	Type **A2** or move the menu bar to Arc 2 and click	Starts the Two-point Arc command
Enter center of arc	Move cursor to center of screen and click	Sets the location of the center of the arc (see fig. 3.3)
Enter start of arc	Hold down Ctrl while using the left-arrow key to move cursor left a little: type **10** and press Enter	Sets the radius to 10" long
Enter the end of the arc	Hold down Ctrl and use the right-arrow key or mouse to move cursor just to right of arc and click	Sets the direction and end of the arc

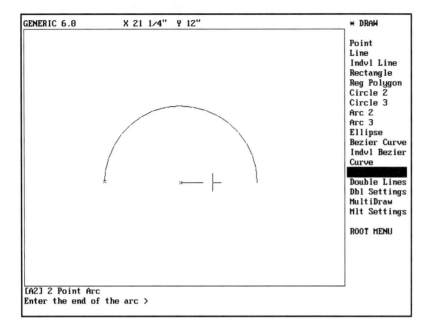

Figure 3.3:

Setting the end point of an arc using Two-point Arc.

You typed a number to set the radius, defining it precisely. Any time the cursor needs to move from one point to another, and you know the exact distance, you can type the number. CADD uses the direction you move the cursor toward as the true direction, or heading, of the line, and then travels the distance you specify. This useful feature is called Direct Distance. If you do not specify the units when you use Direct Distance, CADD assumes that you mean the current display unit.

Notice that you did not have to define the end point of the arc with precision. Because Generic CADD already knew the radius, there was no question as to the path of the arc. All you had to do was move the cursor to a location that would define a line between the center point and the end point. CADD then drew the arc so that it stopped at a point on that line.

Two-point Arc is designed to be used when you know the radius of the arc and the two end points. The next arc, Three-point Arc, is for situations in which you do not know the radius exactly.

Three-point Arc (A3)

When you draw an arc using the Three-point Arc command, you identify a point that is the start of the arc, a point somewhere along the arc, and an end point for the arc. You literally are placing three points along the arc, which means that you do not need to know the radius as long as you know where you want the arc to go. In the steps that follow, you draw a three-point arc that attaches to two points along the first arc (see fig. 3.4).

Using the Three-point Arc Command

Prompt	Input	Description
Command	Select Arc 3 from the menu, or type **A3**	Starts the Three-point Arc command
Enter the start of the arc	Move the cursor toward the construction point along first arc; press third mouse button or type **NP**	Sets the starting point of the arc by attaching to the midpoint of the first arc
Enter a point on the arc	Move the cursor down a little toward right end of first arc; press Enter or click	Sets a point along the span of the arc
Enter the end of the arc	Move cursor to the right end of the first arc; press third mouse button or type **NP**	Attaches the end of the arc to the right end of the first arc

Four-point Arc (A4)

Although this command was dropped from the documentation and the menu with the release of version 5.0, it remains in the software if you choose to use it. In virtually every situation where you might use it, Three-point Arc also works—and with fewer keystrokes. When requested (by typing **A4** because it is not on the menu), the command asks for the center of the arc (same as A3). It asks for the start of the arc (same as A3), and then requests that you identify a point along the arc. Finally, the command asks you to enter the end point of the arc (same as A3). The only difference in operation between Three-point Arc and Four-point Arc is the request for a point along the arc. Because you have defined the radius, this point may or may not be accurate. Generic CADD adjusts the points you enter so that the arc remains a true portion of a circle when drawn.

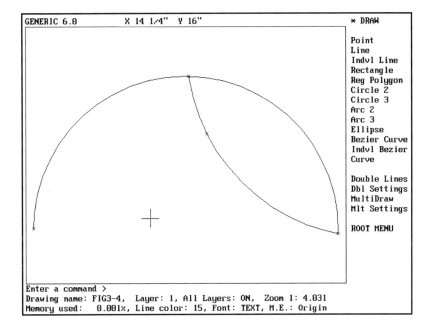

Figure 3.4:

Using Three-point Arc to draw an arc.

Two-point Circle (C2)

Two-point Circle works just like Two-point Arc, except that you do not have to specify an end point. Just click to set the center of the circle, move the cursor to show the radius, and then set a point.

The next hands-on exercise uses Direct Distance, the construction method used earlier to draw a two-point arc. Draw a circle, using the right end of the existing arc as the center point (see fig. 3.5).

Drawing a Circle with Two-point Circle

Prompt	Input	Description
Command	Click on Circle 2 in the menu or type **C2**	Starts the Two-point Circle command
Enter center of circle	Move cursor close to left end of largest arc on screen and press third mouse button, or type **NP**	Sets the center of the circle by snapping to the end of an arc
Enter a point on the circle	Nudge cursor in any direction and type **5**	Sets a radius of 5" and draws the circle

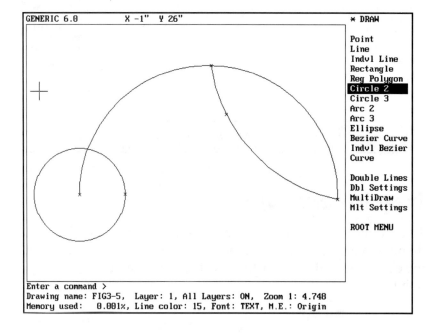

Figure 3.5:

Drawing a circle using Two-point Circle command.

Three-point Circle (C3)

Three-point Circle is useful when you know part of the path for the circle, but you do not know the location of the center point (which means that you do not know the radius). When you enter this command, Generic CADD prompts you to enter three points, one at a time. After you place the first two, CADD's rubber-banding effect shows you what the circle will look like if the location of the cursor is the third point placed. Once the third point is entered, Generic CADD draws the circle.

Be careful not to enter three points in a straight line. This can have unpredictable results. If the three lines are almost in a straight line, you have defined a very large circle.

Drawing a Three-point Circle

Prompt	Input	Description
Command	**DXY**	Erases the previous drawing
Command	**C3**	Starts the Three-point Circle command
Enter first point on circle	Move cursor to left side of screen and click or press Enter	Places the first point on the circle on the left side of the screen
Enter second point on circle	Move cursor to the right and click or press enter	Places a point that will be on the circumference of the circle
Enter third point on circle	Move cursor up and click or press Enter	Places a third point, which defines the circumference of the circle

Drawing Ellipses (EP)

The ellipse is an interesting shape. It is not just a closed curve, and yet it is not a circle, either. Geometrically, the ellipse is defined by the path of a point moving so that it is always the same distance from two points. The ellipse, a popular entity in engineering applications, also is used by architects and construction professionals to define the shape of basins.

There is only one Ellipse command and only one way to define the points on the ellipse, but the CADD database has two choices (Construction and True) for defining the ellipse. To place an ellipse when you select the Ellipse command, you define two axes. The first, called the major axis, sets the length of the ellipse. The actual ellipse passes through the end points of this axis line. The second axis, which Generic CADD defines as the minor axis, sets the width of the ellipse. You may draw the minor axis anywhere up and down the length of the major axis. After you have defined the width, click to set the distance, and Generic CADD draws the ellipse.

Construction Ellipse

After you define both axes of the ellipse, Generic CADD asks whether you want the ellipse to be a True ellipse or a Construction ellipse. If you select the Construction option, Generic CADD draws the ellipse using four connecting arcs. The advantage of selecting a Construction ellipse is that the end points of each arc can be selected later for editing the shape of the ellipse. Additionally, the arc lines can be broken if necessary—a CADD editing technique in which part of a line is removed by using the Object Break (OB) command.

True Ellipse

A True ellipse is constructed from one line and cannot be broken later. Both the True and Construction ellipses can be filled with solid color, using Generic CADD fill commands, or can be cross-hatched by using the hatch routines. The advantage of using the True option is that the Construction ellipse compromises the true ellipse shape to allow for construction by four arcs. If you draw a construction ellipse, change the line colors or line types, and then draw a true ellipse over the first ellipse (using Snap to Nearest Point to select the end points of the axis), you will see that the Construction ellipse is too narrow on the sides and too pointed on the ends. Figure 3.6 shows the two types of ellipses, as well as a True ellipse drawn (in dotted lines) over the top of a Construction ellipse (in solid lines).

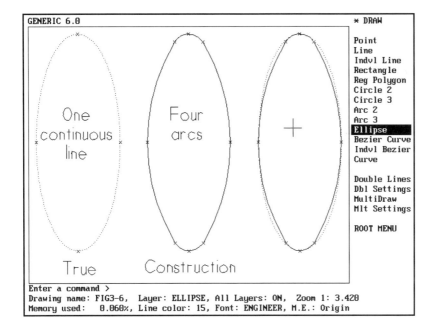

Figure 3.6:

The two types of ellipses: True and Construction.

Drawing Curves

Because of the precise, mathematical nature of Generic CADD and the precision drawing it can do, the program lacks a freehand drawing mode. This is somewhat compensated for, however, by the two curve commands available: Bézier Curve and Complex Curve.

Bézier Curves (BV) and (BW)

Bézier curves are named after the French mathematician who first described them. They are ideal for creating shapes in which the curves are irregular (see fig. 3.7). Each segment of the curve has two control points, which are not on the curve. These control points help to define the shape of the curve; if you later move the control points with commands like Move Point (MP) or the special Bézier Edit (BE) command, you can change the shape of the curve. When you draw a Bézier curve, Generic CADD's rubber-band feature makes placing the curves a visual, intuitive process; the curves flex and bend as you move the cursor. There are two Bézier curve commands. Bézier Curve (BV) is used to draw a series of curves, as in the following exercise. Single Bézier (BW) is for drawing one curved segment. Compare the use of these two commands to the use of Line (LI) versus Individual Line (L1).

Drawing a Bézier Curve

Prompt	Input	Description
Command	Type **BV** or select Bézier Curve from the menu	Starts the Bézier Curve command
Enter first point	Move cursor to left side of screen and click	Sets first point on curve
Enter next point	Move cursor down and click	Sets next point and draws first curve segment
Enter next point	Continue moving the cursor and clicking to set points (press Esc to stop)	Draws a curve with many segments (see fig. 3.7)

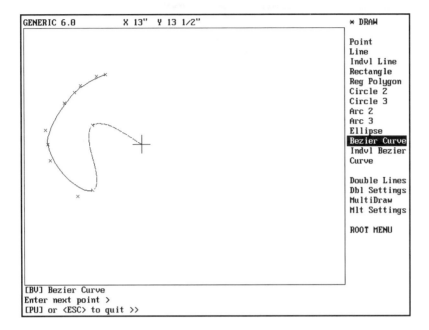

Figure 3.7:
Completed Bézier curves.

Complex Curves (CV)

Complex curves also are known as *spline* curves. They are the automated equivalent of using splines, flexible wooden or plastic strips, to create curves. Although Bézier curves are good for irregularly shaped curved lines, use the Complex Curve command to create smoother curves with more natural shapes. The command is simple to use. After typing CV or selecting Complex Cv from the menu, click to place on the screen points that define sections of the curve. After you have finished, type **PU** for Pen Up (clicking a blank line in the menu also issues the Pen Up command). You cannot press Esc to end the Complex curve as you did for Bézier. The reason is that the complex curve you are drawing is one object, whereas the Bézier command drew several curves in succession. Pressing Esc to end the Bézier Curve command stopped only the last curve from being drawn. If you were to press Esc to finish the complex curve, the last curve drawn—the ONLY curve—would be reversed, and you would be left with nothing.

If you ever plan to import Generic CADD drawings into generic 3D, limit yourself to using only Bézier curves. Spline curves cannot be imported into Generic 3D.

Drawing a Spline Curve

Prompt	Input	Description
Command	Type **CV** or select Curve from the menu	Starts the Complex Curve command
Enter a point on the curve	Move the cursor and click	Sets the first point on the curve
Enter a point on the curve	Continue moving cursor, clicking to place points (to finish the curve, type **PU** or click on a blank line in menu)	Completes the curve (see fig. 3.8)

Figure 3.8:

Drawing a complex curve.

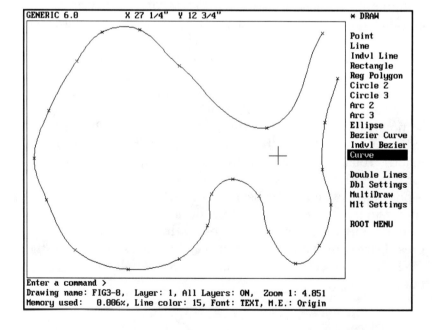

Drawing Polygons

Generic CADD provides two commands for drawing polygons: Rectangle and Regular Polygon. The Rectangle command is used heavily because so many things seem to contain four-sided objects. The command has one limitation, which Regular Polygon can overcome.

Rectangle (RE)

To use Rectangle, type **RE** or select Rectangle from the DRAW menu. The prompt asks for one corner of the rectangle. Move the cursor to where you want one corner of the rectangle and click to set the point. Next, CADD prompts you to enter the opposite corner. Move the cursor up or down, left or right as required, and click to set the point. Notice the rubber-banding rectangle stretching behind as you move the cursor.

Drawing a Rectangle

Prompt	Input	Description
Command	Type **RE** or select Rectangle from the DRAW menu	Starts the Rectangle command
Enter one corner of the rectangle	Move the cursor to the lower left of the screen and click	Sets the first corner of the rectangle
Enter opposite corner	Move the cursor up and to the right; click to set the opposite corner	

In figure 3.9, one corner is placed, and then the cursor is moved to the opposite corner. A rubber-band version of the rectangle stretches behind as the cursor is moved to the opposite corner.

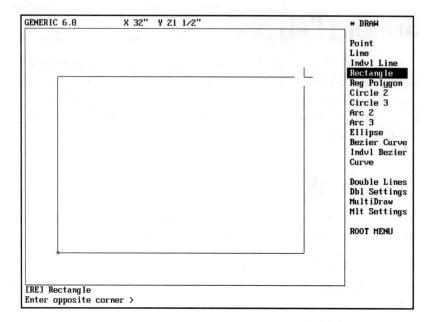

Figure 3.9:

Drawing a rectangle.

When using the Rectangle command, you are limited to creating a rectangle that is vertical or horizontal in placement; this command cannot place a rectangle on-screen rotated at an odd angle. If you need to rotate a rectangle already in the drawing, use the Rotate command. If you have yet to draw the rectangle, use the Regular Polygon command.

Regular Polygon (RP)

Use the Regular Polygon command to make closed objects having anywhere from 3 to 255 sides, each side of equal length, all angles the same. The first thing you are asked to do when using this command is to set the number of sides. If the number in parentheses is the number of sides you want, just press Enter.

When you use this command, you must choose one of two options: Center construction or Side construction. Center construction defines the polygon by having you define the length from the center of the polygon to one corner. Side construction defines the polygon by having you define the length of one side. If one side of the polygon must adjoin another object, Side construction is easier. Use Center construction for free-standing polygons, unless you have a situation that calls for a polygon but which a circle could fit as well (three points being connected by the polygon instead of a circle is one possibility).

Drawing a Regular Polygon

Prompt	Input	Description
Command	Type **RP** or select R Polygon from the DRAW menu	Starts the Regular Polygon command
Change number of sides (5) — Limits: 3 to 255	6	Sets the command to draw a hexagon (six-sided polygon)
(Center construction) or Side Construction	**C**	Selects Center construction
Enter center of polygon	Move cursor to desired location and press Enter	Sets the center point of the polygon
Enter one corner of the polygon	Move the cursor to set one corner, and click to draw the polygon	

Notice the rubber-band effect as you move the cursor to set the corner point. You can move the cursor in any direction from the center point, causing the rubber-band polygon (see fig. 3.10) to spin around the center point until the corner is located.

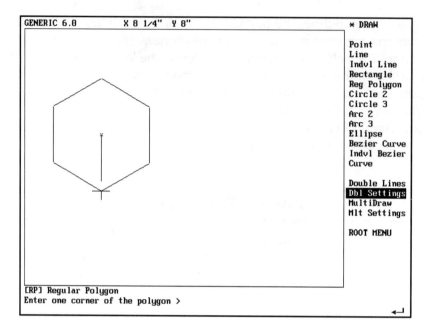

Figure 3.10:

Drawing a regular polygon using the Center construction option.

Drawing a Regular Polygon (Cont.)

Prompt	Input	Description
Command	Press spacebar	Repeats the Regular Polygon command
Change number of sides (6)	Press Enter	Draws a six-sided polygon again
(Center Construction) or Side Construction	S	Uses Side Construction method
Enter one point on the polygon	Move the cursor away from the first polygon and press Enter	Places the starting point of one side
Enter an adjacent corner of the polygon	Hold down Ctrl while moving the cursor; press Enter when the side is the desired length	Defines the length of one side of the polygon

Prompt	Input	Description
Enter polygon location	Move cursor left or right to select polygon orientation; press Enter to finish	Which side of the line should the polygon be on? (see fig. 3.11)

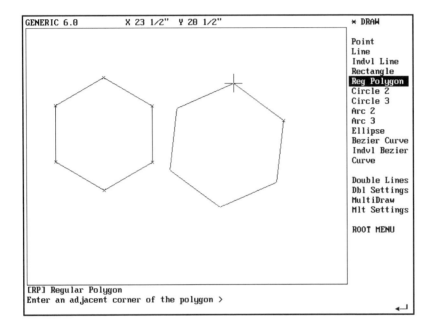

Figure 3.11:

Drawing a regular polygon using the Side construction option.

Drawing Double Lines and Solid Lines

It is not uncommon to need to draw two lines side by side (parallel). The most obvious example is when you draw floor plans—double lines show the thickness of the walls.

The Double Lines command (L2) draws a succession of double lines, just as the Line (LI) command draws a succession of single lines. The width is set using the Double Line Settings command (DB).

Double Line Settings (DB)

The Double Lines command can be set to draw parallel lines, any distance apart. The lines can be drawn to appear as one solid line, and you can choose whether or not the corners are filleted (which means to place an arc where the two lines meet to form a corner). All these options (Left offset, Right offset, Solid, Auto fillet, and Fillet radius) may be set from the Double Line Settings menu, which appears in the prompt lines when you type **DB** at the keyboard or select Double Set from the DRAW menu.

To set the distance between the two lines, use either the right or left offset, or both together. Each offset controls how far the line is from the cursor and the point placed on the screen. Setting both offsets at 3", for example, would draw a 6" wide double line. You can achieve the same effect by setting the right offset at 6" and the left offset at 0.

The way you adjust these settings depends on the way you plan to use the command. If you want one of the lines of the pair to follow a set path, set it at 0 and achieve the distance by setting the other line offset to 6" (or whatever distance). Suppose, for example, that you want to draw a foundation from a set of measurements. Because you want one line to be the outer edge of the foundation, which is what the measurements indicate, you set the left offset at 0 and the right offset at 6".

If, on the other hand, you want both lines to be the same distance from the points you select, set the right and left offsets to be the same distance apart.

The Solid option, if on, uses CADD's solid color fill capabilities to fill the space between the lines with solid color. The color of the fill is controlled by the Color Settings (CS) command or the short-cut Fill Color (FK).

If Autofillet is on, an arc is inserted into each corner. You can set the size of this arc using the Fillet Radius option. The inside arc of the pair (remember, two lines, two arcs) is of the size indicated by this setting; the outside arc is drawn parallel to the first.

Double Lines (L2)

Experiment with the Double Lines command. Use it as you would the Line command, moving the cursor and clicking. To end the command, press Esc, type **PU**, or click on a blank menu line. Some examples of double lines are shown in figure 3.12.

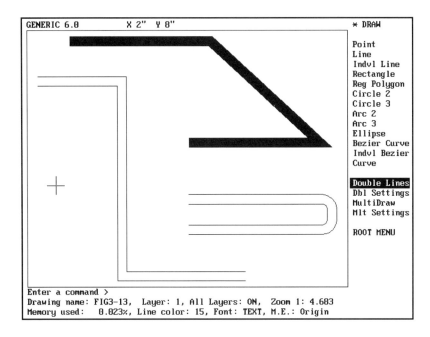

Figure 3.12:

Variations using double lines.

Drawing Multiple Lines and Curves

The Double Lines command is useful but is limited to two lines and works with straight lines only. For additional drawing options, turn to MultiDraw (MU)—new with version 6.0. MultiDraw, found in the DRAW menu, can draw as many as 16 straight lines, Bézier curves, or complex curves at one time. Using the MultiSettings (MS) command (listed as Mlt Settings in the DRAW menu), you can configure each line individually for color, type, width, layer, and the distance it is offset from the cursor. If straight lines are to be drawn, MultiSettings offers the AutoFilleting option. (To set the size of the fillet, use the AutoFillet (AF) command.)

Figure 3.13 shows a sample MultiSettings configuration screen. Five Bézier curves will be drawn, as shown in figure 3.14. Experiment with MultiDraw and MultiSettings on your own. If you have a slow computer (and especially if you do not have a math coprocessor installed) you may want to shut off Rubber-banding from within MultiSettings or by typing RB at the command prompt.

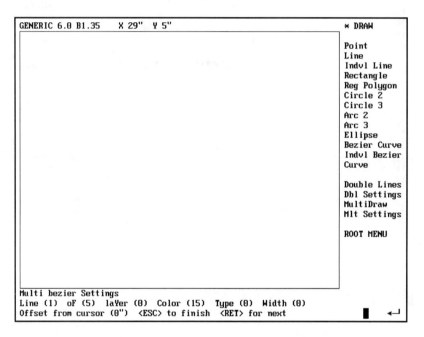

Figure 3.13:

MultiSettings options line for Bézier curve.

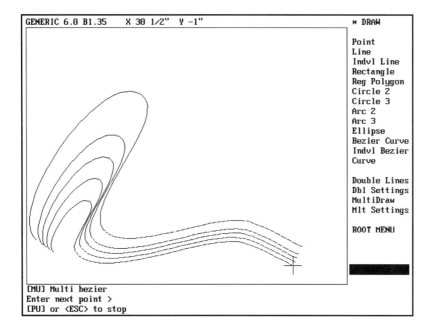

Figure 3.14:

A set of Bézier curves drawn using MultiDraw.

Summary

You have now seen all of Generic CADD's elementary drawing commands. By themselves, they may not seem particularly impressive, but you have only begun to tap the real power of Generic CADD. In the next chapter, which discusses snaps, you start to build on these basics.

Even without the added utility and convenience of snaps and other drawing tools, the DRAW menu commands represent a substantial improvement over manual drafting methods. The objects are geometric entities and are constructed in Generic CADD using mathematical formulas. After the math has been done to draw the object, the fruit of that bit of computer labor can be used again and again. This is not like drawing manually, in which the drafting technician doubles as the calculator and each step that requires the application of geometric principles means starting over.

Tools for Accuracy

Computer users often ask about the differences between paint programs and CADD programs. Although from a technical standpoint they are very different, the differences can be summarized in one word: precision. A program like Generic CADD enables the user to draw with mathematical accuracy of up to six decimal places. A paint program offers no such equivalent. Because there is no direct correspondence between the size of objects in a paint program and the size of objects in the real world, there is no specific scale size for objects in the drawing. In Generic CADD, just the opposite is true. Everything is drawn to its real-world size and can be printed out at any proportional scale the user chooses.

Such precision is fundamental to CADD, which is why it can successfully replace manual drafting. Generic CADD is able to draw with extreme accuracy because everything is located on the coordinate grid. Every point on every object has a unique coordinate address, expressed in terms of its horizontal and vertical distance from the center of the grid (point 0,0). Using these coordinates to identify the exact locations of objects enables you to draw with extreme accuracy. In most cases, you do not need to know these exact locations to draw accurately; Generic CADD calculates them for you. The Snap command's job is to locate exact points on objects. Snap Midpoint, for example, looks for the exact midpoint on a line and snaps the cursor to it. In CADD lingo, to *snap* is to locate and attach to a location. The type of Snap command determines the type of location.

Controlling the Screen Grid

The grid facilitates the operation of the snap commands by providing a reference to all locations in the drawing. You can make the grid visible, which makes it easier to place points on-screen. Like graph paper, the screen grid gives you a visual understanding of the distances between objects. But the grid offers more than just visual guidelines; it can be used to limit the movement of the cursor as a drawing aid.

Grid Size (GS)

The grid consists of dots that appear on-screen at a set distance. You control the spacing of the dots with the Grid Size command, found on the CONSTRAINTS menu. The horizontal and vertical spacing may be controlled separately, as illustrated in figures 4.1 and 4.2. To set the grid size, type **GS** or select Grid Size from the CONSTRAINTS menu. The prompt asks you for the X (horizontal) and Y (vertical) spacing. For each entry, type a distance and press Enter.

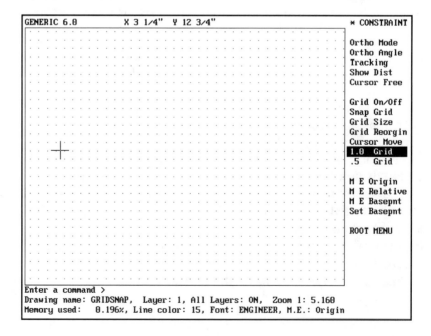

Figure 4.1:

Grid set to a horizontal and vertical distance of 1".

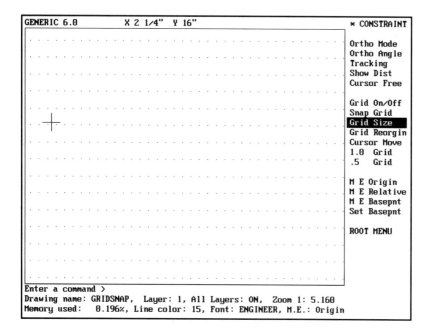

```
GENERIC 6.0        X 2 1/4"  Y 16"                      * CONSTRAINT

                                                        Ortho Mode
                                                        Ortho Angle
                                                        Tracking
                                                        Show Dist
                                                        Cursor Free

                                                        Grid On/Off
                                                        Snap Grid
            +                                           Grid Size
                                                        Grid Reorgin
                                                        Cursor Move
                                                        1.0  Grid
                                                        .5   Grid

                                                        M E Origin
                                                        M E Relative
                                                        M E Basepnt
                                                        Set Basepnt

                                                        ROOT MENU


Enter a command >
Drawing name: GRIDSNAP,  Layer: 1, All Layers: ON,  Zoom 1: 5.160
Memory used:   0.196%, Line color: 15, Font: ENGINEER, M.E.: Origin
```

Figure 4.2:

Grid set to horizontal distance 1", vertical distance 2".

Two preset grid sizes are available from the CONSTRAINTS menu: 1.0" and .5". No two-letter commands are available for these two options; they are menu commands only, provided for your convenience. (These two menu options are examples of menu customization, a topic explored in detail later in the book.) If the grid is not visible when the Grid Size command is invoked, it becomes visible after you finish the required input for the command.

Grid On/Off (GR)

If you want to hide the grid temporarily, or if you have not been using it and you want to make it visible, use the Grid On/Off command, found on the CONSTRAINTS menu. Grid On/Off is a simple toggle that turns the grid display on or off, whatever is opposite of its status when you execute the command.

Snap to Grid (SG)

You can limit the cursor's movement to the points on the grid. To do so, use the Snap to Grid command from the CONSTRAINTS menu. This is one of three snap commands that works as a toggle (the other two are Snap to All Layers [SY] and Component Snap [GC]). If the cursor moves freely about the screen after you type SG, it will then be limited to moving from point to point. When Snap to Grid is on, typing SG again shuts it off.

Start the exercise that follows by turning on the grid, setting its size, and enabling Snap to Grid. In this exercise, you use relative coordinate display, which shows the distance the cursor has moved from the last point placed on the screen.

If you have not already done so, start Generic CADD.

Drawing a Rectangle

Prompt	Input	Description
Command	**GS**	Starts Grid Size command
Change Grid Size X Change Grid Size Y	**1** **1**	Sets Grid size to 1" x 1"
Command	**SG**	Turns on Snap to Grid
Command	**DC**	Turns on display coordinates
...Relative (ON)	**R** and press Enter	Switches on relative display (see fig. 4.3)
Command	Move cursor to lower left of the screen	
Command	**RE**	Starts a rectangle
Enter one corner of the rectangle	Click or press Enter	Places first corner of rectangle

Prompt	Input	Description
Enter opposite corner	Move cursor up and right until coordinate display reads ΔX 8" ΔY 8" and then press Enter	Finishes the rectangle

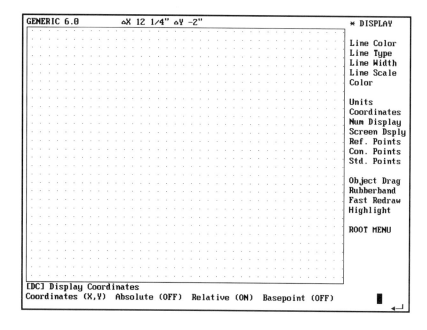

Figure 4.3:

Turning on relative coordinate display.

It was easy to draw an 8" x 8" square using relative coordinate display. The first corner of the rectangle became the 0,0 point in the coordinate display; to finish the figure, you moved up 8" and over 8", using both the grid and the coordinate display as guides (see fig. 4.4).

Using Snaps for Accuracy

The previous chapter covered the basic objects that can be drawn in Generic CADD. But rarely would these objects be drawn in isolation from each other. Normally, one uses a combination of lines, arcs, curves, and other objects to create a drawing. The snap commands, found on the SNAPS menu, make it easy to place these objects where you want them. They may be used whenever CADD prompts you to place a point on the screen. This makes it possible to use snap commands in the middle of any drawing command. Also, because the Line (LI) command is the default operation in Generic CADD, when the prompt says Enter a command, you can enter a snap command to start a line.

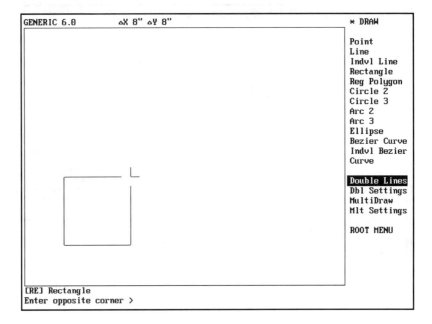

Figure 4.4:

Drawing with relative display coordinates and Snap to Grid.

Snap to Nearest Point (NP)

Perhaps the most commonly used snap command is Snap to Nearest Point (NP). If you have a three-button mouse, the third button should already be programmed to issue this command—how to do this was explained at the end of Chapter 2. (Two-button mouse users can access NP by pressing the Shift key and the first mouse button at the same time.) Snap to Nearest Point looks for the construction point nearest the cursor, and attaches to it the object being drawn, moved, copied, etc. You do not need to know the exact coordinates of this location—the Snap command figures them out for you.

If you have looked at the SNAPS menu, you may have noticed that Snap to Nearest Point is not there. Picking the command from the menu with a mouse would be difficult because the cursor also moves when you select items from the menu (and probably would not be where you needed it to be when the command was issued). Keep this in mind during the discussion of Snap to Closest Point.

If you have a two-button mouse, hold down Shift and press the first mouse button to issue Snap to Nearest Point.

Using Snap to Nearest Point

Prompt	Input	Description
Command	Move cursor near top left corner of square	
Command	**C2**	Starts a two-point circle
Enter center of circle	**NP**	Cursor snaps to top left corner of square (see fig. 4.5)
Enter a point on the circle	Move cursor right until coordinate display reads ΔX 2" ΔY 0" and press Enter	Draws a circle with 2" radius, as shown in figure 4.6 (Snap to Grid helps set the radius accurately)

Snap to Closest Point (SC)

Like Snap to Nearest Point, Snap to Closest Point snaps the cursor to an existing point. But the difference between this command and Nearest Point is that Closest Point asks which Point you want before it snaps. Because of this extra step, you can use Snap to Closest Point from a menu. If you prefer to select commands from the menu instead of typing them at the keyboard, or if you do not have a mouse, you may find yourself using Closest Point frequently.

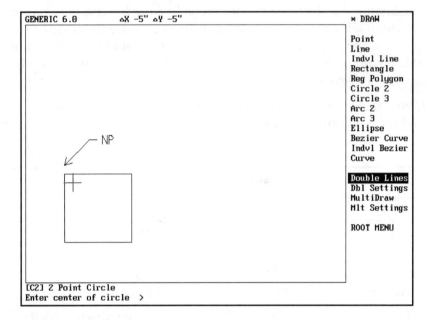

Figure 4.5:

Using Snap to Nearest Point to start the two-point circle.

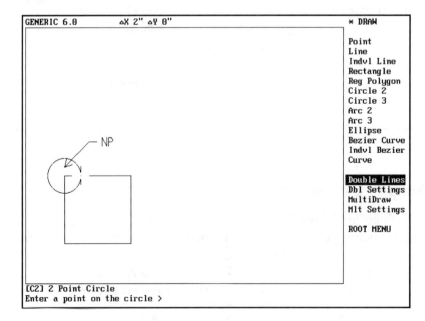

Figure 4.6:

Setting the radius of the two-point circle.

Snap to Midpoint (SM)

Snap to Midpoint locates and snaps the cursor to the exact center point of a straight line, an arc, or a circle. This is a frequently used snap because the midpoint of one line is often the starting place for another object. You also can use Snap Midpoint to draw an arc that connects to a line on both ends. To draw this, you would make a two-point arc and use Snap to Midpoint to define the midpoint of the line as the center of the arc.

In the next exercise, use Snap to Midpoint to move the circle to the exact center of the square. In manual drawing, you would draw diagonal lines connecting opposite corners of the square, and use the intersection of the diagonals to locate the square's center. You can bypass these steps by using Snap to Midpoint.

To move the circle, you use Object Move (OM). It enables you to move a single object such as a line, arc, or circle, displaying a drag image as you move the object to a new location.

Moving the Circle to the Center of the Square

Prompt	Input	Description
Command	**SG**	Turns off Snap to Grid
Command	**OM**	Starts Object Move command
Pick Object	Click on circle	Selects circle for move (see fig. 4.7)
Enter a reference point	**SM**	Invokes Snap Midpoint
Midpoint of	Click on top line of square	Selects midpoint of top line as reference point for move (see fig. 4.8)
Enter new location of reference point	Press spacebar	Repeats Snap Midpoint command
Midpoint of	Click on right side of square	Selects right side of square as new location for reference point (see fig. 4.9)

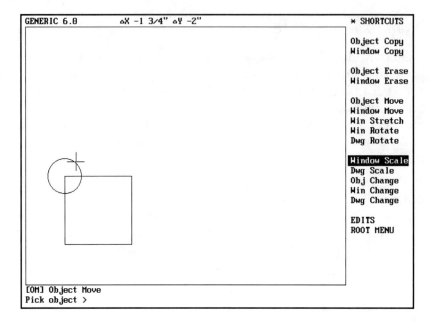

Figure 4.7:

Starting the Object Move command.

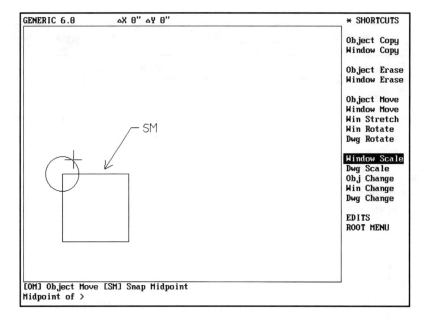

Figure 4.8:

Locating the midpoint by clicking on the top line.

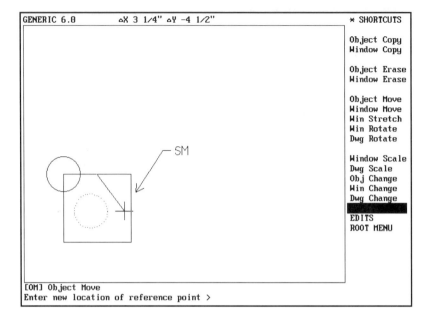

```
GENERIC 6.0        ΔX 3 1/4"  ΔY -4 1/2"              * SHORTCUTS

                                                     Object Copy
                                                     Window Copy

                                                     Object Erase
                                                     Window Erase

                                                     Object Move
                                                     Window Move
                                                     Win Stretch
                                                     Win Rotate
                                                     Dwg Rotate

                    ┌ SM                              Window Scale
                                                     Dwg Scale
                                                     Obj Change
                                                     Win Change
                                                     Dwg Change

                                                     EDITS
                                                     ROOT MENU



[OM] Object Move
Enter new location of reference point >
```

Figure 4.9:

Moving the circle to its new location.

The preceding exercise, placing the circle at the center of the square, is an example of *geometric construction*. You used the existing geometry in a drawing to draw or edit. You placed the center of the circle at the upper left corner of the square (the center of the circle was half the distance of the line from the line's midpoint). By selecting the midpoint of the top line as a new reference point, and by picking the midpoint of the right side as a new reference point, you maintained the "half-the-distance" relationship but transferred that relationship to another line. The center of the circle moved from being half the horizontal distance from the center of the top line, to half the horizontal distance from the line on the right. If you draw lines connecting the midpoints of the top and bottom, and right and left lines, you see that the intersection defines the center of the square, just as the intersection of diagonal lines does.

Now draw another rectangle and put a circle inside it. Use another snap command to copy the circle to a point half the distance between the middle of the rectangle and the top. A new drawing technique, setting the cursor free, helps with this part of the exercise. You also use Ortho Mode in the second exercise, which you have used before.

Drawing a New Rectangle and Circle

Prompt	Input	Description
Command	**SG**	Turns on Snap to Grid
Command	**RE**	Starts a rectangle
Enter one corner of the rectangle	Move the cursor to a point near the top right of the screen and press Enter	Places first point of the rectangle near top of the screen
Enter opposite corner	Move cursor down and right until the coordinate display reads ΔX 6" ΔY -22" and press Enter	Places opposite corner so that dimensions of rectangle are 6" wide and 22" deep (see fig. 4.10)
Command	**C2**	Draws another circle
Enter start of circle	**SM**	Snap to Midpoint places the center of the circle
Midpoint of	Click on left side of rectangle	Selects left side of rectangle (see fig. 4.11)

In the next exercise, use Snap to Nearest Point to select the center of the circle. Whenever Generic CADD draws a circle, it places a construction point at the center. If you set Construction Points to on (PC), you can see the point on-screen. Whether or not the construction point is visible, you can snap to it.

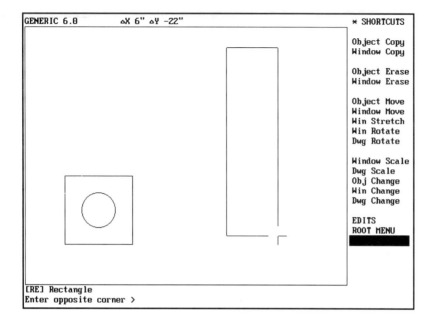

Figure 4.10:

Drawing the second rectangle.

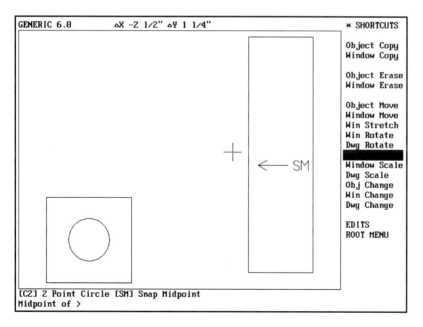

Figure 4.11:

Placing the circle on the left side of the rectangle.

Freeing the Cursor

Prompt	Input	Description
`Enter a point on the circle`	Nudge the cursor up the line; type **1.5** and press Enter	Sets radius of circle at 1.5 inches; draws the circle (see fig. 4.12)
`Command`	**OR**	Turns on Ortho Mode, to limit cursor's movement
`Command`	**OM**	Starts Object Move command
`Pick object`	Click on the circle	Selects the circle as the object to move
`Enter a reference point`	Move cursor inside circle; type **NP** or press third mouse button to Snap to Nearest Point	Snaps to circle's center to select a reference point
`Enter new location of reference point`	**KF** or **CF**	Frees cursor from restriction by Ortho Mode or Snap to Grid (see fig. 4.13)
`Cursor Free is ON`	Move cursor to right, then up to the top of rectangle	Circle's movement is still restricted by Ortho Mode and Snap to Grid, but cursor's is not
	Type **SM** and click on the top line of rectangle	Snap to Midpoint selects new center point of circle (see fig. 4.14)

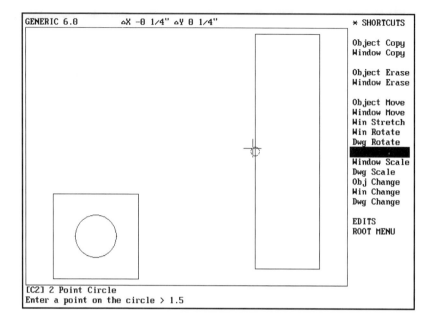

Figure 4.12:

Finishing the second circle.

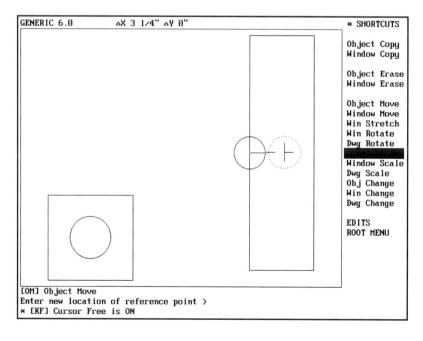

Figure 4.13:

Turning on Cursor Free (KF or CF).

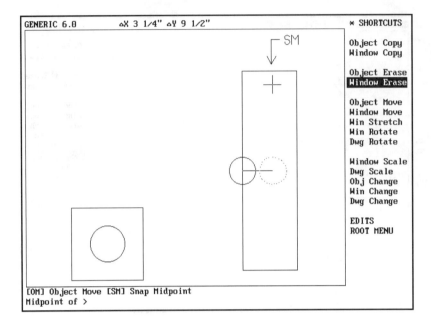

Figure 4.14:

Using the top line's midpoint as a reference for placing circle.

By turning on Ortho Mode, the Object Move command's action is limited to vertical and horizontal movement. When you combined Ortho Mode with Cursor Free in the last exercise, you were able to use the midpoint of the top line to move the circle to a point parallel to the line's midpoint. The intersection of the top and side midpoints locates the exact center of any rectangle.

A full discussion of Cursor Free (KF or CF), with more examples of its use, is in Chapter 5.

Snap Percentage (SR)

Next, try making a copy of the circle, placing it midway between the existing circle and the top of the rectangle. The center of this new circle is on a line that bisects the center of the existing circle and the midpoint of the top and bottom of the rectangle. To do this, use Snap Percentage. Like Snap Midpoint, it reads the distance of a line, arc, or circle and locates a point along its length. But Snap Percentage enables you to set the distance as a percentage of the line's length. (Snap to Midpoint, by comparison, always locates the point that is 50 percent of the distance between the end points.)

Copying the Circle

Prompt	Input	Description
Command	**OC**	Starts Object Copy command
Pick object	Click on the circle	Selects circle as object to be copied
Enter a reference point	Move cursor to left line of rectangle and type **SM**	Selects midpoint of left side of rectangle as the reference point for copy command (see fig. 4.15)
Enter a new reference point or offset	**SR** or select Percentage from the SNAPS menu	Uses Snap Percentage to locate new reference point
Pick object for Snap Percentage	Click on the top half of left line	Selects left line of tall rectangle as object to measure for the Snap Percentage command (see fig. 4.16)
Change percentage (25.000)	If 25.000 is in parentheses, press Enter. If any other number is listed, type **25**	The reference point for the copy of the circle uses a point 25 percent of the distance from the end point of the line (see fig. 4.17)

In figure 4.17, the current value is in parentheses. To accept it without change, press Enter. |
| Enter number of copies | 1 | Makes one copy of the circle (see fig. 4.18) |

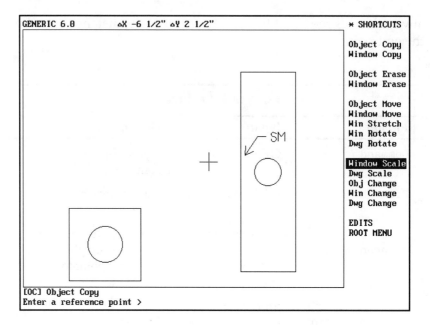

Figure 4.15:

Selecting the midpoint of the rectangle's left side.

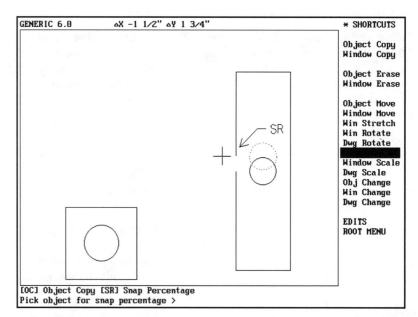

Figure 4.16:

Entering the Snap Percentage command.

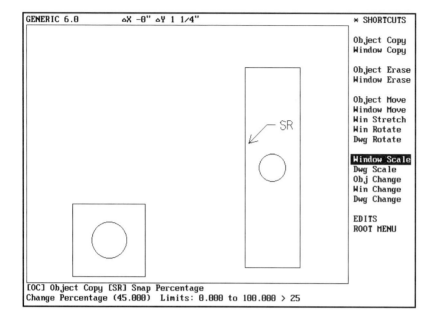

Figure 4.17:

Setting the percentage value for Snap Percentage.

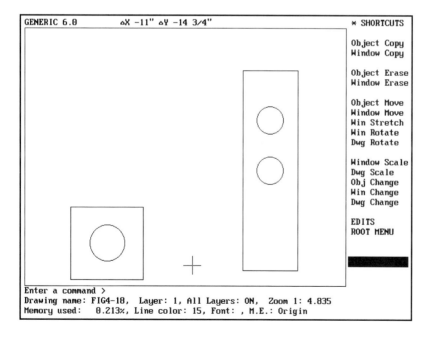

Figure 4.18:

Placing the copy halfway between the rectangle's midpoint and top.

When you use the Snap Percentage command, Generic CADD looks to the end point closest to the point you click on when you select the line. In the previous example, you wanted to snap to a point one-quarter (25 percent) of the way down the line from the top. You clicked on the upper section side of the line. Generic CADD calculated the location for the snap using the upper end of the line as the point of beginning.

On your own, make another copy of the circle at the center of the tall rectangle. (You need to do this before going on to the next hands-on exercise.) Place this copy three-quarters of the way down the height of the rectangle. There are two ways to accomplish this with Snap Percentage. Either use 25 as the percentage, but click near the bottom of the line, or set the percentage to 75 and click near the top of the line again.

Use Snap Percentage to make quick work of drawing pie charts. Generic CADD always starts with the point on the circle that is at 0 degrees—the point straight to the right of the center. From there, it measures counterclockwise. Figure 4.19 shows a circle divided into sections using Snap Percentage. To do this on your own, start each line by using Snap to Nearest Point to snap to the center point of the circle. Then type **SR** for Snap Percentage. Click on the circle to identify it (anywhere is fine), then type in the percentage that matches the size of the wedge you want to draw. Repeat this sequence to mark off additional wedges.

Snap Tangent (ST)

A tangent line is a line that touches a circle or arc without intersecting it. Typical tangent lines are shown in figure 4.20. Note that the two lines touch the two circles and the arc, but never at more than one point.

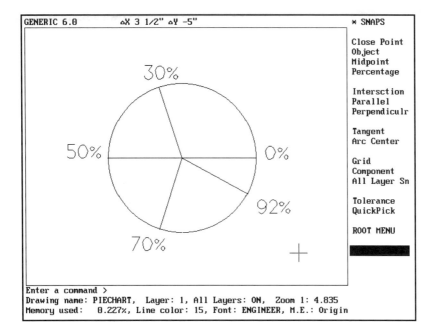

Figure 4.19:

Using Snap Percentage to make a pie chart.

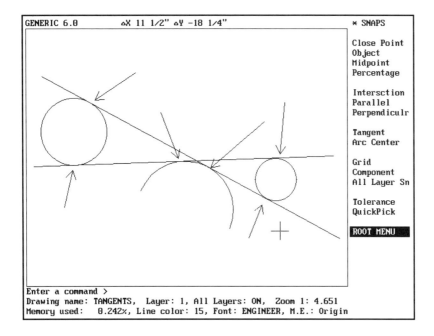

Figure 4.20:

Tangent lines touch circles and arcs without intersecting them.

Draw a tangent line from each circle in the tall rectangle to the circle inside the square.

Drawing Tangent Lines

Prompt	Input	Description
Command	Move cursor to circle inside the square; type **ST**	Starts a new line using the Snap Tangent command to place the first point
Tangent to	Click on top of circle	Selects circle as the starting point of the tangent line (see fig. 4.21)
Enter start point	Click again at the same place	CADD makes the line tangent to this circle, no matter where it goes
Enter next point on line	Move cursor to top circle inside tall rectangle; type **ST**	Identifies top circle in tall rectangle as destination of tangent line (the line also will be tangent to this circle)
Tangent to	Click on upper side of top circle	Draws a line, tangent to a circle on each end (see fig. 4.22)
Command	Click on a blank line in the menu (second mouse button)	Ends the Line command
Command	Move cursor back to circle inside square and type **ST**	Starts the next line
Tangent to	Click on the circle	Identifies circle as the object of the Snap Tangent command

Prompt	Input	Description
`Enter start point`	Click again on the circle	Line begins at a point tangent to the circle
`Enter next point on line`	Move cursor to top of middle circle in tall rectangle and type **ST**	Identifies the middle circle as the end point of the line being drawn
`Tangent to`	Click on middle circle	Draws a line, tangent to the circle on each end (see fig. 4.23)
`Command`	Click on a blank line in the menu (or second mouse button)	Ends the Line command
`Command`	Move cursor to bottom of circle in square and type **ST**	Starts the third line
`Tangent to`	Click on the circle	Identifies the circle as starting point of the line being drawn
`Enter start point`	Click again on circle	Begins line at a point tangent to the circle
`Enter next point on line`	Move cursor to bottom circle in tall rectangle; type **ST**	Identifies the bottom circle as the destination of the line being drawn (see fig. 4.24)
`Tangent to`	Click on bottom circle	Draws the line
`Command`	Click on a blank menu line	Ends the Line command

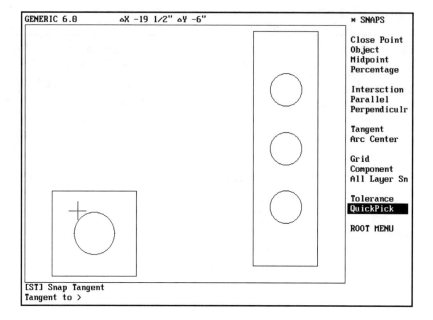

Figure 4.21:

Click on the top of the circle for the Snap Tangent command.

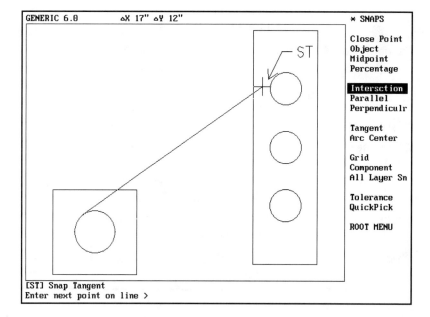

Figure 4.22:

Drawing a line tangent to both circles.

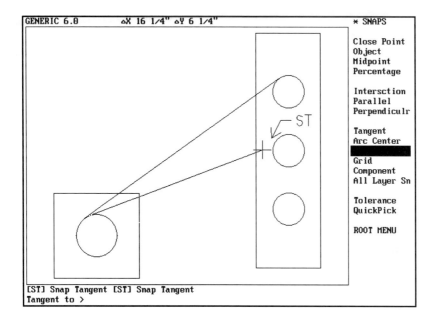

Figure 4.23:

Drawing a line tangent to the middle circle.

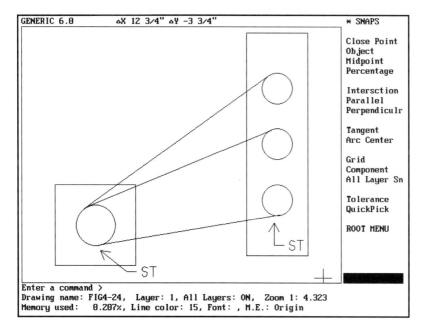

Figure 4.24:

Drawing a line tangent to two circles.

Snap to Arc Center (SN)

When you draw a circle with Generic CADD, a construction point is placed at the circle's center. If you need to connect a line to the construction point, you can just use Snap to Nearest Point. But Generic CADD does not grant this courtesy to arcs, even though, by definition, an arc is a segment of a circle. If you need to know the center point of an arc, you must snap to it with the Snap to Arc Center command. To use this command, type **SN** or select Arc Center from the SNAPS menu, then click on the arc whose center you need.

Snap Perpendicular (SP)

Snap Perpendicular enables you to draw lines that are perpendicular to existing lines, arcs, and circles. (*Perpendicular* means that the angle at which two lines meet is 90 degrees; in the case of arcs and circles, the angle is 90 degrees of the perpendicular line and an imaginary tangent line. If a line is truly horizontal, a line perpendicular to it is truly vertical.) You can enter this snap command either when you are starting the line, or when you are looking to place the end point. In the following section, you use both methods.

In the next exercise, you draw an arc in the upper left portion of the screen. Then you draw a line between the center point of this arc and the top tangent line, making the new line perpendicular to the tangent line.

After drawing a line perpendicular to the top tangent line that connects to the center of the arc, you attach a perpendicular line one inch long to the middle tangent line.

Drawing Perpendicular Lines

Prompt	Input	Description
Command	**OR**	Turns off Ortho Mode
Command	**KF** or **CF**	Turns off Cursor Free

Prompt	Input	Description
Command	**A3**	Starts a three-point arc
Enter start of arc	Move cursor to top left of screen; click to set first point	Places the starting point of the arc
Enter a point on the arc	Move cursor up and right; click to set a point	Sets the direction of the arc
Enter the end of the arc	Move cursor right and down; click to finish the arc	Completes the arc (see fig. 4.25)
Command	Type **SN** or select Arc Center from SNAPS menu	
Center of	Click on arc just drawn	Identifies the arc just drawn by rubber-banding a line from it to cursor
Command	**SP** or select Perpendicular from SNAPS menu	Starts a perpendicular line connecting center of arc to top tangent line
Perpendicular to	Click on top tangent line	Selects a base line, draws a line perpendicular to it, ending at the center of the arc (see figs. 4.26 and 4.27)
Command	**SP** or select Perpendicular from SNAPS menu	Starts a line with Snap Perpendicular command
Perpendicular to	Click on middle tangent line	Selects the base line for next perpendicular line (see fig. 4.28)

continues

Prompt	Input	Description
Enter start point	**SM** and click on the middle tangent line	Selects the midpoint of the middle tangent line as the starting point for the perpendicular line
Enter next point on line	Nudge the cursor upward, type **1"** and press Enter	Tells program to draw a one-inch line from the point placed (see fig. 4.29)
Command	Click on a blank menu line or press Esc	Ends the Line command

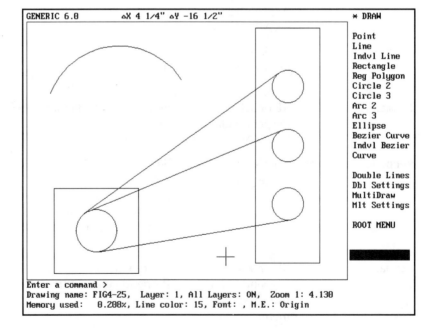

Figure 4.25:

Add an arc to the drawing.

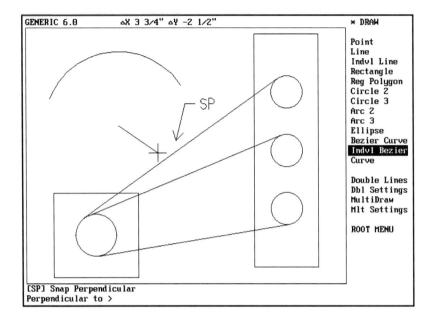

Figure 4.26:

Selecting the top tangent line, draw a line perpendicular to it.

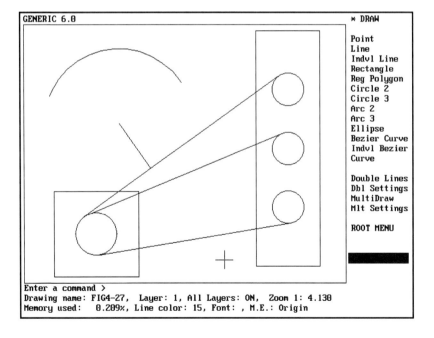

Figure 4.27:

The completed line.

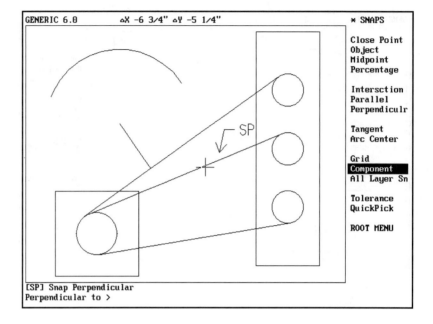

Figure 4.28:

Click on the line that will be the base for the perpendicular line.

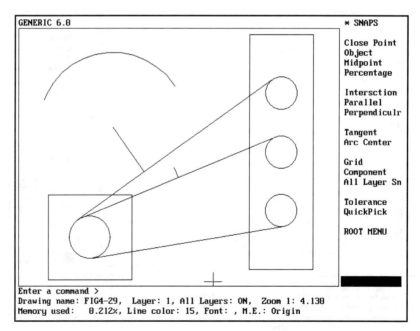

Figure 4.29:

The completed 1" perpendicular line.

Snap Intersection (SI)

So far, all the snaps you have used work on single objects like lines (including arcs and circles) or points. Snap Intersection is an exception. It places a point where two objects cross. The objects can be lines, arcs, or circles in any combination. You can use Snap Intersection any time you need to place a point.

You use Snap Intersection twice in the next section to draw a diagonal line that connects the second and third tangent lines. And you learn how to save a keystroke when using the same snap command to place two consecutive points.

Connecting the Tangent Lines

Prompt	Input	Description
Command	**SI** or select Intersection from SNAPS menu	Starts a new line using SI to place first point
Pick intersection	Using figure 4.30 as a guide, click on top intersection	Selects the first intersection
Place next point on line	Move cursor down and left and press spacebar	Extends the line and selects SI again
Pick intersection	Using figure 4.30 as a guide, click on bottom inter-section	Places the end point of the line at the lower intersection
Command	Click on a blank menu line or press Esc	Ends the Line command

Whenever you are placing points in a drawing and want the same snap command you just used, press the spacebar to repeat it. The last command used is always available by pressing the spacebar.

After you have entered another command, however, you need to type the snap's two-letter code or select it from the SNAPS menu.

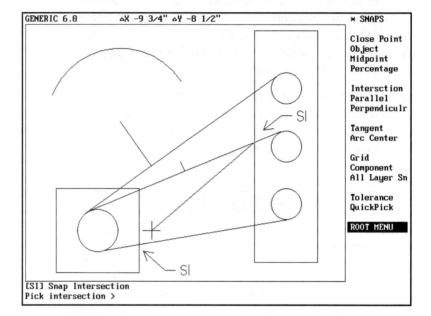

Figure 4.30:

Drawing a diagonal line using Snap Intersection.

Snap Parallel (SL)

Two lines that are the same distance from each other along their entire lengths are parallel. To manually draw a line parallel to another line, you could measure a start point and an end point, both the same distance from the first line, and then connect the points. Using Snap Parallel is much faster.

There are two ways to use Snap Parallel. The first is when you have already started a line you want to make parallel to an existing one. The second method is when you identify a line about to be drawn as a parallel line.

Figures 4.31, 4.32, and 4.33 show how to use Snap Parallel after the line has been started. After you type SL or select Parallel from the SNAPS menu, the prompt line asks you to select which line the new line will be parallel to (see fig. 4.31). Click on the line. Then the program asks you to enter the end point of the line (see fig. 4.32). Place the point, using a snap to identify the point if necessary (see fig. 4.33).

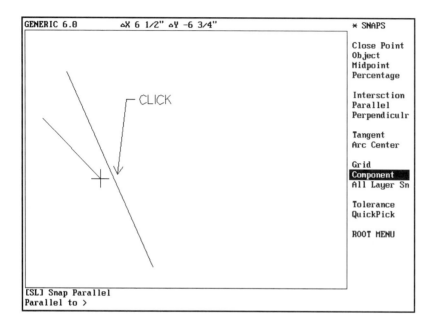

Figure 4.31.

Click on the existing line.

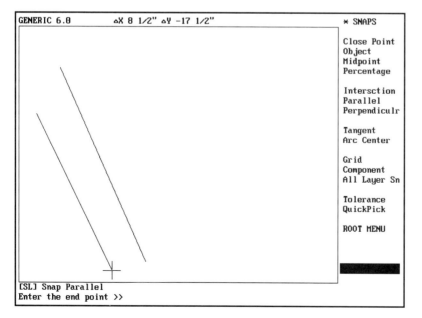

Figure 4.32:

Enter the end point of the parallel line.

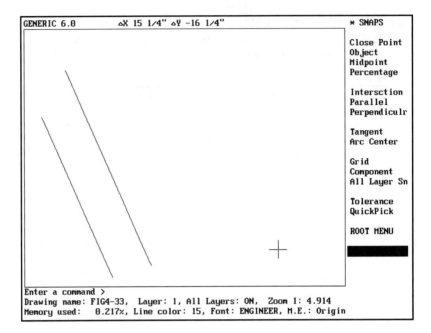

Figure 4.33:

The finished parallel line.

Figures 4.34, 4.35, 4.36, and 4.37 show how to use Snap Parallel before you place the first point on a line. Use this method when the new line must be a specified distance from the first line. You are prompted to select the line the new line will parallel (see fig. 4.34). Next, Generic CADD asks for the distance the new line will be offset from the existing line. If the number shown in parentheses is the distance you need, press Enter. Otherwise, type the new distance and then press Enter (see fig. 4.35). Next, the prompt asks you to enter the start of the line (see fig. 4.36). This is for length only because you have already determined how far the new line will be from the existing line (see fig. 4.35). Click (or snap) to set this point, and then place the end point of the line (see fig. 4.37). Again, the end point you place shows Generic CADD only the length of the line—the distance of this point from the existing line was set when you typed an offset distance.

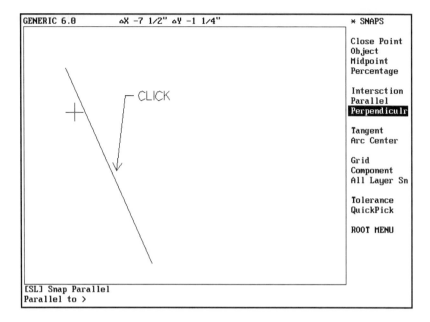

Figure 4.34:

Click on the line that will be parallel to the new line.

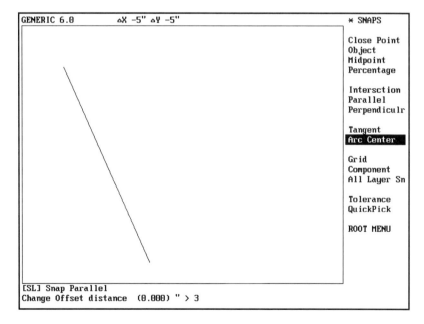

Figure 4.35:

Set the offset distance.

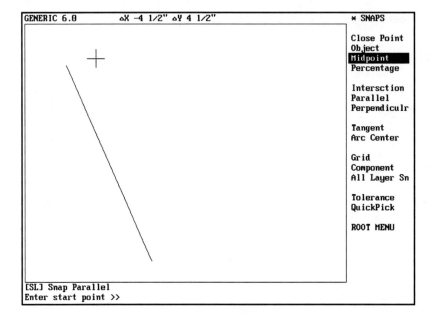

Figure 4.36:

Enter the start of the parallel line.

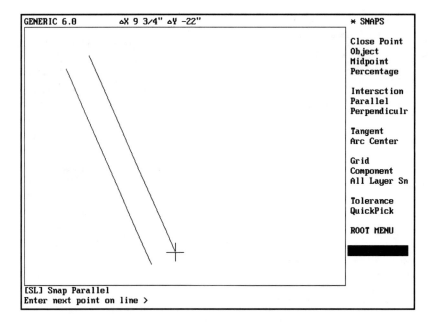

Figure 4.37:

Place the end point of the parallel line.

Snap Object (SO)

If there can be such a thing as a dumb snap, Snap Object is it. It does not calculate a midpoint or a percentage. It does not orchestrate the placement of a parallel line or do anything else even reasonably sophisticated. It just makes sure that the line you are drawing connects to the object you select. It is not limited to a construction point or to a reference point; it can snap to any point on the selected object (Snap Object may be dumb, but it is not stupid).

In the next exercise, you use Snap Parallel to draw a line parallel to the one that extends from the center of the arc at the upper left part of the screen to the top tangent line. You also draw a second arc, parallel to the first one. Because you will take advantage of the Cursor Free (KF) command again, make sure that it is still on (type **KF** or **CF** and read the status—if it says off, you have to type KF or CF again). You will use another Snap command, Snap Object (SO), also.

Snapping to Points with Snap Object

Prompt	Input	Description
Command	**SL**	Starts a line, using the Snap Parallel command to define its location
Parallel to	Click on line extending from center of arc to top tangent line	Identifies the line that will be parallel to the new line (see fig. 4.38)
Change Offset distance (X.000)	2"	Sets a two-inch distance between the two lines (see fig. 4.39)
Enter start point	**SO**	Snap Object sets the start of the line (see fig. 4.40)

continues

137

Prompt	Input	Description
Object to snap to	Click on top tangent line	Selects the top tangent line as object to snap to
Enter next point on line	Move cursor toward top of existing line and snap to nearest point (type **NP** or click on line with third mouse button)	Snap to Nearest Point sets the length of the new line as equal to the first line, as shown in figure 4.41 (note restricted rubber band, even though the cursor can move freely)
Command	Click on a blank menu line or press Esc	Ends the Line command

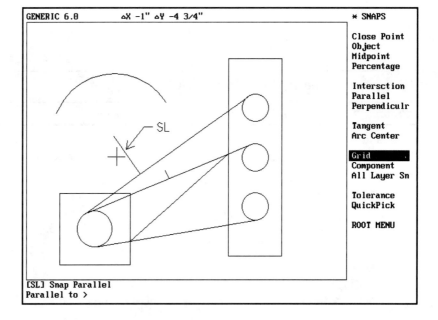

Figure 4.38:

Click on the line that will be parallel to the new line.

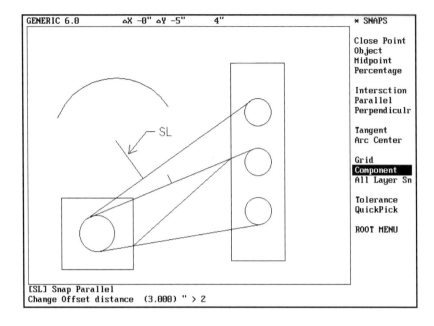

Figure 4.39:

Set the distance between the two parallel lines at two inches.

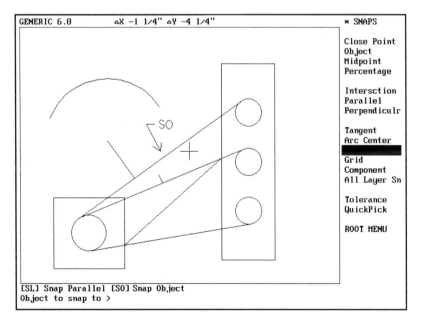

Figure 4.40:

Using Snap Object to identify the starting point.

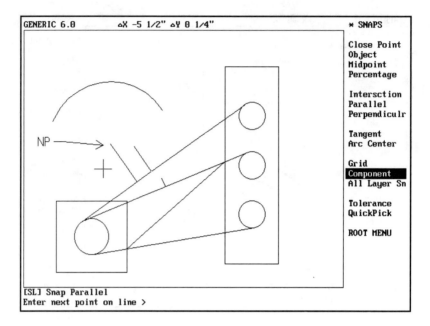

```
GENERIC 6.0        ⊿X -5 1/2" ⊿Y 0 1/4"              * SNAPS

                                                    Close Point
                                                    Object
                                                    Midpoint
                                                    Percentage

                                                    Intersction
                                                    Parallel
         NP                                         Perpendiculr

              +                                     Tangent
                                                    Arc Center

                                                    Grid
                                                    Component
                                                    All Layer Sn

                                                    Tolerance
                                                    QuickPick

                                                    ROOT MENU



[SL] Snap Parallel
Enter next point on line >
```

Figure 4.41:

Use Snap to Nearest Point to set the distance.

Component Snaps (GC)

Component Snaps is a toggle. When it is on, you can snap to construction points on objects that are part of a component. When it is off, the only point on a component that can be snapped is the reference point that identifies it as a component. This command is explored in more detail in Chapter 11, "Components."

Snap to Non-Editable Layers (SY)

If the All Layers Edit command (AL), which was mentioned in Chapter 2, is on, any object on the screen may be edited. If All Layers is off, only the objects on the current layer may be edited. Snap to Non-Editable Layers modifies this slightly by enabling you to snap to objects on visible non-editable layers. If you have hidden the objects on a layer with Layer Hide (YH), they cannot be snapped to, regardless of the status of Snap to Non-Editable Layers.

Like All Layers Edit, Snap to Non-Editable Layers is a toggle; each time you use it, the status switches between on and off.

Redrawing the Screen for Clarity

The bits of light on your monitor that display everything you see are known as pixels. Sometimes, as you draw, a few pixels are unintentionally erased or left on-screen. When you draw a window around an object to erase, for example, the window may erase a bit of a line it crosses even though the line itself is not erased. The redraw commands can clear up unwanted clutter and restore missing pixels.

Redraw (RD)

Redraw, found on the DISPLAY menu, is the command ordinarily used to restore objects to their normal clarity. When you type RD or select this command from the menu, Generic CADD removes and redraws everything in the drawing window. The size of objects does not change (no change in the display scale). The speed of the redraw depends on the speed of your computer equipment and the size of the drawing. Large drawings take more time to redraw than small ones. Having construction points and reference points turned on also can slow down the redraw because their presence means more pixels to display.

Backward Redraw (BR)

If you have a large drawing and find that you need to redraw the screen quite often, you may save time by turning on Backward Redraw, found on the ZOOMS menu.

Backward Redraw is a toggle command. When it is off, the screen redraws items in the order they were drawn. In other words, the first line drawn is the first redrawn. When Backward Redraw is on, and the Redraw command is used, the last line drawn becomes the first line redrawn. The redraw process continues in reverse order until the first line drawn becomes the last line redrawn.

The reason Backward Redraw can be a time-saver is that you usually edit the most recently drawn material. If you must do a redraw before you edit something on-screen, turn on Backward Redraw and issue the Redraw command. The items you drew last redraw first. When everything you need to see is back on the screen, press any key to stop the redraw process. All the objects that do not make it back onto the screen are safe—CADD just did not redraw them. On a slower computer, you can save a minute or more if the drawing is large just by using Backward Redraw and stopping screen redraw when the objects you need are on-screen.

A feature called Quick Pick is introduced in Chapter 9. Quick Pick can speed the search for objects in the drawing; it uses Backward Redraw to set the order in which it searches the drawing's database for objects.

 To gain additional speed in the redraw process, try hiding some of the layers in the drawing.

Window Redraw (WD)

At times, only a small portion of the screen may show stray pixels or have missing pixels. If this is the case, try Window Redraw (WD), found on the ZOOMS menu. You can use it to redraw only the portion of the screen around which you draw a window.

Fast Redraw (FA)

Redrawing large drawings can eat up a lot of time, time you would rather not spend (every time you change the zoom factor) watching Generic CADD redraw what you have created. The Fast Redraw command, on the DISPLAY menu, can help you.

Fast Redraw has seven options, each of which is a toggle. With Fast Redraw, you can do the following:

- Have text redrawn as standard points

- Have arcs redrawn as line segments

- Have all line widths and line types display as width and type zero

- Hide hatch patterns

- Hide solid color fills

- Disable the automatic drawing of layers made visible using Layer Display (YD) or Layer Hide (YH)

- Hide the solid color fills in fillable fonts

If you select the Arcs option, you have an additional choice to make. The number of line segments displayed when Fast Arcs is on can be adjusted. The default is 3, which means that circles are displayed as triangles. You can set Fast Arcs to any number of segments between 3 and 12, but the more segments you choose, the less benefit the command offers.

If you use Fast Redraw to change any of these settings, the new status does not take effect until the next time the screen is redrawn.

Redraws and Multiple Viewports

All redraw commands (as well as zooms, which are covered in Chapter 7) work when Multiple Viewports is in use. How these commands respond depends on the status of Active View (AV). If you have selected one viewport to be active, the redraw command works only in that viewport, no matter what viewport the cursor is in when you execute the command. If no viewport is active, the redraw command operates only in the viewport in which the cursor sits.

Summary

The techniques and tools of manual drafting were developed to serve a specific need—the precise, accurate visual display of design information. To improve upon manual drafting, a CADD program must not only display objects with precision and accuracy but also offer the user the benefits of automation. CADD is only an expensive toy unless it makes drawing objects accurately easier than doing it at the drafting table.

Generic CADD provides a variety of commands to automate and simplify the task of drawing with precision. The on-screen grid provides a visual perspective of relative sizes and interacts with the drawing cursor like a magnet, limiting movement to specific locations. Snap commands use complex mathematics to identify specific locations instantaneously. The different snap commands offer many ways to find the locations of specified points and parts of the basic types of drawing objects. Generic CADD also offers a number of redraw commands, including Window Redraw and Fast Redraw, to improve the clarity of the on-screen image.

Drawing Techniques

The chapters so far have covered the fundamentals of drawing objects on the screen, controlling their display, and using snap commands to move them to precise locations. As you build a drawing, sometimes a new object to be drawn shares a common point or a common length with another object. Taking advantage of these situations in your drawing is known as using existing geometry. The snap commands are all about using existing geometry, and much of the drawing in Chapter 4, including placing the circles inside the rectangles, makes use of existing geometry. You do more of this kind of drawing throughout the later chapters.

In this chapter, you learn more about placing objects in drawings accurately and efficiently. This includes using the various types of keyboard entry to place objects on-screen, more drawing aids, and a few tips for good measure. This chapter shows you that there is always more than one way to draw in Generic CADD; the trick is to use the most efficient method.

When using manual entry, you have three modes available. You also have a variety of ways of controlling the cursor. You can constrain it in several ways, you can have it track where you have been, you can shut off the default rubber banding, or you can operate the cursor without a mouse or digitizer.

Introducing Coordinate Entry Fundamentals

When you draw a line on the screen, it has a start point, a length, a heading (the direction it points), and an end point—and each of these elements has a location. At times, you may not care about any of these aspects; at other times, you may want to be in control of each of these aspects when you draw the line. To sketch a design idea, for example, using the mouse to place lines (combined with the occasional use of Snap to Nearest Point) may be all you need. But if you have to draw an object based on measurements written in a notebook, typing the coordinate locations of each line from the keyboard is easier. Generic CADD calls this *manual entry*.

Everything you draw goes on the coordinate grid, and the location of the cursor on the grid is always displayed in the coordinate display. Chapter 2 demonstrates how the Display Coordinates (DC) command switches the display between absolute, relative, basepoint and polar coordinates. Now you learn how to use each one for drawing.

Absolute Coordinates and Manual Entry Origin

The default coordinate display mode is Absolute Coordinates. If the coordinate display is set to Absolute and reads X 3" Y 3", the cursor is at a location on the grid three inches up from the 0,0 point, and three inches right of the 0,0 point. Thus, the default method of manual entry (keyboard entry) is Origin; every coordinate typed at the keyboard is understood to be in relation to the 0,0 point of the grid, also known as the *Origin Point*. If you press Enter and then move the cursor to the location X 6" Y 6", you create a line similar to the one shown in figure 5.2. Use the following steps to set your display coordinates and manual-entry method to draw this line.

Using Absolute Coordinates

Prompt	Input	Description
`Command`	**SG**	Sets Snap to Grid off (If prompt says ON after you type this command, retype it)
`Command`	**GR**	Sets Screen Grid off (If prompt says ON after you type this command, retype it)
`Command`	**MO**	Sets Manual Entry, Origin ON
`Command`	**DCA**; press Enter	Sets your display coordinates to match figure 5.1
`Command`	**LS**	Sets the screen limits
`Change height limit (X.000)`	**12**	Sets the new height to 12"
`Change width limit (X.000)`	**18**	Sets the new width to 18"
`Command`	**ZL**	Sets the screen view to match the limits
`Command`	**LW8**	Sets line width to 8 (Note that you typed a new line width without waiting to read prompt)
`Command`	**0,0**	Moves the cursor to coordinate location X 0, Y 0
`Command`	**PU**	Issues Pen Up command, so that next movement of cursor does not draw a line

continues

Prompt	Input	Description
Command	3,3	Moves the cursor to coordinate location X 3" Y 3"
Command	6,6	Moves the cursor to coordinate location X 6" Y 6" and draws a line from X 3" Y 3" to here

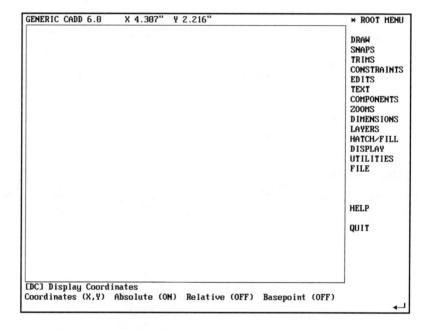

Figure 5.1:

Settings for the Display Coordinates command.

Draw another line using keyboard entry, but first make a change. When you drew the first line, you set Manual Entry to Origin (MO). This means that every coordinate location typed at the keyboard is understood to be so many X units and so many Y units away from the 0,0 point of the grid. Because this 0,0 never changes, you can refer to Manual Entry Origin as creating *absolute* coordinates.

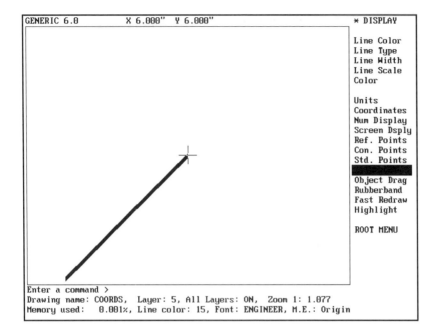

Line Color
Line Type
Line Width
Line Scale
Color

Units
Coordinates
Num Display
Screen Dsply
Ref. Points
Con. Points
Std. Points

Object Drag
Rubberband
Fast Redraw
Highlight

ROOT MENU

Enter a command >
Drawing name: COORDS, Layer: 5, All Layers: ON, Zoom 1: 1.077
Memory used: 0.001%, Line color: 15, Font: ENGINEER, M.E.: Origin

Figure 5.2:

*A line drawn with
Manual Entry Origin.*

Manual Entry Relative

When you set Manual Entry to Relative (MR), every coordinate
location typed at the keyboard is understood to be so many X
units and so many Y units away from the last point placed on the
screen. Because the 0,0 point is always changing, you can refer to
Manual Entry Relative as creating *relative* coordinates. This is an
important distinction that can make a big difference in what you
draw, as you will see.

Using Manual Entry Relative

Prompt	Input	Description
Command	**PU**	Issues Pen Up command
Command	**0,0**	Moves the cursor to coordinate location X 0, Y 0

continues

Prompt	Input	Description
Command	**PU**	Issues Pen Up command
Command	**LW0**	Sets Line Width to zero
Command	**MR**	Sets Manual Entry to Relative (relative to last point entered)
Command	**3,3**	Moves the cursor three inches up and three inches right of last point placed (X 0, Y 0)
Command	**6,6**	Moves cursor six inches up and six inches right of last point placed

In figure 5.3, you see a line drawn using the same numbers as coordinates as the first line, but it looks quite different with Manual Entry Relative in effect.

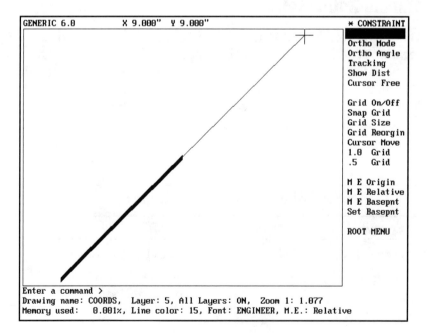

Figure 5.3:

The same line with Manual Entry Relative.

Notice the difference? When the first line was drawn, Generic CADD interpreted everything from the keyboard using only absolute coordinates. When the second line was drawn, Generic CADD interpreted everything from the keyboard using only relative coordinates. With absolute, every coordinate was a set distance from the 0,0 point on the grid. With relative, every coordinate was a set distance from the last point placed.

There is one oddity here. Although you used the Manual Entry Relative (MR) command to tell Generic CADD how to interpret what you typed at the keyboard, you never told it to change how it displays coordinates at the top of the screen. Did you notice in figure 5.3 and in your drawing that the coordinate display at the top of the screen says X 9" Y 9"? The display still tells you where the cursor is by using absolute coordinates, even though the keyboard commands are interpreted as relative coordinates. You can change the coordinate display so that it matches the manual-entry method in operation.

Relative Coordinates

When you are drawing with Manual Entry Relative, typing 6,6 and having the coordinate display read X 9" Y 9" can be confusing. You can use the display coordinate (DC) command to change the coordinate display readout so that it shows the position of the cursor, relative to the last point placed, matching the method of manual entry in use.

Changing the Coordinate Display Readout

Prompt	Input	Description
Command	**DC**	Starts Display Coordinates command
Coordinates (X,Y) Absolute (OFF) Relative (ON) Basepoint (OFF)	**R**	Turns Relative coordinate display on, and turns Absolute coordinate display off (see fig. 5.4)
...Relative (ON)	Press Enter	Saves the changes and ends the command

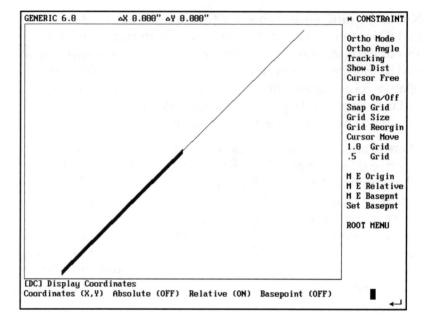

```
GENERIC 6.8              ∆X 0.000"  ∆Y 0.000"              ⋇ CONSTRAINT

                                                          Ortho Mode
                                                          Ortho Angle
                                                          Tracking
                                                          Show Dist
                                                          Cursor Free

                                                          Grid On/Off
                                                          Snap Grid
                                                          Grid Size
                                                          Grid Reorgin
                                                          Cursor Move
                                                          1.8  Grid
                                                          .5   Grid

                                                          M E Origin
                                                          M E Relative
                                                          M E Basepnt
                                                          Set Basepnt

                                                          ROOT MENU




   [DC] Display Coordinates
   Coordinates (X,Y)  Absolute (OFF)  Relative (ON)  Basepoint (OFF)
```

Figure 5.4:

Display coordinates now show relative coordinates.

After you finish this command, the cursor relocates itself to the origin point (absolute 0,0). But be warned—it still considers X 9" Y 9" the relative 0,0 point on the screen and will base its next action accordingly. This is a good time to re-orient the cursor, something you need to do from time to time when drawing with relative coordinates and Manual Entry Relative.

Re-Orienting the Cursor

Prompt	Input	Description
Command	Press Enter	Makes the current cursor location the last point placed
Command	**PU**	Issues Pen Up command (automatic Line command status is off)

Polar Coordinates

The *Cartesian coordinates* you have used so far, both absolute and relative, identify a position. *Polar coordinates* identify a distance and a heading. Switch the screen to display polar coordinates, so you can explore how the polar readout works.

Setting Polar Coordinates

Prompt	Input	Description
Command	**DC**	Initiates Display Coordinates command
Coordinates (polar) ...**A**bsolute (OFF)	**C**	Changes coordinates to Polar (see fig. 5.5)
...**C**oordinates...	Press Enter	Ends command

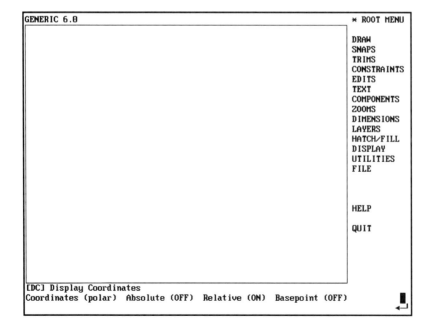

Figure 5.5:

Polar coordinates as the active coordinate method.

Like Cartesian coordinates, polar coordinates can be absolute (based on the origin point of the drawing) or relative (based on the last point placed). When they are relative, the readout on the screen identifies the distance and heading of the cursor based on the last point placed. When polar coordinates are absolute, the readout on the screen identifies the distance and heading of the cursor based on its distance and angle from the origin point. Either way, zero degrees always points to 3 o'clock, and the headings proceed counterclockwise around the circle. Figure 5.6 shows several polar headings.

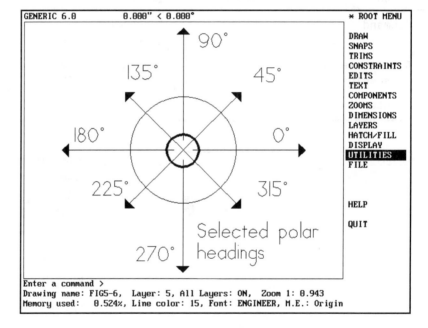

Figure 5.6:

Examples of polar headings.

Follow the steps below to gain practice using polar coordinates.

Using Polar Coordinates

Prompt	Input	Description
Command	**DXY**	Erases the drawing
Command	Use the mouse to move the cursor to the middle of the screen and press Enter	Places the start point of a new line

Prompt	Input	Description
Command	3,<90	Moves the cursor 3" on a 90-degree heading from the last point placed; draws a line
Command	2,<45	Moves the cursor 2" on a 45-degree heading from last point placed; draws a line
Command	4,<180	Moves the cursor 4" on a 180-degree heading from last point placed; draws a line
Command	2,<315	Moves the cursor 2" on a 315-degree heading from last point placed; draws a line
Command	3,<270	Moves the cursor 3" on a 270-degree heading from last point placed; draws a line

Your screen should look like the one in figure 5.7. Save this drawing as SHAPE1.CGD. You will use it in a later chapter.

Prompt	Input	Description
Command	DS	Issues the Drawing Save command
Save File as	Name the file SHAPE1	Saves the drawing as SHAPE1.CGD

Basepoint Coordinates and Manual Entry Basepoint

A *basepoint* in Generic CADD is a temporary origin point you can place anywhere on the coordinate plane. It remains invisible and unused until you set Manual Entry to Basepoint (MB). Then it becomes active, and all keyboard entry is evaluated using the current basepoint. The coordinate display can be set to show either Cartesian (X,Y) or polar coordinates. Whenever Manual Entry is set to Basepoint, a diamond (♦) precedes each number in the coordinate display.

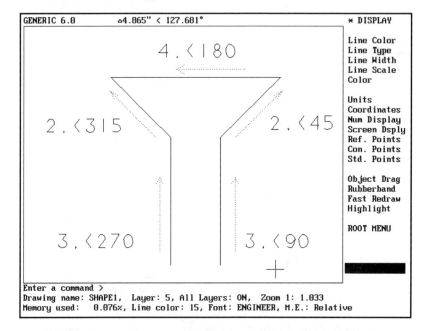

Figure 5.7:

A shape drawn by typing polar coordinates.

Using the basepoint is useful when you want to draw lines that connect to a distant point or to enter a series of coordinates (such as surveyor's data) that all relate to a specific location. The location of the basepoint is set using the Basepoint (BP) command and is expressed in absolute X,Y terms, no matter the mode of manual entry or coordinate display currently in effect.

Choosing and Using a Coordinate Display Method

Here are a few points to remember when choosing a method for manual entry and setting the status of the display coordinates.

- When you select absolute, relative, or basepoint display using the Display Coordinates command, be careful how you make the selection. When you turn on a selection, the alternative selections are turned off automatically. But if you turn off a setting that is on, it switches to off and the others stay off as well, leaving you with no coordinate-display format in effect.

- Be careful to match the manual-entry method with the appropriate coordinate display. It would be confusing to have manual entry set to relative, for example, but have the coordinate display show absolute coordinates.

- Choosing a manual-entry method is usually a three-step process. First you choose the manual-entry method (Origin, Relative, or Basepoint). Then you choose the appropriate coordinate readout to match (polar or Cartesian). Then you select the display type to match the manual-entry method you selected (Absolute for Origin, Relative, Basepoint). If you plan to enter only one or two lines using a manual-entry method, and you do not need to rely on the coordinate display, skipping this process is safe. Just do not forget to return the manual-entry method to Origin.

Using Cursor Control Commands

The shy star of this chapter is the drawing cursor. Earlier, the chapter covered the various ways to describe the location of the cursor on the coordinate plane. Generic CADD gives you several ways to limit the movement of the cursor.

The cursor control commands discussed here are all in the CONSTRAINTS menu. In addition to these commands, the grid commands (Grid On/Off, Grid Size, and three grid settings) are on the CONSTRAINTS menu.

Ortho Mode (OR)

You already are familiar with Ortho Mode. Once Ortho Mode is on (it is a toggle), all lines entered into the drawing are limited to increments of 90 degrees. If you are drawing something with all horizontal and vertical lines, Ortho Mode is an easy way to keep the lines straight.

The Ctrl key works with the Ortho mode as a temporary toggle. If you press Ctrl while drawing, the status of Ortho mode is reversed. If Ortho mode is on, and you need to draw one diagonal line, do not bother to turn Ortho mode off. Just press Ctrl, draw the diagonal, then release Ctrl. If you need one perfectly horizontal line, but Snap to Grid and Ortho mode are off, press Ctrl to make Ortho mode active temporarily. Ortho mode is a powerful drawing tool that you return to again and again throughout the rest of this book.

Ortho Angle (OA)

It is possible to adjust the angles used by Ortho mode. They will still be in increments of 90 degrees, but you can rotate the base heading of Ortho mode from 0 degrees (3 o'clock) to any other angle. If you create isometric drawings, set Ortho Angle to 30 degrees to help you draw lines at the proper angle.

In figure 5.8, the polygon on the left was drawn using Ortho Angle at zero degrees. The one on the right was drawn with Ortho Angle at 30 degrees. (Remember, the Rectangle [RE] command always draws a figure perpendicular to the edges of the screen, no matter what Ortho Angle is set to.)

Tracking (TK)

Tracking enables you to move from one point to another, leaving a trail as you go, in search of a specific point on the screen. Whenever you must enter a point, Tracking is available by typing TK at the prompt. As you move from point to point using Tracking, a line extends back to the last point you placed. When you click to select another point, Tracking forgets about any points selected earlier in Tracking mode and attaches the line to the latest point placed. After you have found your way to the point you need, type **PU** to end Tracking. The last point selected during Tracking is the point you need to finish whatever command was in operation when you started Tracking.

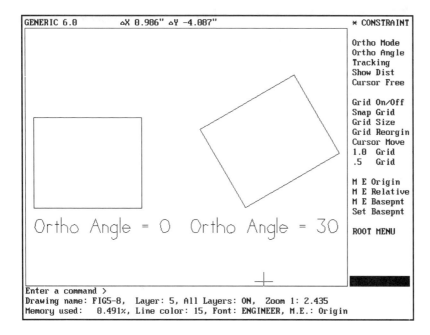

Figure 5.8:

Two polygons drawn with Ortho Mode on.

Tracking is used most often when moving objects and placing components. Hands-on examples showing the use of Tracking are in Chapters 9, 10, and 11.

Cursor Free (CF)

Normally when you draw in Generic CADD, a "rubber band" is attached to the cursor. If you are placing the end point of a line, this rubberband stretches back to the first point placed. If Cursor Free is on (it is a toggle), the cursor becomes detached from the rubberband. As demonstrated in Chapter 4, this enables you to use snap commands that would otherwise be unavailable. You can limit the placement of lines with Ortho mode, and still use nearby points as references to snap to.

Cursor Movement (CM)

If you do not have a mouse or digitizer and must rely on the arrow keys as your only way to move the cursor, you need to be familiar with Cursor Movement (CM), located in the CON-STRAINTS menu. Users who have pointing devices may never need it. If you are using the screen grid and moving the cursor with the arrow keys, Cursor Movement forces the cursor to move only one grid point at a time. Cursor Movement is a toggle, which you should turn on only if you are using the arrow keys and Snap to Grid.

Tandem Cursor

Tandem Cursor, introduced in Chapter 2 with other elements of the Screen Display (DI), is included here to make the discussion of Controlling the Cursor complete.

Tandem Cursor controls the relationship between the drawing cursor (the crosshairs) and the menu bar. If Tandem Cursor is on, both cursors appear all the time, and their movement is linked. If Tandem Cursor is off, only one of the cursors is visible at any one time. Most of the time the drawing cursor is the visible one, but if you move it off the screen to the right, the drawing cursor disappears and the menu bar appears.

Users of earlier versions of Generic CADD generally keep Tandem Cursor set on; they are familiar with that setting because there was no choice before version 6.0. There is one potential benefit to switching to Tandem Cursor off, however. When the cursors are not linked, the first mouse button can be used with both cursors. When the crosshair cursor is active, the first mouse button identifies points and executes commands, as usual. When the menu bar is active, the first mouse button selects the highlighted command. If Tandem Cursor is on, the user *must* use the second mouse button to select items from the menu.

Summary

This chapter focused on cursor movement and the various ways to identify the position of the cursor. Knowing the position and heading of the cursor helps us to use more than one way to place objects in the drawing.

In this chapter, you learned how to draw by typing in coordinates at the keyboard. This is referred to in Generic CADD as manual entry. Manual entry takes three forms, depending on what you use as a reference for your data. Manual Entry Origin uses the 0,0 point of the coordinate grid to calculate the locations of objects, Manual Entry Relative uses the last point placed as a reference, and Manual Entry Basepoint uses a temporary 0,0 point (that you designate) as a reference.

Generic CADD offers two ways to show the location of the cursor on the drawing screen—by using X,Y coordinates (Cartesian coordinates) or by using polar coordinates, which show the heading of the cursor and its distance from point 0,0. What either coordinate method defines as 0,0 depends on the style of operation you choose: Absolute (Origin), Relative, or Basepoint.

In addition to the different methods of manual entry and coordinate display, there are ways to control the movement of the cursor. Ortho mode limits the cursor to increments of 90 degrees. Ortho Angle sets the base angle for ortho mode. Cursor Free allows the cursor to separate from the rubberband line, and Tracking enables you to move from one point to the next in the middle of a drawing command without drawing anything, leaving a temporary trail as the cursor moves.

As your knowledge of Generic CADD increases, you will find ways to take advantage of each of these systems.

The next chapter detours from the techniques of drawing to focus on the techniques of adding text to drawings. A few well-placed words of explanation can make the difference between a good drawing and a great one.

Labeling and Explaining the Drawing

When most people see Generic CADD for the first time, they are impressed by the program's many ways to draw and reshape objects. They applaud the program's ability to place dimensions in the drawing automatically, and they are impressed to see on-screen dimensions recalculate when an object changes shape. Show them text in drawings, however, and most people respond with a shrug. After all, text is text. You type in some words, and they appear in the drawing. No big deal, right? Wrong.

The capability to create and place text in a drawing is one of Generic CADD's best timesaving features. If you had to create legible text by drawing each character, it would take you hours to annotate a drawing. And what style, or typeface, would you use? Could you maintain consistency from letter to letter?

Generic CADD is not a word processing program; it is a graphics program. Text that you place in a CADD drawing is not the same as the text you are familiar with in word processing programs. Generic CADD uses the computer's graphics environment, rather than the text-based environment most word processing programs use. Any text that appears inside the drawing window is actually drawn with lines and curves. The look of the text must conform to generally accepted type styles, called *fonts*.

With the introduction of version 6.0, text handling takes a big leap forward. As part of Generic CADD's increased compatibility with AutoCAD, all 19 standard AutoCAD fonts are now included in Generic CADD. And with an impressive bit of legerdemain, 10 new typeset-quality typefaces also are included. Printed to a laser printer or quality plotter, these new fonts rival the quality you expect from a desktop publishing program. Compare the quality of these fonts with the fonts shipped with any other CADD program on the market; you will be favorably impressed.

Understanding Text Fundamentals

The purpose of text in a CADD drawing is to convey information. This sounds simple enough, but information can be conveyed in many ways. The right fonts for displaying text are a powerful enhancement to any drawing. Consider the following examples of what you can do with fonts.

- **Draw attention.** Bold fonts (especially the new typeset-quality filled fonts in Generic CADD 6.0) focus attention on specific portions of documents.

- **Organize information.** The careful selection of fonts can help to show the relative importance of information, as the use of italic and bold text does in a manuscript.

- **Impart a theme.** Documents created for specific clients often have greater appeal if a type style identified with the client can be used, aiding in visualization of the completed project. With 37 fonts to choose from, each with countless ways to adjust (slant, size, justification, etc.), it is possible to create type style that offers clients a unique look.

- **Display a logo.** Many clients, especially those working on joint projects, want their company name included on the final documents in the type style of their choice.

- **Convey an emotion.** Advertisers have long used type styles to arouse emotion or convey an attitude. Type styles can look whimsical, formal, traditional, or state-of-the-art to set the tone of the document.

- **Perpetuate a tradition.** Sometimes fonts are chosen simply because documents have always been done that way. Some of the fonts included with Generic CADD match hand-lettering styles that have been taught in drafting courses for generations.

- **Greater simulation of the actual product.** By using the actual production type style in a design document, instrumentation and panel labeling can be accurately designed, evaluated, and modified for full effectiveness.

Generic CADD includes three basic steps for using text: selecting the font, setting placement and size options, and placing the text in the drawing. Commands are available to execute these steps, as well as to edit text already placed in a drawing (to edit as text and to "edit" the look, as you would edit any other part of a CADD drawing), to import text from other files, and to create new fonts for use in Generic CADD.

Preparing To Place Text

Before you add text to a Generic CADD drawing, you must select the font you want to use and specify the size, the justification mode, as well as several other options. Many of the available settings rarely change whereas others change every time you use text. All the necessary commands are options under the Text Settings (TS) command.

If you place some text in a drawing and then make adjustments to any part of the Text Settings command, only the text you place after changing the settings is affected. The text already in the drawing does not change. (To change the font of text already part of the drawing, use the Text Change command, discussed later in this chapter.)

Selecting a Font

To select a font, start the Text Settings command by typing **TS** at the prompt line or by selecting SETTINGS from the TEXT menu; press **F** for Font. A list of the available fonts appears in the menu (see fig. 6.1). (Although no longer on the menu as a separate command, the Font Select command, available in earlier versions of Generic CADD, can still be accessed by typing FS.)

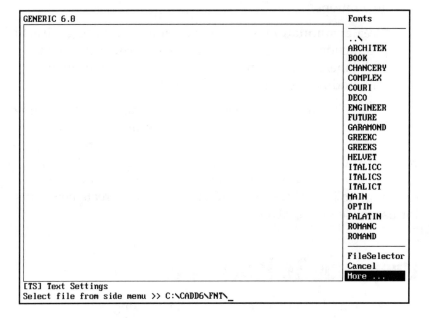

Figure 6.1:

Available fonts appear in the menu.

Depending on the video system you have and the number of fonts you have installed on your hard drive, you may or may not be able to see the entire list of available fonts. Select the More option to view the rest of the list. If you have fonts in other directories on your hard drive, select the backslash symbol (..\) in the menu to view another directory or use File Selector. If you do not need to change any other text setting, end the command by pressing Enter after you have selected the font.

If you have used older versions of Generic CADD, please note that the program no longer gives you the MAIN font as a default. The default font is now the last font used.

Generic CADD 6.0 offers 37 fonts. If you seek even greater variety, two volumes of additional fonts are available separately from Autodesk Retail Products, and several third-party vendors have fonts for sale. You also can create your own fonts, as discussed later in this chapter. Figures 6.2 through 6.6 show most of the fonts available in Generic CADD 6.0.

```
GENERIC 6.0 B1.35    X 14.976"   Y 6.532"              Fonts
                                                       ..\
   MAIN             TEXT                               ARCHITEK
                                                       BOOK
   AaBbCcDdEeFfGgHh    AaBbCcDdEeFfGgHh                 CHANCERY
   IiJjKkLlMmNnOoPp    IiJjKkLlMmNnOoPp                 COMPLEX
   QqRrSsTtUuVvWwXx    QqRrSsTtUuVvWwXx                 COURI
   YyZz 0123456789     YyZz 0123456789                 DECO
                                                       ENGINEER
                                                       FUTURE
   SIMPLEX          COMPLEX                             GARAMOND
                                                       GREEKC
   AaBbCcDdEeFfGgHh    AaBbCcDdEeFfGgHh                 GREEKS
   IiJjKkLlMmNnOoPp    IiJjKkLlMmNnOoPp                 HELVET
   QqRrSsTtUuVvWwXx    QqRrSsTtUuVvWwXx                 ITALICC
   YyZz 0123456789     YyZz 0123456789                 ITALICS
                                                       ITALICT
                                                       MAIN
   ITALICS          DECO                               OPTIM
                                                       PALATIN
   AaBbCcDdEeFfGgHh    AaBbCcDdEeFfGgHh                 ROMANC
   IiJjKkLlMmNnOoPp    IiJjKkLlMmNnOoPp                 ROMAND
   QqRrSsTtUuVvWwXx    QqRrSsTtUuVvWwXx
   YyZz 0123456789     YyZz 0123456789                 FileSelector
                                                       Cancel
                                                       More ...
[TS] Text Settings
Select file from side menu >> C:\CADD6\FNT\_
```

Figure 6.2:

These six fonts are from previous versions of Generic CADD.

Start Generic CADD and select a font by following the steps in this hands-on exercise:

Changing a Font

Prompt	Input	Description
Command	**TS**	Starts the Text Settings command (see fig. 6.7)
Font...	**F**	Select a font
Select file from side menu	Move menu bar to Engineer and click second mouse button, or press Home	Selects Engineer as the new font for text in the drawing

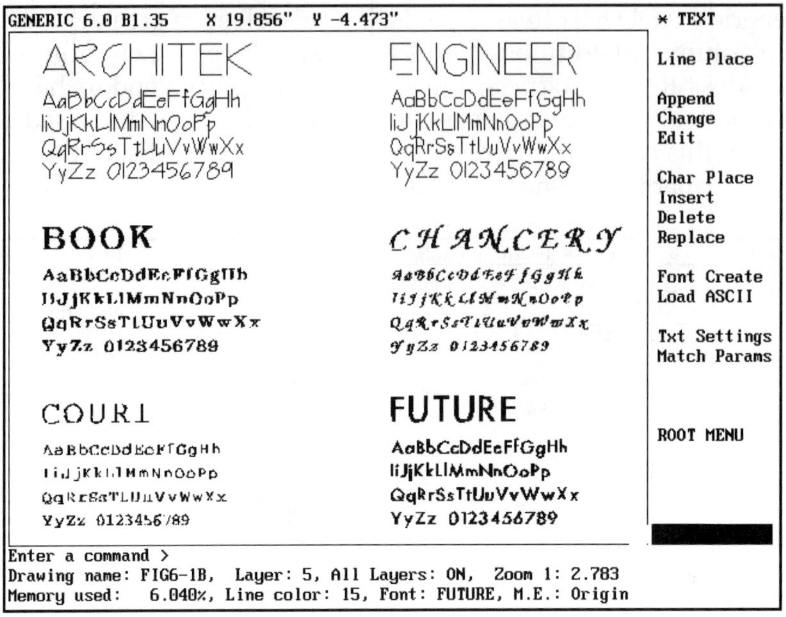

Figure 6.3:

Architek and Engineer are single-line fonts; the others are filled.

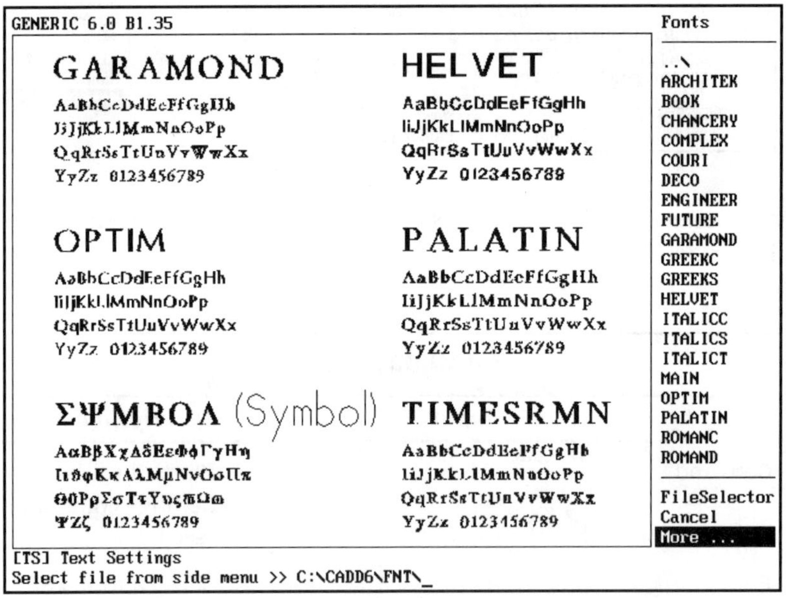

Figure 6.4:

These six fonts are all filled.

```
GENERIC 6.0 B1.35    X 24.858"  Y 6.968"              Fonts

                                                       ..\
  ΓΡΕΕΚΧ (Engineer)    ΓΡΕΕΚΣ (Greeks)               ARCHITEK
  AαBβXχΔδEεΦφΓγHη      AαBβXχΔδEεΦφΓγHη               BOOK
  ΙιϑϑΚκΛΛΜμΝνΟοΠπ      ΙιϑϑΚκΛΛΜμΝνΟοΠπ               CHANCERY
  ΘϑΡρΣσΤτΤυ∇∈ΩωΞξ      ΘϑΡρΣσΤτΤυ∇∈ΩωΞξ               COMPLEX
  ΨψΖζ 0123456789      ΨψΖζ 0123456789                COURI
                                                       DECO
                                                       ENGINEER
  ITALICC              ITALICT                         FUTURE
  AaBbCcDdEeFfGgHh     AaBbCcDdEeFfGgHh                GARAMOND
  IiJjKkLlMmNnOoPp     IiJjKkLlMmNnOoPp                GREEKC
  QqRrSsTtUuVvWwXx     QqRrSsTtUuVvWwXx                GREEKS
  YyZz 0123456789      YyZz 0123456789                 HELVET
                                                       ITALICC
                                                       ITALICS
  ROMANC              ROMAND                           ITALICT
  AaBbCcDdEeFfGgHh    AaBbCcDdEeFfGgHh                 MAIN
  IiJjKkLlMmNnOoPp    IiJjKkLlMmNnOoPp                 OPTIM
  QqRrSsTtUuVvWwXx    QqRrSsTtUuVvWwXx                 PALATIN
  YyZz 0123456789     YyZz 0123456789                 ROMANC
                                                       ROMAND

                                                       FileSelector
                                                       Cancel
                                                       More ...
[TS] Text Settings
Select file from side menu >> C:\CADD6\FNT\_
```

Figure 6.5:

These six fonts also are found in AutoCAD.

```
GENERIC 6.0 B1.35    X 24.736"  Y 5.005"              Fonts

                                                       ROMANS
  ROMANS              ROMANT                           ROMANT
  AaBbCcDdEeFfGgHh    AaBbCcDdEeFfGgHh                 SCRIPTC
  IiJjKkLlMmNnOoPp    IiJjKkLlMmNnOoPp                 SCRIPTS
  QqRrSsTtUuVvWwXx    QqRrSsTtUuVvWwXx                 SIMPLEX
  YyZz 0123456789     YyZz 0123456789                 SYASTRO
                                                       SYMAP
                                                       SYMATH
  SCRIPTC             SCRIPTS                          SYMBOL
  AaBbCcDdEeFfGgHh    AaBbCcDdEeFfGgHh                 TEXT
  IiJjKkLlMmNnOoPp    IiJjKkLlMmNnOoPp                 TIMESRMN
  QqRrSsTtUuVvWwXx    QqRrSsTtUuVvWwXx
  YyZz 0123456789     YyZz 0123456789

  SYASTRO             SYMAP

                                                       FileSelector
                                                       Cancel
                                                       More ...
[TS] Text Settings
Select file from side menu >> C:\CADD6\FNT\_
```

Figure 6.6:

These six fonts also are found in AutoCAD.

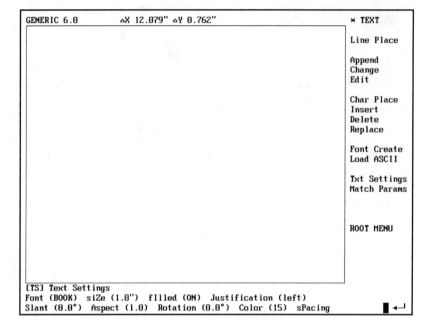

Figure 6.7:

The Text Settings command options.

Text Size

Text size, along with the font, is perhaps the most often adjusted text setting. The order in which these settings are presented is the order you should follow when preparing to place text. Because many of the other settings rely on the size of the text, it should be set before Aspect, Justification, Spacing, and so on.

If you plan to print or plot your drawing at a certain scale, set the text size accordingly. If, for example, you need to print the drawing at a scale of 1" = 1' (1/12 scale), and you want your text to be 1/4" tall on paper, set your text size to 3" (1/4" × 12). A required scale on paper of 1/4" = 1' (1/48 scale), with text 1/4" high on your printout would require a text size of 12" (1/4" × 48).

To set the size of text (see fig. 6.8), start the Text Settings command and then press **Z**, or use the first mouse button to click on siZe in the prompt lines. Type in the new size and press Enter.

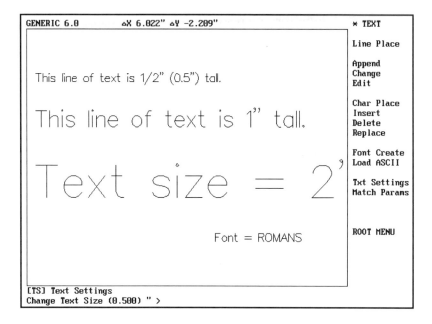

Figure 6.8:

The Size option of Text Settings.

Filled Text

Of the fonts included with Generic CADD 6.0, 10 are outline fonts that can be filled with a solid color. This has the effect of making the characters (letters, numbers, punctuation, and symbols) look as if they were printed by a desktop publishing program instead of a CADD program. Some Generic CADD users—primarily those who use Generic CADD for technical illustration—also use draw or desktop publishing programs, such as CorelDRAW! or PageMaker. They draw in Generic CADD but import the final drawing to the other program to add typeset-quality text. Having these new fillable fonts available in Generic CADD should reduce the need for using a second program just to add text to finish a CADD drawing.

Using the new typeset-quality text does not mean that you must use a laser printer. These fonts look exceptional on any device Generic CADD can print to. Now pen plotters and dot-matrix printers can produce the same quality as laser printers. Do not let the way these fonts look on-screen keep you from using them;

even on a VGA monitor, the resolution of the drawing on the screen is much less than the resolution of the printed drawing (even printed to a 9-pin dot-matrix printer). The higher the resolution you select, of course, the better the fonts look.

The Fill option is a toggle; it affects only the 10 fonts that can be filled (and any fillable fonts you create, as is explained later in this chapter). If Fill is on, all placements of a fillable font in the drawing will have solid color fill. The color of the fill is always the color of the text. If Fill is off, any fillable text in the drawing is left unfilled (see fig. 6.9).

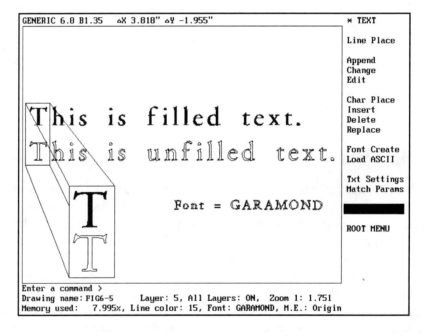

Figure 6.9:

An example of filled and unfilled text.

Note that this setting operates differently than most commands that affect appearances in Generic CADD. All occurrences of a fillable font in the drawing are affected by the toggle. You cannot mix filled and unfilled text in one drawing. If you set Fill off, place some words in the drawing, and then set Fill on and place some more text, the final appearance of both placements of text depends on the status of the Fill setting when you print the drawing. You can take advantage of this by setting Fill off until you are ready to print. Because solid color fills cause slow redraws, you can save time by leaving the setting off until you are ready to print. (Another way to increase redraw speed is to use Fast Redraw, as explained in Chapter 4.)

If you must use both filled and unfilled fonts in a drawing, use the Explode (EX) command on the characters you want unfilled. The Explode command, explained fully in Chapter 10, strips characters of their identity in the drawing database. CADD sees the lines that make up these characters as unrelated to each other and leave them unfilled. To completely explode text placed as lines, you have to explode the characters twice. The first use of Explode changes lines of text to individual characters, but the program still sees them as text characters and fills them if the fill toggle is on. The second use of the Explode command finishes stripping the characters of their identity as text; they remain unfilled, even if the fill toggle is on.

If you use filled text, it is best to not adjust the Slant or Aspect of the text (as explained later in this chapter). These fonts were designed to look just like their namesakes in typography. Changing the Slant or Aspect can easily change the text you are placing into a caricature of the font rather than a variation.

The fill toggle is the only Text Settings option that applies to text placed by dimensioning commands. Dimensioning is covered fully in Chapter 13.

Text Justification

The Justification option affects only text placed as lines, not text placed as individual characters. You have three choices with this command: Left, Center, and Right. When you use the Text Line Placement (TL) command to place a block of text (one or more lines), you are asked to select a starting point, also known as the *insertion point*. Justification uses the insertion point to determine where to place text.

Left justification means that the left edge of the text is flush with the left margin, as with the text you are reading now. The insertion point is the leftmost point of the line, and the reference points of all other lines in the block line up immediately below the first point. All of the text is placed to the right of the point.

Center justification means that for every line of text placed in the drawing (while this command is in effect), half of the line is to the left of the insertion point and half is to the right.

Right justification means that the right edge of the text is flush with the right margin. The first line's insertion point is the rightmost point of the first line, and the reference points of all other lines are immediately below the first line's reference point.

Figure 6.10 illustrates a single paragraph, placed using each of the three justification options. Each line in the center of the drawing shows where the cursor was placed to start each insertion of text.

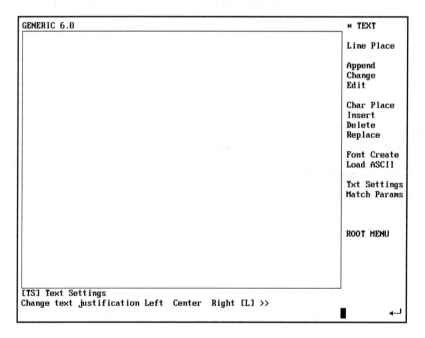

Figure 6.10:

Three justification options.

Text Slant

The Slant option enables you to make each character slant forward or backward, for an italicized effect (see fig. 6.11). You can adjust the slant between negative 45 degrees and positive 45 degrees. The default, for text standing straight up, is zero degrees.

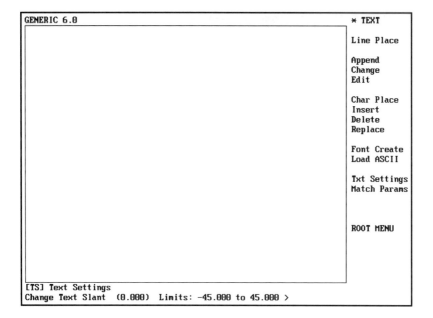

Figure 6.11:

Text slant.

Text Aspect

Aspect, which controls the width of each character, is independent of the actual size of the text. The default setting is 1, meaning that text will be the width it was when the font was designed. Setting the Aspect at 2 doubles the width of each character (see fig. 6.12). The maximum value for Aspect is 10; the reasonable minimum is .1. Assigning a negative value to Aspect causes each character to be placed as a mirror image of the normal character.

If space is limited, Aspect can sometimes be used to create display text that is no taller than other text in the drawing but stands out because of the width change.

Changing the Aspect command affects newly placed text only; any characters already in the drawing do not change to the new aspect.

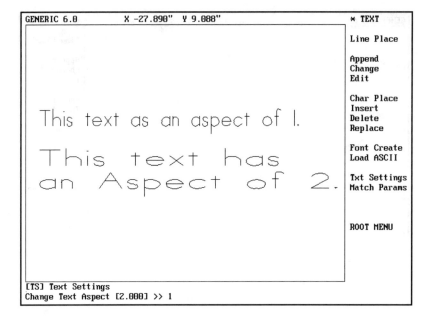

Figure 6.12:

Text Aspect.

Text Rotation

By using the Text Rotation option of Generic CADD's Text Settings command, you can place text at any angle. Positive numbers give an upward slant; negative numbers give a downward slant. The default is zero degrees, for horizontal text. Figure 6.13 shows some of the effects you can achieve with the Text Rotation option.

Text Color

Any color available on your system in Generic CADD can be used as the color for text, through the Color option of Text Settings. After typing TS, type **C** for color. The color palette for your system appears in the menu. Type the corresponding number and press Enter, or use the menu bar to choose a color.

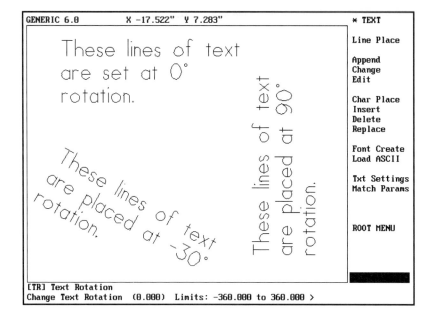

Figure 6.13:

Examples of text rotation.

Text Spacing Options

All of the Text Settings options discussed so far affect the look of the characters and their placement on the screen. The next set of options control the spaces between the characters and between the lines. The three spacing options are available under the sPacing option of Text Settings. Press **P** from the Text Settings menu to reach these choices (see fig. 6.14).

Between Character Spacing

Between Character, the first option listed for the Text Spacing command, controls how much space is placed between characters. The default, which generally results in the best-looking placement, is 20 percent. This means that CADD places between characters a space that is 20 percent of the text size in use. Figure 6.15 illustrates the use of the Between Character space option. To set the Between Character space, type **C** at the sPacing options menu.

177

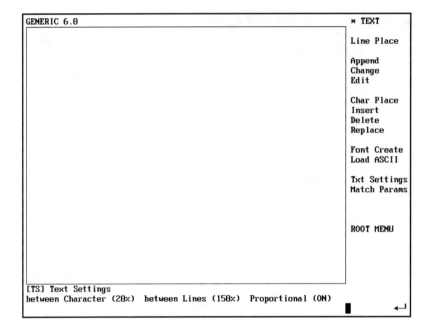

Figure 6.14:

Using the sPacing option of Text Settings.

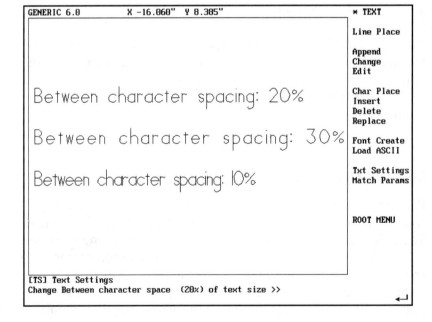

Figure 6.15:

Different spacings, set by using the Between Character option.

Between Line Spacing

Between Lines, the second spacing option, controls how much space is placed between lines when more than one line of text is placed in the drawing. The default spacing is 150 percent, using text size as the measurement. You can see samples of different spacing in figure 6.16.

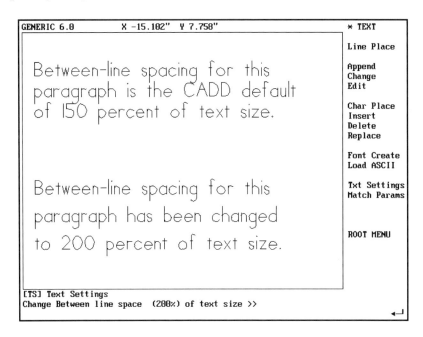

Figure 6.16:
Different line-spacing effects.

Each line of text placed in the drawing has a reference point at the beginning of the first line. The Between Lines option adjusts the distance from the reference point of the first line to the reference point of the next line, and all lines thereafter. When you need to place more than one line of text, 150 percent (the default) usually is the best choice.

Proportional Spacing

The Proportional Spacing option is a toggle. The default setting is on, which means that as text is placed (using the Text Line command only; more on that shortly) the spacing between characters is varied to produce more reasonable text. The Between Character space of each character is taken into consideration by Generic CADD in determining the placement of each character in the line. An "i," for example, takes up less space on the line than a "w." Observe the difference in figure 6.17.

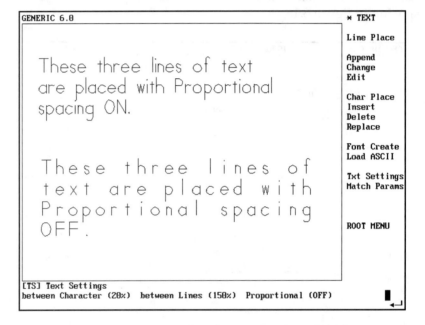

Figure 6.17:

The Engineer font, showing proportional spacing on and off.

If the Proportional Spacing option is off, all text is set in monospace, meaning that an "i" takes up as much space on the line as a "w." Between Character spacing is the same for each character when Proportional Spacing is off.

Placing and Editing Text

After you have set all the text-spacing options, you can focus on placing text in your drawing. Generic CADD provides two methods for placing text in your drawing: as lines of text placed as one unit or as individual characters.

Each line of text placed with the Text Line command is considered by Generic CADD to be one entity. Each line has one reference point at the beginning of the line. The Text Edit (TE) command is used to edit lines of text, if necessary. Justification and proportional spacing work only with text lines, not with text placed as individual characters. The other settings work with both styles of text placement. To edit text placed as individual characters, use Text Insert (TI), Text Delete (TD), or Text Replace (TX), explained later in the chapter.

Placing Text

As mentioned earlier, two commands place text in a drawing: Text Line Placement (TL) and Text Character Placement (TP). Both commands are found in the TEXT menu.

The Text Line Placement command is the preferable method of placing text in a drawing. Text lines are more easily edited than text placed as individual characters, they can be justified and proportionally spaced, and they take up less memory in the drawing file. But to place only a few characters in a drawing, consider using Text Character Placement instead. Individual characters are easier to move, and can be quickly exploded (reduced to lines, which then can be edited individually). Text placed using the Text Line Placement command also can be exploded, but this requires an additional step.

Text Line Placement (TL)

The Text Line Placement command enables you to enter one or more lines of text. CADD treats each line as a single entity, not as individual characters or as lines, arcs, and so on. After you type **TL** or select Text Line from the TEXT menu, the Enter starting point prompt appears. Move the cursor to the place where you want the first line to start and click your mouse to select the point. Then type each line of text, pressing Enter to place the line in the drawing. As you type, the text appears at the bottom of the screen in the prompt line. A rectangle (called a *bounding box*) is drawn to represent the text. If you need to change what you have typed, and it still is in the prompt line, press Backspace or the arrow keys to move through the text. Pressing Backspace deletes one character to the left, just as it does in most word processors. When you press Enter at the end of the line, the bounding box is replaced by the text. To overwrite existing text, press Insert, and type new characters over the existing ones.

After typing your last line of text, press Enter to place the line, and then press Esc to end the Text Line Placement command. The (PU) command usually works whenever you need the Esc key, but not when you are entering text. If you were to type PU, the letters would be placed in the drawing, not interpreted as a command.

Now try a few text operations. In the following exercise, you set up a grid and place a left-justified paragraph on the upper part of an 8.5" by 11" rectangle. After you are finished, your screen should look like figure 6.18.

Placing the First Paragraph

Prompt	Input	Description
Command	**GS**	Places a grid on the screen
Change grid size X	Type **.5** and press Enter	Sets the grid spacing to .5"
Change grid size Y	Press Enter	Accepts .5" as height spacing for grid
Command	**SG**	Starts Snap to Grid command; if response shows "off," type **SG** again
Command	**TS**	Starts Text Settings command
(Text Settings screen)	**Z**	Sets size of Screen drawing text
Change Text Size	Type **.25** and press Enter	Sets size to 1/4"

Prompt	Input	Description
(Text Settings screen)	**F**	Selects font
Select font...	Type **Engineer** and press Enter twice	Selects Engineer as new font
Command	**RE**	Draws a rectangle
Enter one corner of the rectangle	Type **0,0** and press Enter	Sets the bottom corner at coordinate location X 0, Y 0
Enter opposite corner	Type **8.5, 11** and press Enter	Sets the top corner at coordinate location X 8.5", Y 11'''
Command	**ZA**	Starts Zoom All command
Command	**TL**	Starts the Text Line Placement command
Enter starting point	Type **.5,10** and press Enter	Places insertion point at X .5", Y 10"
>	Type **This text is one-quarter inch tall. If** (press Enter) **printed at full size, it will be one-quarter** (press Enter) **inch tall on paper.**	Displays and places the text in the drawing (press Enter at the end of every line and press Esc to end the command)

By typing three characters at once, you can go into a command quickly, choosing an option at the same time. You use this technique in the next exercise as you change text slant and size and place a second paragraph of text. The results are shown in figure 6.19.

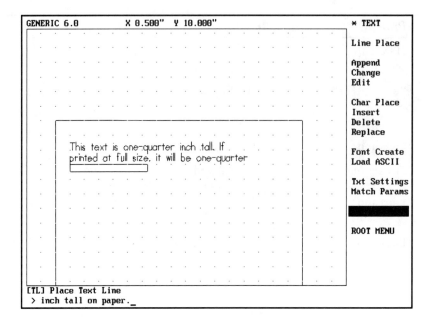

Figure 6.18:

Place the first paragraph at the top of the drawing.

Placing the Second Paragraph

Prompt	Input	Description
Command	**TSS**	Starts Text Spacing Slant command
Change Text Slant	Type **15** and press Enter	Changes slant to 15 degrees
Command	**Z**	Starts Text Size command
Change Text Size (0.250)	Type **.5** and press Enter twice	Changes text size to .5"
Command	**TL**	Starts the Text Line Placement command

Prompt	Input	Description
Enter starting point	Move cursor to X .5 Y 8 and press Enter	Places insertion point at X .5", Y 8"
>	Type **This text is one-half** (press Enter) **inch tall, placed at a** (press Enter) **slant of 15 degrees.** (Press Enter and Esc)	Displays and places the text in the drawing

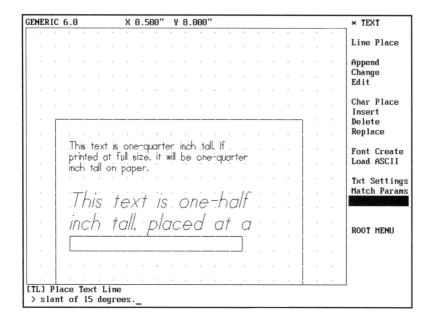

Figure 6.19:

Add the next paragraph of text.

The next paragraph's text is a full 1" tall and centered in the rectangle. Do not try to put too many words on a line. Figure 6.20 shows the resulting text.

Placing the Third Paragraph

Prompt	Input	Description
Command	**TSS**	Starts Text Spacing Slant command
Change Text Slant	Type **0** and press Enter	Returns text slant to normal (zero degrees)
...Justification	**J**	Justifies text
Change text justification	Type **C** (do not press Enter)	Centers text
Command	**Z**	Starts Text Size command
Change Text Size	Type **1** and press Enter twice	Displays new text size as 1" and ends command
Command	**SG**	Turns off Snap to Grid command
Command	**TL**	Starts Text Line Placement command
Enter starting point	Type **4.25,4.5** and press Enter	Displays insertion point for next paragraph
>	**This text** (press Enter)**is 1"** **tall** (press Enter and Esc)	Displays and places two lines of centered text

Finally, along the rectangle's right edge, place a line of text at a rotation of 90 degrees, as shown in figure 6.21.

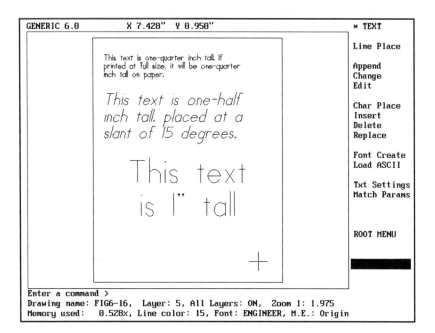

Figure 6.20:

Enter two lines of centered text.

Placing the Fourth Paragraph

Prompt	Input	Description
Command	**SG**	Turns on Snap to Grid
Command	**TR**	Shortcut to the Text Rotation command
Change Text Rotation	Type **90** and press Enter	Sets new text placement angle to 90 degrees
Command	**TZ**	Shortcut to the Text Size option
Change Text Size	Type **.25** and press Enter	Sets new Text Size to .25"
Command	Type **TSJR** and press Enter	Sets text justification to Right

continues

Prompt	Input	Description
Command	**TL**	Starts the Text Line Placement command
Enter starting point	**8,10.5**	Sets insertion point at X 8" Y 10.5"
>	Type **This text is one-quarter inch tall, and is rotated 90 degrees.** Press Enter and Esc	Displays and places one line of right-justified text

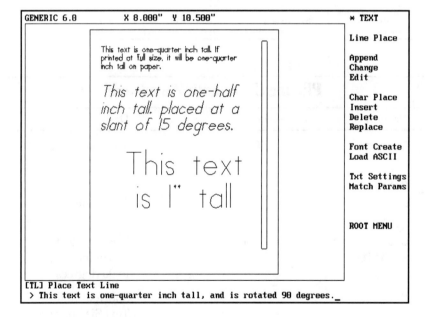

Figure 6.21:

Place a line of text along the right edge of the sheet.

Text Character Placement (TP)

Use the Text Character Placement command when you do not want the text you place to be tied together as a single entity, as it is with the Text Line Placement (TL) command. All of the Text

Spacing options (except Justification and Proportional spacing) apply to Text Character Placement.

With Text Line Placement, after you identify an insertion point you are stuck with that location for the text you need to place. The Text Character Placement command, however, gives you the option of moving the insertion point for each character you place, if you choose. This feature is used to place a number at each corner of a rectangle in the next exercise.

Here is the sequence of commands: after typing TP or selecting Char Place from the TEXT menu, move the cursor to the location in the drawing where you want the first character placed. Press Enter or the first mouse button to identify the location. Type the character you need (in this case, the numeral 1). Instead of pressing Enter or Esc, press the first mouse button. An I-shaped cursor appears, replacing the normal Text Character Placement cursor (a flat line). When the I-shaped cursor is on the screen, you may use the mouse to move it to any other location on the screen (see fig. 6.22). When you click at the new location, the text-placement cursor returns. Type the required characters. After you finish entering text with Text Character Placement, press Esc.

Changing to the I-Shaped Cursor

Prompt	Input	Description
Command	**RE**	Draws a rectangle
Enter one corner of the rectangle	Move cursor to X 2, Y 2 and press Enter	Places upper left corner of the rectangle
Enter opposite corner	Move cursor down and right to X 6, Y .5 and press Enter	Places lower right corner of the rectangle
Command	Type **TR0** and press Enter	Sets Text Rotation to zero degrees
Command	**TP**	Starts Text Character Placement command

continues

Prompt	Input	Description
Enter text starting point	Move cursor near top left corner of rectangle and click first mouse button or press Enter	Sets starting point for text placement
Enter a character	Click first mouse button; text placement cursor is replaced by I-shaped cursor	Displays I-shaped cursor; starting point may be changed or text settings altered

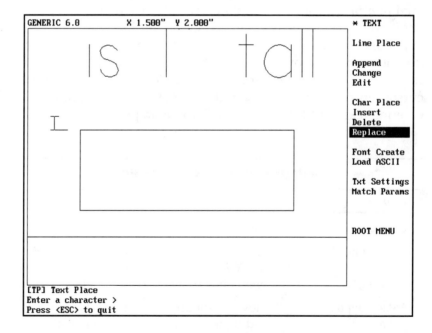

Figure 6.22:

The I-shaped cursor used with Text Character Placement command.

Text settings can be changed when the I-shaped cursor is on the screen, as in the following exercise (see fig. 6.23).

Changing Text Settings

Prompt	Input	Description
Enter a character	Type **TSA2** and press Enter twice	Changes Text Spacing Aspect to double width
Enter a character	Click first mouse button	Returns to text placement cursor
Enter a character	**1**	Places the numeral 1 at the top left corner of the rectangle
Enter a character	Click first mouse button	Switches to I-shaped cursor

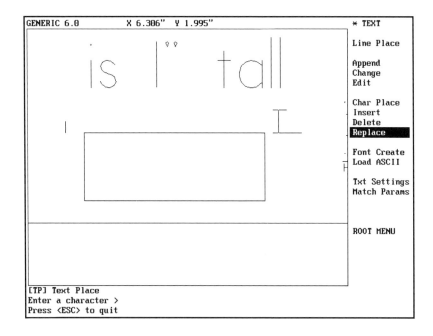

Figure 6.23:

Using the I-shaped cursor to select a new placement point.

In the next exercise, you put a numeral at each corner of the rectangle (see fig. 6.24). Notice that while moving from corner to corner, you are still in the Text Character Placement command and remain there until you press Esc.

Numbering the Rectangle's Corners

Prompt	Input	Description
Enter a character	Move I-shaped cursor to top right corner of rectangle	Selects new placement point for text
Enter a character	Click first mouse button and type **2**	Identifies new placement point for text; places numeral 2 at top right corner of rectangle
Enter a character	Click first mouse button	Switches to I-shaped cursor
Enter a character	Move I-shaped cursor to bottom left corner of the rectangle and click first mouse button	Selects new placement point at bottom left corner of rectangle
Enter a character	3	Places the numeral 3
Enter a character	Click the first mouse button; move I-shaped cursor to bottom right corner of the rectangle and click first mouse button	Selects new placement point at bottom right corner of the rectangle

Prompt	Input	Description
Enter a character	4	Places the numeral 4
Enter a character	Press Esc	Ends Text Character Placement command

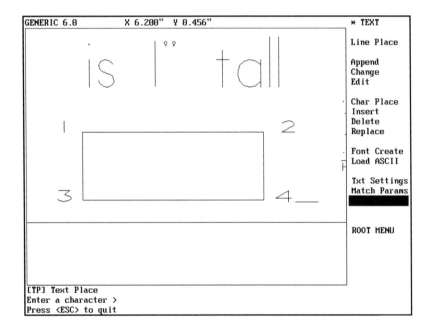

Figure 6.24:

Each corner has been numbered.

Editing Text

Whenever you work with text, changes frequently are necessary. Working with text in Generic CADD is no exception. You need to become familiar with the various text editing commands available.

Each of the two text-placement commands has corresponding editing commands. Use Text Edit (TE) and Text Append (TA) for text placed using Text Line Placement. Text Insert (TI), Text Delete (TD), and Text Replace (TX) are for text placed with Text Character Placement.

In Generic CADD, editing also means changing objects in the drawing. The lines that make up text characters also can be edited as objects, so that you can change their color, size, line type, and so forth. The Text Change (TG) command, a special version of the Change (CG) command, is exclusively for text placed using Text Line Placement. The Explode command, discussed in Chapter 10, must be used before object-editing any text placed with Text Character Placement.

Text Edit (TE)

The Text Edit command, found in the TEXT menu, is used to make changes to text placed in a drawing with the Text Line Placement command. To use Text Edit, type **TE** or select Edit from the TEXT menu, and click on or very near the reference point of the line you want to edit. Just use the first mouse button. (You do not need to use Snap to Nearest Point.) A bounding box appears around the line, and the text appears in the prompt line at the bottom of the screen. Use Backspace, the left-arrow and right-arrow keys, and Del to make changes to your text, just as you would in a word processor. When finished, press Enter.

When first used, Text Edit is in insert mode. If you move the text cursor to the middle of the line and type any letters, the characters to the right move to make room for the new text. If you prefer to use overtype mode (in which any new text replaces old text) press Insert. The small text cursor is replaced by a large one. To return to insert mode, press Insert again. (The Insert key switches between the two choices. No menu command or two-letter command for this function is available.)

Fast Text, one of the features of the Fast Redraw (FA) command introduced earlier in the book, can be used to speed your work with text. Follow the steps below to edit the second paragraph on the screen.

Preparing Text for Editing

Prompt	Input	Description
Command	**FA**	Displays Fast Redraw options
fast Text (OFF)	Type **T** and press Enter	Turns on Fast Text and exits command
Command	**ZW**	Starts the Zoom Window command
Place window	Draw a window around the second paragraph of text (which begins This text is one-half...)	Provides a close-up view of the paragraph to be edited (see fig. 6.25)
Command	**TV**	Starts Fast Text View command to redraw Fast Text so that it is visible
Place window	Draw a window around the reference points of the three lines in the second paragraph	Redraws the second paragraph to make it readable; leaves other text in Fast Text mode (see fig. 6.26)

In the next exercise, you edit the first line of the second paragraph. When you click on the reference point of a line with the first mouse button, the line to be edited appears in the prompt line and a bounding box surrounds the text on-screen. Reference points appear in the illustrations for clarity, but are not required to be visible when you follow these instructions.

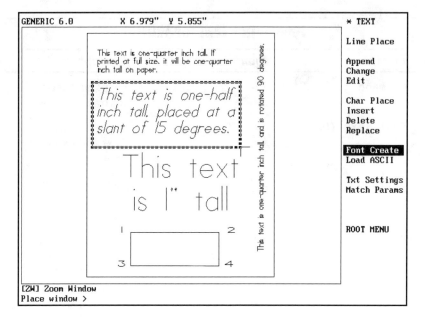

Figure 6.25:

Drawing a Zoom Window around the second paragraph.

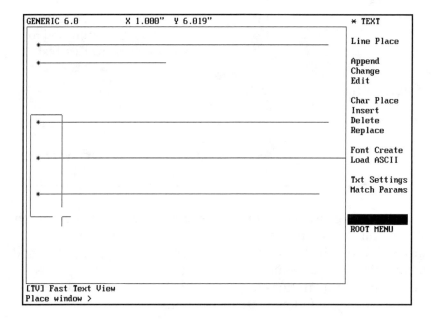

Figure 6.26:

Draw the Text View window around reference points of the lines.

Editing Text

Prompt	Input	Description
Command	**TE**	Starts Text Edit command
Pick text line to edit	Move cursor to the reference point of the first line in the paragraph; click on it	Selects the first line of the second paragraph for editing
>	Use Backspace key to erase one-half; type **1/2"** and press Enter	Edits line (see fig. 6.27)

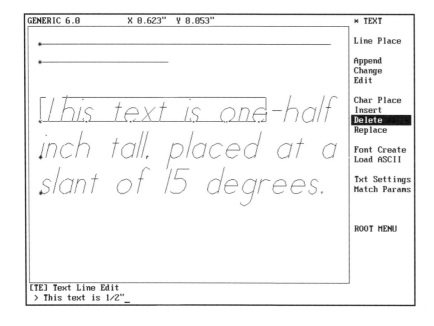

Figure 6.27:

Press Backspace to erase old text, and then type in new text.

Note that when you select the line to be edited, a bounding box appears on the screen to surround the line, but the line itself remains on-screen. After you make the changes and press Enter, the text line is redrawn. Because the Fast Text command is on, only a straight line appears, and the old text remains (stray pixels, so to speak). Use the Redraw command (RD) to restore the screen.

Editing Another Line

Prompt	Input	Description
Command	**RD**	Redraws the screen
Command	Type **TV** and draw a window around the paragraph	Uses Text View to view the second paragraph
Command	**TE**	Displays the Text Edit command
Pick text line to edit	Click on or near the reference point of the second line in the second paragraph	Selects the second line of the second paragraph
>	Place cursor under the t in tall, press Backspace to erase inch, and then press Enter	Removes the word inch from the beginning of the second paragraph (see fig. 6.28)

Text Append (TA)

A complicated drawing may have many separate objects and several blocks of text. You may labor over it for hours, and then set it aside to work on another project. What if a week goes by, and the client tells you that you need to insert one line of text? What font did you use? At what size? How far down from the last line should you place the new text?

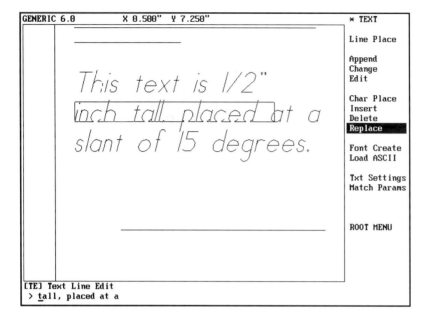

Figure 6.28:

Use Text Edit to erase the word "inch" from the second line.

The Text Append (TA) command can save a great deal of time whenever new lines of text need to be added to an existing block of text. After you type **TA** or select Append from the TEXT menu, the prompt asks you to click on the line of text. Then the command automatically adjusts every element of the Text Settings command as needed to add new material to the existing block. You may enter one line or several, just as you would with the Text Line Placement command.

Text Append works with lines of text only, not with text placed using the Text Character Placement (TP) command.

Text Change (TG)

Use the Text Change command when you want to change the appearance of the text, but not the context. Text Change is a special version of the Change (CG) command for text; it enables you to change the font, the justification, and the between-character spacing of text placed with the Text Line Placement (TL) command. Using Text Change, you also can switch proportional text to monospace (and vice versa) and change the slant and aspect of text already in the drawing.

The Text Change command does not work with text placed using Text Character Placement. To change text placed as individual characters, use the Explode command to reduce the text to lines, arcs, and so on, and then use the Change (CG) command. See Chapter 10 for more information.

In the next exercise, try changing fonts, as shown in figure 6.29.

Changing Fonts with the Text Change Command

Prompt	Input	Description
Command	**RD**	Redraws the screen
Command	Type **TV** and draw a window around the second paragraph	Redraws the second paragraph
Command	Type **TG** or select Change from the TEXT menu	Displays the Text Change command
Window...	Type **W** or click on Window in the prompt line	Uses Window selection to identify the text to change
Place window	Draw the window around the three reference points of the three lines in the second paragraph	Selects the second paragraph as the text to be changed
<RET>to accept...	Press Enter or click on <RET>urn in the prompt line	Ends selection process
...Font...	**F**	Changes the font of selected text

Prompt	Input	Description
Select font from side menu	Move menu bar to Architek, and click second mouse button	Selects Architek as new font for the selected text
Text Line Change	Press Enter	Ends Change command
Command	**FAT**	Uses the Fast Redraw command to turn off Fast Text
Command	**RD**	Redraws the screen

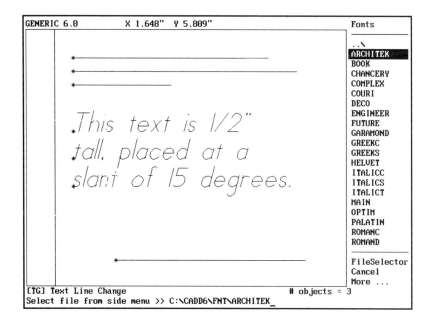

Figure 6.29:

Select Architek as the new font for the selected text.

Text Insert (TI)

Text Insert, found in the TEXT menu, is the first of three commands for editing text placed using Text Character Placement (TP). Use it to place a letter in an existing line. After you type **TI** or select the command from the menu, you are prompted to identify a character. Generic CADD moves this character (and all those following) one space to the right. You then type the character to be added to the line.

The command is good for one character only; if you need to insert more than one character, use the Text Replace (TX) command, discussed in the next section.

In the next hands-on exercise, you place a pound sign (#) in front of the numeral 1, near the rectangle.

Editing with the Text Insert Command

Prompt	Input	Description
Command	**ZA**	Starts the Zoom All command
Command	Type **ZW** and draw a window around the rectangle at the bottom of the screen; be sure to include the number at each corner	Provides a close-up view of the rectangle
Command	**TI**	Starts the Text Insert command
Point to insert location	Move cursor to the numeral 1 and click on the reference point	Places another character in front of the numeral 1
Enter character to insert	#	Places the pound sign in front of the numeral 1 (see fig. 6.30)

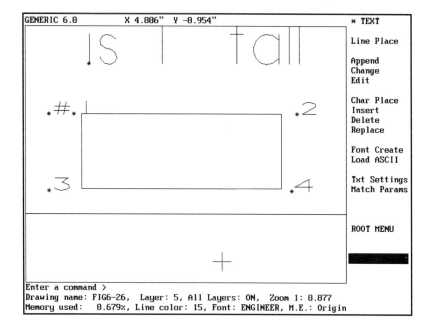

Figure 6.30:
Text Insert is used to place "#" in front of "1."

Text Replace (TX)

Of the three commands used to edit single-entity text (text placed with Text Character Placement), Text Replace is the only one that can affect more than one character. After you type **TX** or select Replace from the TEXT menu, you are prompted to select the character to be replaced. When you click on a character, a text cursor appears beneath it. Type a letter, number, or other character to replace it. The new character replaces the old, and the cursor moves to the next space. You may continue to replace characters or add new text if no other characters are present. If you press Enter, the text cursor moves down a line from where you started, and you may continue to enter new text. To finish, press Esc.

Using Text Replace to Multiple Characters

Prompt	Input	Description
Command	TX	Starts the Text Replace command
Enter Text Starting Point	Move the cursor to the numeral 3	Selects the 3 as the character to be replaced
Enter a character	a	Replaces the numeral 3 with a lowercase a
Enter a character	Press the right arrow key eight times, bringing the text cursor directly under the numeral 4	Moves the text cursor to the numeral 4
Enter a character	b	Replaces the numeral 4 with a lowercase b (see fig. 6.31)

Text Delete (TD)

The Text Delete command is straightforward. Type **TD** or select Delete from the TEXT menu, and click on the character you want to delete. The character disappears. If it was part of a row of characters placed at the same time, the characters to the right of the deleted character move left one space to fill the gap. Feel free to try using Text Delete to eliminate any of the text characters surrounding the rectangle in the preceding exercise.

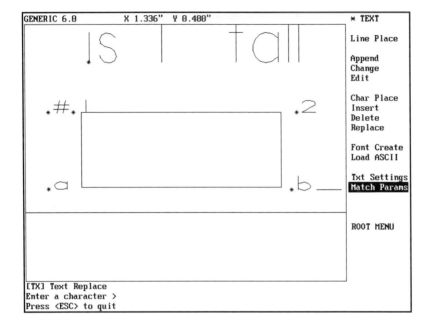

Figure 6.31:

Using Text Replace to replace numbers with letters.

Loading Text Files into a Drawing

Although Generic CADD makes placing text in a drawing as convenient as possible, it is a drafting and design program, not a word processor. If you need to place a significant quantity of text in a drawing, first prepare the text in a word processor and then import it into CADD, using the Load ASCII (LA) command.

ASCII is a standard format for text files. Virtually all word processors and text editors, as well as most spreadsheets and database programs, can save text in ASCII format, even if they normally save text in a different format. Any text file that has been saved in ASCII format can be imported into Generic CADD by using the Load ASCII command.

Some of the files in which Generic CADD stores configuration data are in ASCII format. In the following exercise, you load one of them into a drawing.

Loading an ASCII File

Prompt	Input	Description
Command	**DS**	Saves the drawing
Save file as	**TEXT**	Establishes TEXT as name of the file
Command	**DXY**	Removes the drawing
Command	**LA**	Starts the Load ASCII command
Select file from side menu	**CONFIG6.FIL**	Loads file CONFIG6.FIL from the CADD6 directory (see fig. 6.32)
Enter placement point	When bounding box appears, move cursor so that the entire box is visible; click to select the placement point	The bounding box represents the size of the text file when drawn on the screen (see fig. 6.33)
Command	**ZA**	Starts the Zoom All command

While the bounding box is on-screen, before you click to select a placement point, you can change the rotation, slant, spacing, or aspect of the text, using the commands discussed earlier in this chapter.

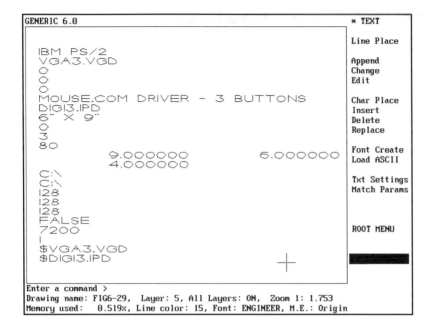

Figure 6.32:

Complete CONFIG6.FIL file. (Yours may be different.)

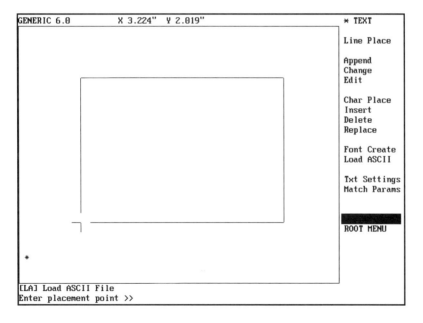

Figure 6.33:

Text first appears as bounding box, showing text block size.

Placing a Schedule in a CADD Drawing

The Load ASCII command has various uses. For many users, being able to import ready-made schedules (such as construction or purchase details that relate to the objects in the drawing) is a real timesaver. Although the details of creating a schedule depend greatly on the type of drawing to be done (ranging from designing machine parts to drafting home-remodeling projects), you need to keep certain fundamentals in mind.

The Load ASCII command brings text into the drawing as text lines. It determines the length of a line as one paragraph, using the end-of-paragraph marks invisibly embedded within the text file to identify lines. You can save time by setting the length of the lines before you import the file (by editing the text into short paragraphs in your word processor).

If you need to place the text inside a legend box, take time to consider the line spacing before you import the text. Is 150 percent of text size as a between-line spacing the correct distance, or do you need to adjust it higher or lower? Take time also to consider the between-character spacing.

Be sure to put the text on a layer by itself, so that it is easy to hide or erase. To do so, select a new layer, using Layer Current (YC) before you import the text file with Load ASCII.

Chapter 15 also discusses this topic, which covers the new Bill of Material utility program included with Generic CADD 6.0.

Creating New Fonts

Suppose that you need a special look for your text, but not one of the fonts in Generic CADD is appropriate. You can create your own font. The command is Font Create (WT), in the TEXT menu. Creating a complete font takes a great deal of time and requires much planning. The letters must conform to a common style and should blend well. The letters also should contain as few arcs or

Bézier curves as possible, if you are concerned about redraw speed.

Text characters in the new font must not contain any existing text characters or components unless they have been exploded first to reduce each character or component to separate objects.

Saving new characters as a font may be confusing the first time you try it. Generic CADD saves the character you create to the file of the currently active font, as named by the use of the Text Settings command. So that you do not ruin an existing font by redrawing some of its characters, before you create a new character, use the Text Settings command to name a font not already defined.

The following exercise shows how to save an object as a character in a new font.

Saving a New Font Character

Prompt	Input	Description
Command	**DXY**	Erases the drawing
Command	Type **C2** and draw a modest circle	Draws a circle as part of a new text character to be created
Command	Type **RE** and draw a square around the circle	Draws a square to complete the object to be made into a new text character
Command	**FS**	Selects text font
Select font	**DODO**	Names the new font
File C:\CADD6\ FNT\DODO.FNT Not Found!! Is this a new font?	**Y**	Tells CADD that DODO is to be considered a new font

continues

Prompt	Input	Description
Selected font is DODO		Any objects now saved as a character become part of a font called DODO
Command	**WT**	Starts Window Create command
Draw window	Draw the window around the circle and the square	Identifies the objects to be saved as a text character
Enter the character to be defined	**O** (capital O)	Object becomes capital O in the new font (see fig. 6.34)
Enter a point at the lower left of character	Move the cursor to the lower left corner and click	Identifies the location of the new character's reference point
Command	**TP**	Tests the new font
Select text starting point	Move the cursor anywhere and press Enter	Selects where the text should go
Enter a character	**O**	New character appears on-screen

If you have created a new font and want it to be fillable, like the desktop-publishing-quality fonts included with Generic CADD, you must take one additional step after all the characters in the font have been identified. You use a utility program (called FILLFONT) in the \CADD6 directory to make new fonts fillable.

FILLFONT runs from the DOS prompt; it is not executable from *Inside Generic CADD 6*, 2nd Ed., unless you use the Shell to Executable (SH) command to leave CADD temporarily. (To do this, type **SH COMMAND.COM** and press Enter twice. Type **EXIT** at the DOS prompt to return to Generic CADD.)

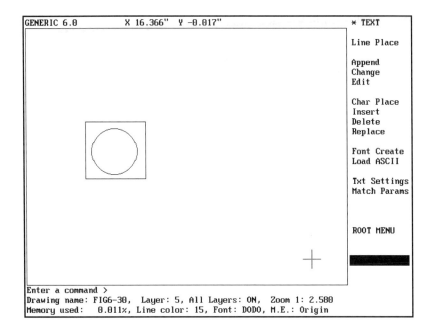

```
GENERIC 6.0          X 16.366"   Y -0.017"              * TEXT

                                                         Line Place

                                                         Append
                                                         Change
                                                         Edit

                                                         Char Place
                                                         Insert
                                                         Delete
                                                         Replace

                                                         Font Create
                                                         Load ASCII

                                                         Txt Settings
                                                         Match Params


                                                         ROOT MENU

                    +

Enter a command >
Drawing name: FIG6-30,  Layer: 5, All Layers: ON,  Zoom 1: 2.580
Memory used:   0.011%, Line color: 15, Font: DODO, M.E.: Origin
```

Figure 6.34:

The circle in the square is a new font.

All characters in a font you want to designate as fillable must follow the rules CADD uses to fill objects with solid color (see Chapter 12, "Drawing Enhancements," for more information). Lines, arcs, circles, spline curves, and Bézier curves may be used to create the characters. All end points on all objects in the characters must meet exactly, and not overlap.

Before using FILLFONT the first time, it is a good idea to move the utility program to the font directory (most likely \CADD6\FNT, unless you identified another directory for fonts when you installed Generic CADD). The move ensures that you can use the utility program without always having to type a file's DOS path first. The easiest way to get both the utility and the font to convert into the same directory is to use the DOS COPY and ERASE commands. Assuming that all your fonts are stored in a directory called \CADD6\FNT, at the DOS prompt of the \CADD6 directory, type: **COPY FILLFONT.EXE C:\CADD6\FNT** and press Enter. Then, while still in the \CADD6 directory, type **ERASE FILLFONT.EXE** and press Enter so that you do not have two copies of the utility on your hard drive. (If you have DOS 5.0 or equivalent, use MOVE instead of

COPY to eliminate the step of erasing the copy from the \CADD6 directory.)

After you have defined all the characters of the font, exit CADD and go to the \CADD6\FNT directory (assuming that you moved FILLFONT to this directory). To use the utility, at the DOS prompt type **FILLFONT**, followed by the name of the font you want to identify as fillable. If the font is called DODO, for example, type the following:

FILLFONT DODO.FNT

and press Enter.

There are two other ways to take advantage of FILLFONT. The utility can be used to strip a fillable font of the ability to be filled, and it can be used to rename a font as it is being made fillable.

To designate FUTURE.FNT as unfillable (as shipped with Generic CADD 6.0, it is a fillable font), you would type:

FILLFONT /U FUTURE.FNT

and press Enter.

The rename option is useful if you want two versions of a font, one fillable and the other not fillable. To create two versions of DODO.FNT, type:

FILLFONT /R DODO.FNT

and press Enter.

The utility program prompts you for the name to give to the fillable version of the font. In this example, it would be a good idea to respond by typing **DODOFILL.FNT** and pressing Enter.

The resulting fillable font is called DODOFILL.FNT; the unfillable font, DODO.FNT.

Summary

The ability to add text to a Generic CADD drawing should not be taken for granted. If text in a CADD drawing had to be drawn character by character, as it does in manual drafting, it would add hours to the process of completing a drawing.

Text in Generic CADD has special properties that distinguish it from the other types of objects used to create drawings. Text may be placed as lines or as single characters, and special editing commands are available for each type of text. Because Generic CADD sees text as an entity different from other objects in the drawing, most editing commands used in drawing do not work on text.

By placing lines of text, you can use proportional spacing and a choice of justification styles. If you place text as individual characters, you easily can change the placement of one letter without affecting others in a line. CADD text is not the same as text used by your word processor. In many instances, the text needs to conform to the traditional look of drafting text. Most of the fonts shipped with Generic CADD match traditional drafting fonts. Others match the look of typeset-quality fonts available in desktop publishing programs.

All text characters in Generic CADD are made from lines, arcs, circles, and Béziers, linked together by the program to create a font, a style of text. If one of the 37 fonts shipped with the program does not match a style you need, you can create a new font. Additional fonts are available from Autodesk Retail Products and other sources.

Knowing how to place and edit text is an important step on the road to mastering Generic CADD, as important as learning to use the basic drawing and editing commands. The next two chapters take the basics you have learned so far and amplify them in two important areas: adjustment of the screen display and the printing of drawings.

Getting around the Screen

Your drawings become increasingly complex as you continue using Generic CADD. As a result, you may want to examine small portions of a drawing to be sure that all objects are precisely constructed.

Most of the items you draw will have a real-scale size larger than the screen display, although drawings by machinists and electronic engineers are exceptions. To ensure accuracy, you must be able to view a segment of a drawing close up. To avoid distraction, restricting the view to certain objects also is helpful.

Generic CADD provides a variety of ways to view a drawing and to adjust the view to suit your needs. These commands are explored in this chapter, using SHAPE1.GCD, the drawing you created in Chapter 5.

Most of the commands for controlling the screen display are found on the ZOOMS menu. Although these commands control the display scale for objects on the screen, only one of them requires you to choose a specific scale.

Think of your computer monitor as the eyepiece on a video camera. You can zoom in for a close-up view or zoom back for a wide-angle shot. You do not have to calculate a specific scale to get these views with the video camera; you just press the button to adjust the lens.

In addition to the zoom commands, you can use the layer commands to limit what appears on the screen. Chapter 2 points out the benefit of dividing the drawing into several layers. If you are drawing a complicated schematic or construction plans with many overlapping sets of information, draw related portions on their own layer to make them easy to hide or display.

The MultiView command, introduced in Chapter 2, also can simplify working on complicated drawings. As you learn in this chapter, combining layer management with the use of MultiView can get tricky.

Experimenting with these commands demonstrates how easy and convenient they are. They quickly will become essential to your CADD work.

Using Zoom Commands

All the zoom commands are found in the ZOOMS menu, shown in figure 7.1. If you learn only a few of the two-letter commands, some of the zoom commands should be among them. Flipping back and forth through the menus to change the view on the screen can be tedious; let the two-letter commands save you time.

If you have not already done so, load SHAPE1.GCD, which you created in Chapter 5. (A copy of SHAPE1.GCD is on the optional disk available for use with *Inside Generic CADD 6*, 2nd Edition.)

Loading the SHAPE1 Drawing

Prompt	Input	Description
Command	**LO**	Starts the Load command
Load	**D**	Six choices are listed; choose D to load a drawing
Select from side menu	**A:\SHAPE1**	Loads drawing from optional disk

Prompt	Input	Description

If you want to load a drawing from an earlier drawing session instead of a drawing from the optional disk, use the menu to locate the directory of the drawing, and select the drawing with the menu bar, or type in the directory and file name at the prompt.

Prompt	Input	Description
Enter an insert origin. Press <RET> for 0,0	Press Enter	Places the origin drawing at 0,0 point on screen

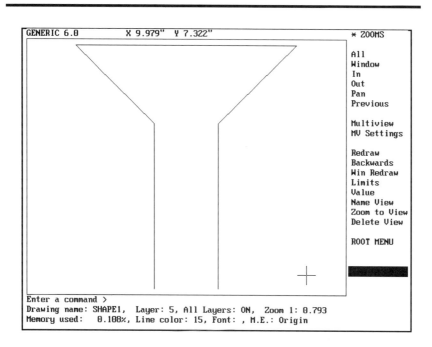

Figure 7.1:

The ZOOMS menu in Generic CADD, with SHAPE1.CGD loaded.

Zoom All (ZA)

When you load the SHAPE1.GCD file, the entire drawing fills the screen, as in figure 7.1. This is the same view provided by the Zoom All command. Whenever you use one of the other commands and want to see the entire drawing again, type **ZA** and CADD displays it.

If you want to know the scale of the drawing as it appears on-screen, the current scale is always visible in the prompt lines, listed as the Zoom. For the current view of SHAPE1, the zoom scale is 1:0.793. This means that one unit in the real world of the drawing (inches, in this case) equals 0.793 inches on-screen. The exact scale on your monitor may vary according to the size of the screen and the resolution it provides.

Zoom Limits (ZL)

The Limits command, discussed early in the book, is used to define a boundary for your work. The Zoom Limits command redraws the screen to show the limits you have chosen. If your entire drawing fits inside the limits, it will be visible, although not necessarily at the same scale as drawn by the Zoom All command.

After you type **ZL**, the screen is redrawn to the dimensions of the screen limits. Figure 7.2 shows SHAPE1, redrawn using the Zoom Limits command with the limits set to 12" x 18".

Figure 7.2:

SHAPE1.GCD redrawn using the Zoom Limits command.

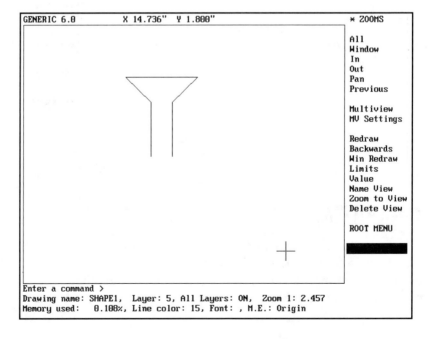

Zoom Window (ZW)

At times, you may want to get a close-up view of a small portion of the drawing. The easiest way to do this is to use the Zoom Window command. When you type **ZW** or select Window from the ZOOMS menu, you are prompted to draw a window around the portion of the drawing you want to see close up. Your first mouse click sets the first corner of the zoom window. When you click the mouse the second time to set the opposite corner of the window, Generic CADD calculates the zoom scale needed to draw only the objects inside the window and displays these objects on the screen. Figure 7.3 shows where to place the window for the following exercise; figure 7.4 shows a view of the top left corner of SHAPE1.GCD after the Zoom Window command has been completed.

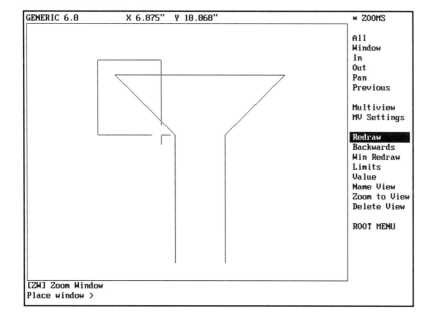

Figure 7.3:

Where to place the window to execute the Zoom Window command.

Placing a Zoom Window

Prompt	Input	Description
Command	**ZA**	Starts Zoom All command
Command	**ZW**	Starts Zoom Window command
Place Window	Move cursor above and left of corner and click to set first point; move cursor down and right to draw window; click again to finish window and execute Zoom Window command	Identifies part of drawing to be zoomed

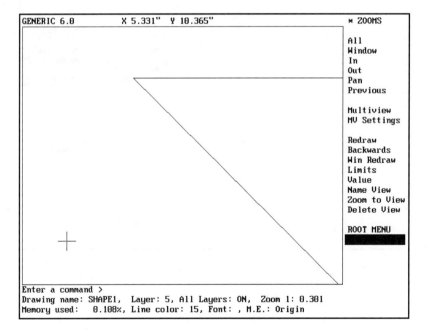

Figure 7.4:

The view after completing the Zoom Window command.

Zoom Previous (ZP)

You just completed a Zoom Window command. The zoomed view on the screen before this was a Zoom All view of the drawing. If you wanted to go back to the Zoom All view, you could type **ZA** again, for Zoom All. Typing **ZP**, for Zoom Previous, would be a better choice, however.

Why is Zoom Previous a better choice? When Zoom All is invoked, it must calculate the dimensions of the drawing and then calculate how best to fit the drawing on the screen. The Zoom Previous command does not calculate anything; it just knows the coordinates of the last zoom and adjusts the screen to match. If you have a very complicated drawing, one that takes a long time to redraw, using Zoom Previous instead of a zoom command that requires calculation saves time. If you are using SHAPE1.GCD, the redraw time of the two commands is virtually the same because the drawing is small; the time difference is greater if the drawing is complicated.

Zoom In (ZI) and Zoom Out (ZO)

The Zoom In and Zoom Out commands are like two sides of a coin. Zoom In redraws objects at twice the currently displayed size; Zoom Out redraws objects at half that size.

The key to these two commands is the placement of the cursor. Each command prompts you to select the center of the new view. Do this by moving the cursor to the location you want and clicking the first mouse button (or pressing Enter). If the center of this new view is any kind of point (construction, standard, or reference), you can use Snap to Nearest Point (NP or third mouse button) to select that point as the center of the zoom. Generic CADD then recalculates the zoom value, either doubling or halving it, and makes your chosen location the center of the display.

To gain an ever-tighter or ever-wider view of a portion of the drawing, use either command several times in succession. Each time, the displayed view is either half as large (Zoom Out) or twice as large (Zoom In) as the previous view. Figure 7.5 shows where to click when using the Zoom In command; figure 7.6 shows the new view after you use the Zoom In command on the last view.

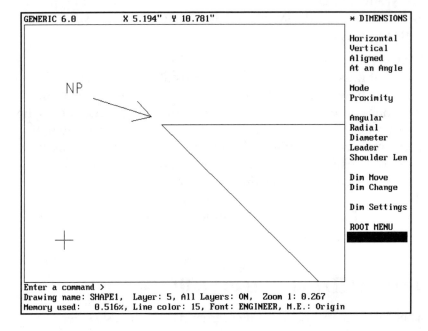

Figure 7.5:

Snap to Nearest Point sets center of new view for Zoom In command.

If you have used older versions of Generic CADD, you may be familiar with the Zoom Up and Zoom Back commands. Zoom In and Zoom Out are those same commands, renamed. The old two-letter commands, ZU and ZB, are still available if you want to use them.

Zooming with Zoom In

Prompt	Input	Description
Command	**ZI**	Starts Zoom In command
Enter center of zoom	Move cursor to corner and type **NP**, or press the third mouse button	Selects the corner as the center of the new view

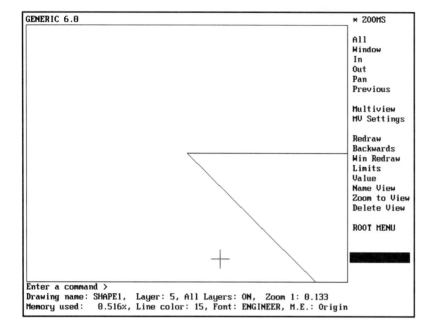

Figure 7.6:

The view after Zoom In command is used.

Zoom Value (ZM)

If you need to see objects on-screen at a certain scale size, use the Zoom Value command. A setting of 2 makes objects appear at half their actual size (two inches in the drawing displays as one inch on-screen). This command can be used in a pinch when you need to measure something but do not have a ruler. (This is measuring's equivalent of bringing the mountain to Mohammed.) First, draw a ruler using the Copy command to mark off sixteenths of an inch along a line seven inches long. Use the Zoom Value command to redraw the line at a 1:1 view, so that one inch on-screen equals one inch in real-world units. Then place your object on-screen and measure it against the CADD ruler you have just created. Voilá! Instant ruler; perfect measurement!

Figure 7.7 shows the display after the Zoom Value command has been used to set the screen to a 1:1 view, with the corner as the center of the display.

Setting the Screen to a 1:1 View

Prompt	Input	Description
Command	**ZM**	Starts the Zoom Value command
Enter zoom value 1	**1**	Sets new zoom value at 1:1
Enter new center of screen	Move cursor to corner and type **NP** or press third mouse button	Identifies center of new display

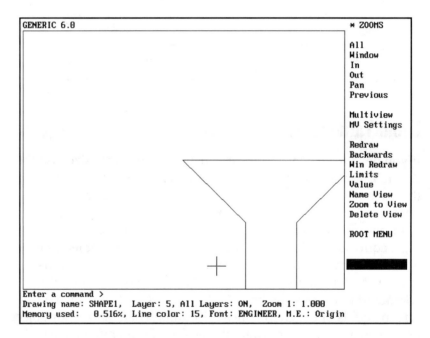

```
GENERIC 6.0                                          * ZOOMS

                                                     All
                                                     Window
                                                     In
                                                     Out
                                                     Pan
                                                     Previous

                                                     Multiview
                                                     MV Settings

                                                     Redraw
                                                     Backwards
                                                     Win Redraw
                                                     Limits
                                                     Value
                                                     Name View
                                                     Zoom to View
                                                     Delete View

                                                     ROOT MENU


Enter a command >
Drawing name: SHAPE1,  Layer: 5, All Layers: ON,  Zoom 1: 1.000
Memory used:   0.516%, Line color: 15, Font: ENGINEER, M.E.: Origin
```

Figure 7.7:

Set a zoom value of 1 to display the object at full scale.

Pan (PA)

Sometimes you may want to slide the display without changing the zoom value. The Pan command shifts the view without changing the zoom value. To use it, type **PA** or select Pan from the

ZOOMS menu. When you click on a location, Generic CADD calculates how to adjust the display so that the point you select becomes the center of the display, without changing the zoom factor.

Utilizing Preselected Views

If you are working with a large drawing, you may want to return often to several locations in the drawing, either while you are creating it or after you have finished. You can define these special locations as views and bring them to the screen by using the Zoom View (ZV) command. Use the Name View (NV) command to save the views. When you no longer need a saved view, delete it with the Delete View (NX) command.

Name View (NV)

The first step in using a preselected view is to name it. Use any of the zoom commands to set the screen the way you want it, and then use the Name View command to save the coordinates and zoom value for later use. In the following exercise, you zoom in on the corner again with the Zoom Window command, and then save the close-up view as a named view.

Naming a View

Prompt	Input	Description
Command	**ZW**	Starts the Zoom Window command
Command	**NV**	Starts the Name View command
Enter view name	**LCORNER**	Names the current display, saving the view for future use

Zoom View (ZV)

To use a Named View, type **ZV** or select View from the ZOOMS menu. After you are prompted for the name of the view, type the name or select it from the menu. The screen is redrawn to the zoom value and coordinates of the named view.

Note that a named view saves the view, not necessarily the objects in the view. If you save a view and then erase something in that view, the object is no longer visible when you summon the named view.

Delete View (NX)

If you decide you do not need a particular preselected view, use the Delete View command to remove it from the drawing. Type **NX** or select Delete View from the ZOOMS menu. Type the name of the view to be deleted, or select the name of the view from the menu.

Using Zooms from Other Commands

All zoom commands can be used as nested commands, which means that you can use them while you are doing something else. Whenever you can place a point on the screen or move the cursor, you can use a zoom command to change the display on-screen.

In the steps that follow, a line is drawn connecting the left corner with the bottom right of the object on-screen. You start with a tight view of the corner, and then change the view in the middle of the Line command to view the lower right portion of the object. To set up the drawing for the following exercise, change the current layer before you draw the line.

Another way to accomplish this sort of task is to use MultiView. Each view is put in a viewport, and then the line is drawn from point to point by moving the cursor from one viewport to another. This topic is explored shortly.

Zooming from within the Line Command

Prompt	Input	Description
Command	**YC100**	Changes current layer to Layer 100
Command	Move cursor to top left corner, type **NP** or press third mouse button	Starts a new line at the corner (see fig. 7.8)
Command	**ZA**	Starts Zoom All command to see entire drawing
Command	Move cursor to bottom right of object and press third mouse button, or type **NP**	Finishes the line by connecting to the bottom right of the object (see fig. 7.9)
Command	Press Esc, or click a blank line in the menu with second mouse button	Ends the Line command

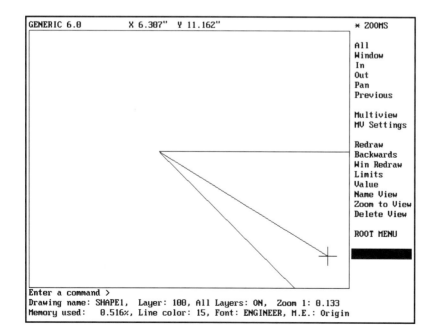

Figure 7.8:

Start a line by using Snap to Nearest Point.

227

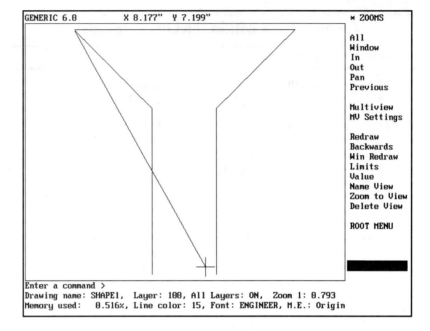

Figure 7.9:

A Zoom All view, executed in the middle of drawing a line.

Taking Advantage of Your Layer Organization

Using the zoom commands makes it easy to get a close-up or wide-angle view of a drawing. Occasionally, however, you need to control what appears in a specific view. If you have planned ahead and divided the drawing into different layers, you can hide and display layers as you choose.

Layer Hide (YH)

To remove from view the objects on a specific layer, use the Layer Hide (YH) command, found in the LAYERS menu. After you select the command, a list of layers that have data on them appears in the menu (see fig. 7.10). If a delta symbol (Δ) precedes a layer number (or name), that layer holds data. The c identifies the current layer, and dots indicate which layers are visible.

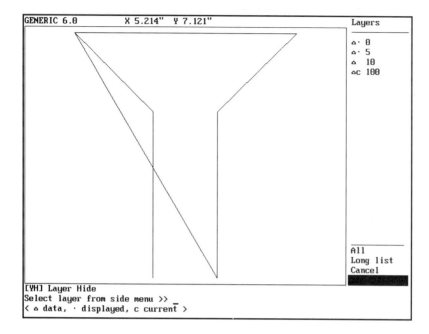

Figure 7.10:

The status of every layer in use is shown in the menu.

When you click on the layer you want to hide, it disappears from the screen. You can continue selecting layers, or you can press Enter to end the command. You cannot hide the currently active layer.

Do not confuse Layer Hide with Layer Erase (YE or YX). Layer Hide simply removes objects from view; Layer Erase deletes all objects on a layer.

Layer Display (YD)

To restore a hidden layer, use the Layer Display command, also found on the LAYERS menu. It works just like Layer Hide, except that the layer(s) you select are displayed, not hidden. Press Enter without selecting a layer to end the command.

Both Layer Hide and Layer Display act as toggles, but only within the command. If you use Layer Hide to hide a layer, for example, it immediately disappears from the display. Selecting the same layer again before you end the Layer Hide command causes the layer to reappear.

Using Multiple Viewports with Layers

Chapter 2 introduces the use of Multiple Viewports (VP) and mentioned the possible adjustments. If you divide your drawings onto various layers, using Multiple Viewports with your layer-management scheme can save you time moving between layers as you edit.

Layers is one of the options in the Viewport Settings (VS) command, found in the ZOOMS menu. If you choose Global, any layer command you use works on all viewports. If you hide Layer 5, for example, it is hidden in every viewport. If you choose Viewport, any layer-management command you select works only in the currently active viewport.

As you may recall from Chapter 2, when a viewport is active (using AV), any redraw commands you use are limited to the active viewport. In figure 7.11, an active viewport is used with the Layer Hide and Layer Display commands. (The menu has been shut off, using the VM command, to provide additional room for the viewports). One by one, each of the three viewports along the left side of the screen was made the active viewport. (Press **AV** to select an active viewport; use the Tab key to move from one to another.) In each viewport, a different layer was selected as the current layer and all other layers were hidden. The drawing being used has three layers, each of which is represented in one of the small views.

The Viewport toggle in Viewport Settings is in effect only when Active Viewport (AV) is on.

This can be helpful in scenarios similar to the following:

- A landscape designer can put the underground sprinkler system on one layer, shrubs on another, and rock work on a third, and (by assigning each a viewport) look at all of them simultaneously without interference from the other elements

- To test the way various layers look when combined, drafting professionals in any field can divide the screen into equal-sized viewports, each with different combinations of layers.

- Use of the Selection and Filtering commands described in Chapter 10 can be made more intuitive by combining selected entities on a layer and setting aside a viewport for the objects.

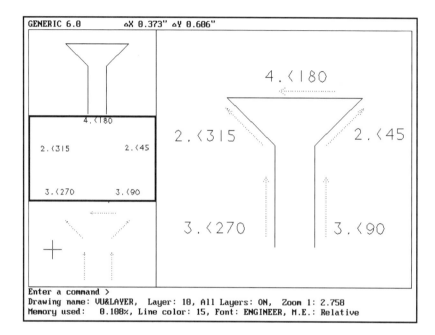

Figure 7.11:

Using Multiple Viewports to display various layers.

 Although an explanation of macros lies ahead, here is a macro to automate the selection of four viewports with layer management set to Viewport. To use the macro, type **MA**, press a function key, and then type the following characters, exactly as they appear here:

VP,10,AV,++,PU,VS,L,++,!;

Resetting Origin Points

The coordinate grid is at the heart of Generic CADD. Every object in a drawing is saved in memory using coordinate reference points. On occasion, however, you need to change the origin point of the drawing or adjust where the on-screen grid starts.

Grid Re-Origin (GO)

If you turn on the grid when objects already are on-screen, they may not line up with the grid. You can adjust the origin point of the grid with the Grid Re-Origin command, in the CONSTRAINTS menu.

In the following exercise, you turn on the grid, setting it to 1/4" spacing, and then move the grid so that it lines up with the drawing. In figure 7.12, the screen grid is set at 1/4" x 1/4" spacing. The view is zoomed to the bottom of the object. Note that the grid points do not line up with the end points of the lines. In figure 7.13, the origin of the grid has been moved to the bottom left of the object. Note how the grid points and the end points of the lines now match up.

Moving the Grid

Prompt	Input	Description
Command	**GS**	Initiates Grid Size command
Change Grid Size X	**.25**	Sets the grid spacing height to .25"
Change Grid Size Y	**.25**	Sets the grid spacing width to .25"
Command	**GO**	Starts the Grid Re-Origin command
Enter new origin	Move cursor to the bottom left of the object and type **NP**, or click third mouse button	Uses Snap To Nearest Point to move the origin point of the screen grid to the bottom left of the object

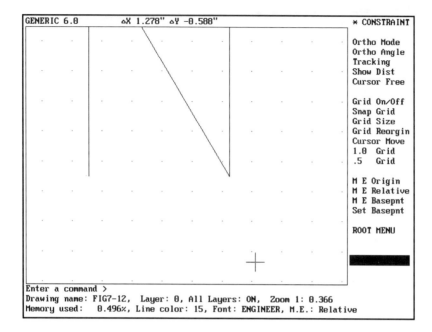

Figure 7.12:

The screen grid set at 1/4" x 1/4" spacing.

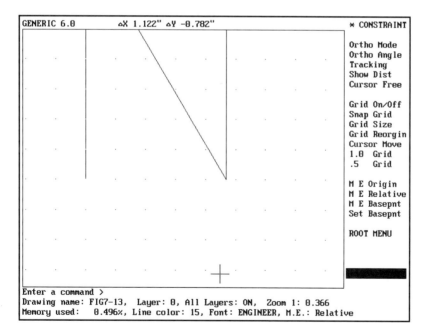

Figure 7.13:

Grid origin moved to the bottom left of the object.

Drawing Re-Origin (DO)

The Drawing Re-Origin command is found on the UTILITIES menu. It changes the location of the drawing's 0,0 origin point. This command should be used rarely, and its use should be carefully considered.

Although moving the 0,0 location may sound like no big deal, it can have far-reaching effects. When you create a named view, the Named View command saves the center of the view as a coordinate location relative to the origin point. The Zoom Limits command uses the origin point as the lower left corner of the new display. If you change the location of the origin point, all these settings are affected.

Why would Generic CADD offer such a command? Sometimes, changing the drawing origin is the easiest way to achieve harmony in a drawing. If you are combining two completed drawings to make one new one, you may have to adjust the origin to properly align the two. Be sure, however, that you will not regret changing the origin; you cannot use the Undo command to reverse the change. To change the origin, type **DO** and locate a new 0,0 point, either by moving the cursor and clicking or by typing a coordinate location.

 If you type a location, be sure that you are not typing what you believe to be an absolute coordinate location when Manual Entry Relative is on—you will get the wrong location as the new origin.

If you use the Drawing Re-Origin command, give yourself a safety net. Place a Standard Point (PO) command at the true 0,0 of the drawing before you start. If you goof, or if you just want to return the origin to its original location, type **DO** again and use a snap command to snap the origin to the standard point.

Summary

The zoom commands make it easy to see any part of the drawing, at any scale. You can zoom up close for a tight view or look at the entire drawing, no matter how large it is.

Zoom commands can be used from inside other commands, a feature that enables you to adjust the view as you draw or edit, for an extra measure of precision and control. Being able to summon a zoom command from within other commands is an example of *nested command structure* in Generic CADD. With a capability to change the view while drawing, the user can focus on the work to be done, rather than on the settings and zoom scale of the display.

Generic CADD offers 256 possible layers to draw on. Planning ahead to take advantage of layers gives you a variety of benefits, including the ability to quickly modify the view on-screen by using Layer Hide and Layer Display. Any combination of layers may be visible or hidden at any time. Using Layer Hide and Layer Display with Multiple viewports offers additional flexibility in viewing and editing various layers.

Understanding the use of zooms and layer display prepares you for success in the next chapter, which covers printing drawings. Any view you can create on-screen can be sent to a printing or plotting device. Knowing how to create the right view makes it easier to create the correct printed version of your work.

Printing and Plotting

 ll plotting and printing operations in Generic CADD are activated from the output menu, a text screen that appears whenever you select PRINT, PLOT, or POST-SCRIPT in the FILE menu. Most of the functions of the Output menu are the same, no matter what type of output device you select; Generic CADD considers all output to be plotting. This is reflected in the terminology of the menus, such as Plot Scale and Start Plot. The menu choices and commands used to set up the page, to determine the style of plot, and to preview the plot are the same for plotters, printers, and PostScript devices. The choices under the options portion of the menu vary according to the output device you need.

In addition to PRINT, PLOT, and POSTSCRIPT in the FILE menu, you can reach the Output menu by using two two-letter commands. Plot (PL) uses the Selection process covered in Chapter 10, and enables you to plot all or selected portions of your drawing. After you select the objects to be plotted, you see the main output menu (see fig. 8.1). The Drawing Plot (DP) command automatically selects all objects on all currently displayed layers and immediately places you in the output menu.

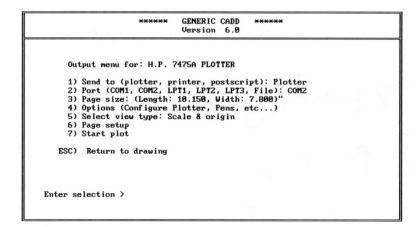

```
******  GENERIC CADD  ******
        Version  6.0


Output menu for: H.P. 7475A PLOTTER

1) Send to (plotter, printer, postscript): Plotter
2) Port (COM1, COM2, LPT1, LPT2, LPT3, File): COM2
3) Page size: (Length: 10.150, Width: 7.800)"
4) Options (Configure Plotter, Pens, etc...)
5) Select view type: Scale & origin
6) Page setup
7) Start plot

ESC)  Return to drawing



Enter selection >
```

Figure 8.1:

The Generic CADD output menu.

Choosing an Output Device

The first line of the output menu, Output menu for:, indicates the specific device to which output is sent. Select the device—a plotter, a dot-matrix or laser printer, or a PostScript printer—from the first option on the menu.

If you access the output menu using either the DP or PL two-letter commands, the first line is set for the most recently used device. Generic CADD remembers all the settings for each type of device. Whenever you switch from one device to another, Generic CADD recalls such settings as the type of plotter printer, the output port, the number of plotter pens, and so on.

If you use one of the three lists on the FILE menu (PRINT, PLOT, or POSTSCRIPT), the device is set automatically, and the first line of the output menu and default value shown for the first option reflect this.

Plotters

Plotters fit into two broad categories: Pen/Pencil and Raster. Pen plotters, which use pens (or sometimes pencils) to physically draw the plot line by line, are slow but normally can accept a wide range of media, such as paper, transparency film, Vellum, and Mylar. Color is limited only by the pens available.

The Raster category includes electrostatic plotters, thermal plotters, dot-matrix plotters, and laser printers with plotter emulation capabilities. The plotters in this category typically "buffer" the plot data (store the data in memory) and then draw the entire plot at once. These devices usually generate a complicated plot in less time than nonbuffering devices, but often are limited in the types of media they can accept. Many plotters in this category are not capable of color output.

All plotters are sent data in a "plotter language," which describes the drawing in vectors or lines. This language is closer to Generic CADD's method for storing drawing data than to the bit-map language of dot-matrix printers. As a result, Generic CADD generally can create plotter code faster and more easily than printer code.

If you have a laser printer that can emulate a plotter, such as a Brother HL-8e or a Hewlett Packard LaserJet III, you should take advantage of this capability and configure Generic CADD for a plotter instead of a printer. You also should configure for a plotting device if you use a product such as Plotter in a Cartridge with a printer such as the Canon LBP-8II or the HP LaserJet II. In these cases, treating the printer as a plotter speeds output and, in the case of the HP LaserJet III, improves quality.

To select a plotter as the output device, choose option 1) `Send to (plotter, printer, postscript):` from the main output menu. The output format menu then appears. Select 1) `Plotter`. Generic CADD automatically returns you to the main output menu after you make your choice.

To configure your plotter's specific brand and model, select 4) `Options` from the main output menu. This places you in the Options: Plotter menu. Then select 1) `Configure new plotter`. Generic CADD may prompt you to enter a path to the PLOTTERS.TPL file. This file, which contains all the plotter configuration choices, normally is stored in the default CADD directory (C:\CADD6). Type **C:\CADD6** (or the drive and directory where you installed Generic CADD), and press Enter. As figure 8.2 illustrates, Generic CADD lets you choose from a list of plotters (30 per screen).

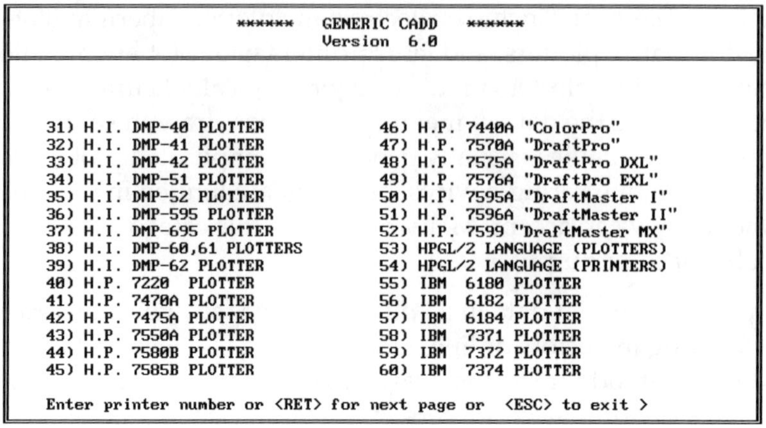

```
                    ******  GENERIC CADD  ******
                            Version  6.0

    31) H.I. DMP-40 PLOTTER          46) H.P. 7440A "ColorPro"
    32) H.I. DMP-41 PLOTTER          47) H.P. 7570A "DraftPro"
    33) H.I. DMP-42 PLOTTER          48) H.P. 7575A "DraftPro DXL"
    34) H.I. DMP-51 PLOTTER          49) H.P. 7576A "DraftPro EXL"
    35) H.I. DMP-52 PLOTTER          50) H.P. 7595A "DraftMaster I"
    36) H.I. DMP-595 PLOTTER         51) H.P. 7596A "DraftMaster II"
    37) H.I. DMP-695 PLOTTER         52) H.P. 7599 "DraftMaster MX"
    38) H.I. DMP-60,61 PLOTTERS      53) HPGL/2 LANGUAGE (PLOTTERS)
    39) H.I. DMP-62 PLOTTER          54) HPGL/2 LANGUAGE (PRINTERS)
    40) H.P. 7220  PLOTTER           55) IBM  6180 PLOTTER
    41) H.P. 7470A PLOTTER           56) IBM  6182 PLOTTER
    42) H.P. 7475A PLOTTER           57) IBM  6184 PLOTTER
    43) H.P. 7550A PLOTTER           58) IBM  7371 PLOTTER
    44) H.P. 7580B PLOTTER           59) IBM  7372 PLOTTER
    45) H.P. 7585B PLOTTER           60) IBM  7374 PLOTTER

    Enter printer number or <RET> for next page or  <ESC> to exit >
```

Figure 8.2:

Selecting a plotter.

If you do not see your plotter listed on the first page, press Enter so that you can see the next 30 options. When you find your plotter, type its corresponding number and press Enter. For the HP LaserJet III, choose the option labeled HPGL/2 LANGUAGE (PRINTERS). If your plotter is not listed, refer to your plotter manual to see what other plotters it emulates. Many plotters emulate one of the Houston Instrument or Hewlett-Packard models (indicated on the menu as H.I. or H.P.).

After you choose a plotter, you are returned to the options menu. Press Esc to return to the main output menu. Now, you must tell the program how the plotter you selected is connected to your computer. Choose 2) Port (COM1, COM2, LPT1, LPT2, LPT3, File): from the main output menu. Most plotters use a serial connection and are thus connected to either COM1 or COM2. Select the number that represents the port to which the plotter is connected, and press Enter. If you selected a COM port, Generic CADD prompts you to confirm the configuration of the serial port (see fig. 8.3).

Generic CADD suggests parameters that usually represent the factory configuration for most plotters. You should check to make sure that the plotter and Generic CADD are configured for the same settings. If they are not, change either the configuration or the plotter so that the settings match. Your plotter cannot operate correctly if the serial port settings for Generic CADD and the plotter are different. Refer to the documentation included with Generic CADD for more information on default settings for most plotters. When the settings are correct, press Esc to return to the main output menu.

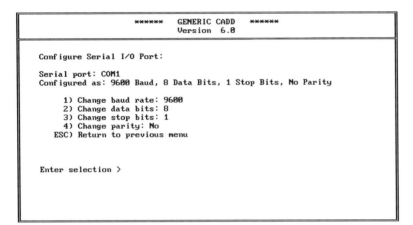

```
******    GENERIC CADD    ******
          Version  6.0

Configure Serial I/O Port:

Serial port: COM1
Configured as: 9600 Baud, 8 Data Bits, 1 Stop Bits, No Parity

    1) Change baud rate: 9600
    2) Change data bits: 8
    3) Change stop bits: 1
    4) Change parity: No
  ESC) Return to previous menu


Enter selection >
```

Figure 8.3:

Serial port parameters.

Dot-Matrix and Laser Printers

Dot-matrix printers and laser printers form images on paper by printing a series of dots, referred to as *raster* or *bitmap graphics*. For Generic CADD to plot a drawing on this type of printer, it must convert the drawing from its own object/vector format into a raster image. Generic CADD then converts the raster image into printer code and sends it to the printer. This process often involves the calculation of millions of dots, which are then sent to the printer. The calculation and transmission of this volume of information to the printer can be time-consuming.

Many laser printers can emulate plotters or support the PostScript page-description language. Plotter languages and the PostScript language are vector-based and do not require Generic CADD to convert the drawing to a raster image. For this reason, laser printers that can emulate plotters should be treated as plotters by Generic CADD. Similarly, printers that are PostScript-compatible should be configured as PostScript devices.

To select a printer as the output device, choose 1) Send to (plotter, printer, postscript): from the main output menu, then select 2) Printer from the output format menu. Generic CADD automatically returns you to the main output menu after you make your choice.

Configuring for the specific brand and type of printer is much like configuring for a plotter. Select 4) Options from the main output menu. This places you in the Options: Printer menu. Next, select 1) Configure printer. Generic CADD may prompt you to enter a path to the .TPR files. Just as with the plotter configuration files, these files contain all the printer configuration choices. These files normally are stored in the default CADD directory (C:\CADD6). Type **C:\CADD6** (or the drive and directory where you installed Generic CADD 6.0) and press Enter. Generic CADD displays a list of printer brands to choose from (see fig. 8.4).

Figure 8.4:

Selecting a printer brand.

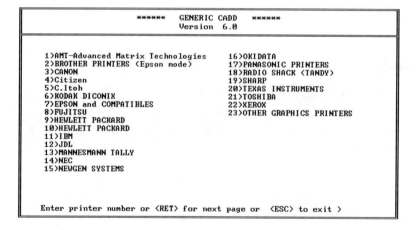

```
******    GENERIC CADD   ******
            Version  6.0

1)AMT-Advanced Matrix Technologies    16)OKIDATA
2)BROTHER PRINTERS (Epson mode)       17)PANASONIC PRINTERS
3)CANON                               18)RADIO SHACK (TANDY)
4)Citizen                             19)SHARP
5)C.Itoh                              20)TEXAS INSTRUMENTS
6)KODAK DICONIX                       21)TOSHIBA
7)EPSON and COMPATIBLES               22)XEROX
8)FUJITSU                             23)OTHER GRAPHICS PRINTERS
9)HEWLETT PACKARD
10)HEWLETT PACKARD
11)IBM
12)JDL
13)MANNESMANN TALLY
14)NEC
15)NEWGEN SYSTEMS


Enter printer number or <RET> for next page or  <ESC> to exit >
```

Type the number that corresponds to your printer, and press Enter. If you do not see your printer brand listed, refer to your printer manual to see what printers it is compatible with. Most 24-pin printers, for example, emulate one or more of the Epson 24-pin (LQ) model printers.

After you choose a brand of printer, Generic CADD displays a list of models and resolutions (see fig. 8.5). Most printers fit into broad categories such as 8/9-pin or 24-pin (8- and 9-pin printers are really the same, because most 9-pin printers only use 8 pins for printing graphics). Usually you see several choices for each type of printer, each offering a different resolution. Most printers are capable of printing at several resolutions. When in doubt, start with the low-resolution choice and run a test print; then try the other options. Higher resolutions yield higher quality output but take longer to print. You may want to configure for a low or medium resolution for draft-quality check prints and reconfigure to high or very high resolution for presentation-quality output.

```
              ******   GENERIC CADD   ******
                       Version  6.0

              *****  Select Printer Model  *****

   1) IBM GRAPHICS PRINTER - LOW RES
   2) IBM GRAPHICS PRINTER - MED.
   3) IBM GRAPHICS PRINTER - HIGH
   4) IBM GRAPHICS PRINTER - VERY HI
   5) IBM COLOR PRINTER - LOW RES.
   6) IBM COLOR PRINTER - MED. RES.
   7) IBM INKJET - BLACK & WHITE
   8) IBM INKJET - COLOR
   9) IBM 24 PIN - LOW RES.
  10) IBM 24 PIN - MED. RES.
  11) IBM (AGM) 24 PIN - LOW RES.
  12) IBM (AGM) 24 PIN - MED. RES.
  13) IBM (AGM) 24 PIN - HIGH RES.
  14) IBM (AGM) 24 PIN - V. HIGH RES


      Enter Printer Model or  <ESC> to exit >
```

Figure 8.5:

Selecting a printer type and resolution.

After choosing a printer, you need to tell Generic CADD how that printer is connected to your computer. Choose 2) Port (COM1, COM2, LPT1, LPT2, LPT3, File): from the main output menu. Most printers use a parallel connection and thus are connected to LPT1, LPT2, or LPT3. Select the number that represents the port to which the printer is connected, and press Enter. If you have a serial printer and you select a COM port, Generic CADD prompts you to confirm the configuration of the serial port (refer to fig. 8.3).

Most serial printers use the 9600 baud, 8 data bits, 1 stop bit, and no-parity settings. Make sure that the printer and Generic CADD are configured for the same settings. If they are not, change the configuration for either Generic CADD or the printer so that the settings match. Your printer cannot operate correctly if the serial port settings for Generic CADD and the printer are different.

When the settings are correct, press Esc to return to the main output menu.

As with plotting, you do not need to configure for a printer each time you run Generic CADD, except when you switch resolutions. When you exit Generic CADD using the Quit command, or update the environment with EN, Generic CADD saves your printer settings and recalls them the next time you use the program.

PostScript Printers

If you have a printer, such as the Apple LaserWriter or NEC Colormate PS, which supports the Adobe PostScript language, you should configure Generic CADD for PostScript output.

To select a printer as the output device, choose 1) `Send to (plotter, printer, postscript)`: from the main output menu, then select 3) `Postscript` from the output format menu. Generic CADD automatically returns you to the main output menu after you make your choice. You do not need to configure for the individual brand or model of printer because all PostScript devices are the same in Generic CADD.

After choosing PostScript as the output format, you need to tell Generic CADD how the PostScript printer is connected to the computer. Choose 2) `Port (COM1, COM2, LPT1, LPT2, LPT3, File)`: from the main output menu. Select the number representing the port to which the printer is connected and press Enter. If you have a serial printer and selected a COM port, Generic CADD prompts you to confirm the configuration of the serial port (refer to fig. 8.3).

Page Setup and Basic Plot Types

The process for setting up the page, determining the plot type, and previewing the plot is the same no matter what output device you use. Normally, when preparing to plot a drawing, you need to go through the following steps: selecting the size of paper, selecting the type of plot (view, fit, scale), and previewing the position and appearance of the drawing on the paper.

Setting the Page Size

The first step in plotting a drawing is setting the page size. The page size represents the area Generic CADD is allowed to use when plotting a drawing. The page size you set in Generic CADD should be smaller than the size of the paper being used. Not only is allowing for a little white space around your drawing aesthetically pleasing but, more important, most output devices also have a maximum image size that is smaller than the physical paper size.

Plotters have a safety margin at the front and back of the page, and those that move the paper during plotting must allow an area at the sides of the sheet for the pinch rollers. Laser printers also have pinch rollers and usually cannot print within a quarter-inch of either side of the sheet. Unless you override the settings, most lasers also have a default top and bottom margin of one-half inch.

To select a page size, choose 3) `Page size:` from the main output menu. Generic CADD prompts you to choose from a selection of standard sizes. If you have configured for a plotter, the sizes listed represent the maximum allowable plot area for standard architectural and engineering sheet sizes (A, B, C, and so on). If you have configured for a dot-matrix printer, Generic CADD suggests two standard sizes for narrow- and wide-carriage paper.

Choose one of the sizes listed and press Enter. If you want to specify a size that is not listed, choose the option labeled `User selected size`. Generic CADD prompts you for the width and length of the paper. (Remember, do not enter the physical size of the paper unless your device is capable of printing to the entire sheet.)

Current View

Choose 5) `Select view type:` from the main output menu. Generic CADD prompts you to select the type of view you want to plot. Generic CADD provides three standard plot view types (see fig. 8.6). After you choose one of the three options, Generic CADD returns you to the main output menu. The `Fit full drawing` and `Specify scale & origin` options also can be activated when in page preview mode.

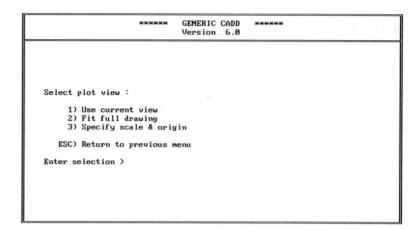

****** GENERIC CADD ******
Version 6.0

Figure 8.6:

Plot view types.

The first of the three view options is Use current view. This option tells Generic CADD to plot the current view to fit the selected page size. The printed drawing, however, does not match what you see on the screen because the height and width ratio of the screen and the page size are rarely the same, which usually results in extra material (not visible on-screen) at the top and bottom of the plot. If you are using Multiple Viewports, the current view comes from the active viewport, if one is set.

This option is desirable when you want a quick printout of some portion of your drawing at no specific scale. This plot type is one of the easiest to do but offers the least amount of control over the plot created. You should use one of the other two options for more serious plots.

Start in the drawing screen and use one of the zoom commands to center a portion of the drawing on-screen. Then type **DP** to get to the output menu. After verifying that the output device, port, and page size are correct, choose the Use current view option.

To preview the image that is to be plotted, choose 6) Page setup from the main output menu. Generic CADD prompts you with Fast redraw? (Y/N). Press **N**, or click the second mouse button. Generic CADD then shows your drawing and a solid box (drawn using the cursor color) that represents the area to be plotted (see fig. 8.7). Press Enter to return to the main output menu.

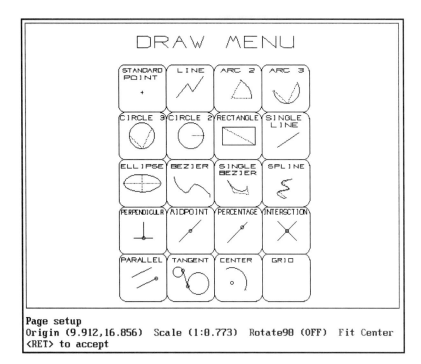

Figure 8.7:
Page preview.

If all the other settings (plotter type, output port, paper size and so on) are correct and the output device is loaded with paper and on-line, select 7) Start plot. Generic CADD begins plotting the drawing.

Fit Full Drawing

The second plot-view type is Fit full drawing. When you select this option, Generic CADD calculates the plot scale required to plot the entire drawing as large as possible on the page size you have selected. Generic CADD automatically centers the drawing on the page, but does not calculate the resulting rotation in the largest plot. This option is most useful when you want to plot the entire drawing and the scale of the resulting plot is not important.

Because Generic CADD does not calculate the best orientation, it is often a good idea to use the Page setup option to see whether the drawing would plot larger if rotated. Choose 6) Page setup

from the main output menu. Generic CADD prompts you with
Fast redraw? (Y/N); press **Y**, or click with the first mouse button.
Generic CADD then shows a light blue dashed box with an X
drawn from the corners (see fig. 8.8). The dashed box represents
the extents of the drawing and is fit around the outermost objects
in the drawing. A solid box (drawn using the cursor color) is
placed over the dashed box. The solid box represents the paper—
in other words, the area that is to be plotted.

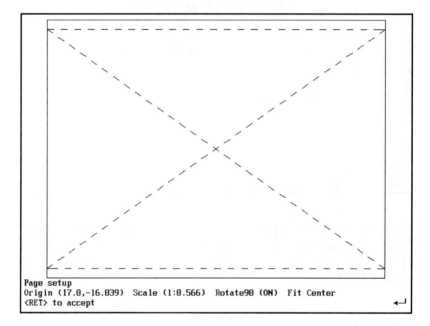

Page setup
Origin (17.0,-16.039) Scale (1:0.566) Rotate90 (ON) Fit Center
<RET> to accept

Figure 8.8:

*Page preview in fast
redraw mode.*

If you believe that the drawing would fit better on the page if it
were rotated 90 degrees, press **R**. Generic CADD rotates the
dashed box that represents the drawing and aligns the lower left
corners of the two boxes. If you press **F**, Generic CADD fits and
centers the drawing to the paper, using the new rotation. If you
liked it better the first way, press **R** and then **F** again to rotate the
drawing back to the previous view. When you are satisfied with
the orientation and fit, press Enter to return to the main output
menu.

If all the other settings (plotter type, output port, paper size, and so on) are correct and the output device is loaded with paper and on-line, select 7) Start plot. Generic CADD begins plotting your drawing.

Plotting to Scale

To be useful to other people, most drawings of real-world objects (as opposed to charts or schematic diagrams) must be plotted to scale. Generic CADD expresses the plot scale as a ratio of 1:*nn*, where one unit measured on the plotted drawing is equal to *nn* units in the real world. The units on both sides of the ratio are shown only if they differ.

Architects and surveyors typically express scale as a ratio of Y inches to X feet. In many cases, one or the other side of the ratio is assumed to be one. The expression *quarter-inch scale* refers to a ratio of one quarter inch to one foot, for example. The expression *one to a hundred scale* means that one inch equals 100 feet.

To convert a traditional scale to Generic CADD format, both sides of the ratio must be in the same units (feet or inches, for example). You then bring the value on the left side to one. The process to convert traditional 1/4" to 1' scale into Generic CADD plot scale, for example, is as follows:

1. 1/4": 1'   Starting ratio
2. 1/4": 12"   Convert right side to inches
3. 4×1/4": 4×12"   Multiply both sides by 4
4. 1": 48"   CADD plot scale

Following the preceding example, "eighth-inch scale" becomes a plot scale of 1:96, whereas "one inch to a hundred feet" becomes a plot scale of 1:1200.

To plot a drawing to scale, first set the page size using the third option on the main output menu. (If the page size is not set correctly, page setup does not correctly represent the plotted drawing.) Then select 6) Page setup from the main output menu. If the entire drawing is to be plotted, type **Y** at the Fast redraw? (Y/N) prompt. If only a portion of the drawing is to be plotted, answer **N** to this prompt.

After Generic CADD has drawn the page setup screen (see fig. 8.9), press **S** to set the scale. Generic CADD indicates the current plot scale and prompts you to enter a new value. Enter only the right half of the plot scale, and press Enter. Generic CADD redraws the page setup screen and aligns the lower left corners of the drawing and the page outline.

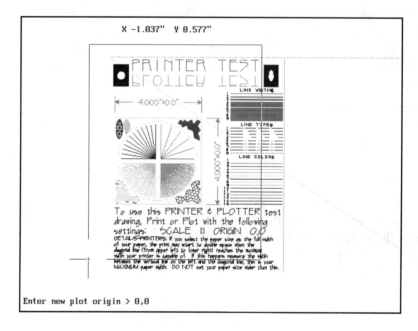

Figure 8.9:

Page preview, setting scale, and origin.

If the drawing fits better rotated on the page, press **R** to rotate the drawing. Generic CADD again redraws the screen and aligns the lower left corners. If the entire drawing is to be plotted, press **C**. Generic CADD centers the drawing on the page. If the entire drawing does not fit on the page, you need to choose a new plot scale (press **S**) and center the drawing on the paper again.

If only a portion of the drawing is to be plotted, press **O** to locate the origin for the page outline. You may now use the pointer to drag the page outline and position it over the portion of the drawing that you want to plot. While dragging the page frame, you can use commands such as Zoom In (ZI), Zoom Out (ZO), Zoom Window (ZW), and Pan (PA) to better position the page outline. The origin in this case refers to the lower left corner of the page outline.Thinking of the page outline as a viewfinder may help—whatever is located inside the page frame is plotted.

You also can use manual entry to position the page frame at a specific location in the drawing. After you press **O** to locate the plot origin, type **MO** to ensure that manual entry values are relative to the origin of the drawing.

Positioning the plot origin with the manual entry set relative to last point or relative to basepoint can be extremely frustrating. If rotation is off, enter manual entry coordinates as you usually would and press Enter. If rotation is on, the process is a little trickier. Because the drawing is rotated, you have to rotate the coordinate values to properly position the page outline. To rotate the coordinates, transpose the X and Y values and multiply the Y value by -1. You would enter **5,-2**, for example, to place the corner of the page outline at 2,5. This is necessary only when the drawing has been rotated to fit the paper.

When you are satisfied with the scale and the position of the page outline relative to the drawing, press Enter to return to the main output menu.

If all the other settings (plotter type, output port, paper size, and so on) are correct and the output device is loaded with paper and on-line, select 7) Start plot. Generic CADD begins plotting the drawing.

Plot Options and Their Effect on Output

The choices available under 4) Options on the output menu depend on which output device you selected. The first choice on the printer and plotter versions of this menu is used to configure for the specific model of printer or plotter connected to Generic CADD. All three versions of the options menu provide a choice that lets you select the number of copies to be plotted.

The other choices generally enable you to tailor the output in various ways, such as selecting the number of plotter pens or the line width used for PostScript output.

Plotter Options

The plotter options menu provides choices for configuring the plotter, drawing arcs and circles, configuring the plotter pen settings, importing a plotter command file, and setting the number of copies to be plotted (see fig. 8.10).

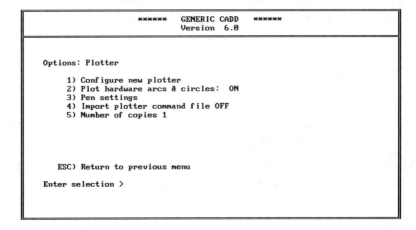

```
****** GENERIC CADD ******
Version 6.0


Options: Plotter

        1) Configure new plotter
        2) Plot hardware arcs & circles:  ON
        3) Pen settings
        4) Import plotter command file OFF
        5) Number of copies 1




    ESC) Return to previous menu
Enter selection >
```

Figure 8.10:

The options menu for plotter output.

Configure New Plotter

Selecting 1) `Configure new plotter` enables you to change the specific model of plotter being used, as discussed earlier.

Plot Hardware Arcs & Circles

Select 2) `Plot hardware arcs & circles:` to turn hardware arc support on or off. *Hardware arcs and circles* means that the printing device has a built-in capability to draw circles and arcs. The program only needs to specify the size. Not all plotters offer this feature. Generic CADD indicates `not supported` if your plotter does not support accurate internal routines to draw arcs and circles.

Plotters that use the DM/PL protocol (a plotting language used by several manufacturers) support hardware arcs, but the accuracy level of the protocol is too low to be used effectively with Generic CADD; DM/PL rounds the arcs to the nearest degree.

Plotters that support internal arc and circle functions usually draw these entities using relatively few line segments, or facets (256 for a full circle). Frequently, when the arcs or circles in a drawing are relatively large, you can see the individual line segments. Generic CADD uses a larger number of line segments, which usually results in a smoother arc. Hardware arcs should be enabled only if you are creating a plot file to import the drawing into another graphics program. For everyday plotting, you usually should leave this option off.

Pen Settings

Choosing 3) Pen settings displays a separate menu with the different pen settings options (see fig. 8.11). These options are used to control the pen speed, width, number of pens, and so on.

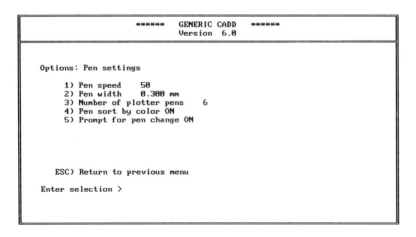

```
****** GENERIC CADD ******
        Version  6.0


Options: Pen settings

    1) Pen speed      50
    2) Pen width     0.300 mm
    3) Number of plotter pens    6
    4) Pen sort by color ON
    5) Prompt for pen change ON




  ESC) Return to previous menu

Enter selection >
```

Figure 8.11:

The options menu for pen settings.

The first choice under pen settings is 1) Pen speed. If you are using an electrostatic, thermal, pencil, or laser printer in plotter-emulation mode, this option should be set to 50 (the maximum value possible). You may need to use a lower pen speed to prevent skipping or fading, depending on which pens and media you are using. Some plotters sense the pen type and adjust automatically. Because the optimum pen speed varies with both the type of pen and the media, you need to experiment to find what speed works best with a given combination of pens and media.

Roller ball pens generally can be run at full speed without much difficulty. Fiber-tip and ceramic-tip pens require a fast to medium speed. Technical or drafting pens usually work best at a medium to slow setting. Transparency pens require a very slow setting.

The second option is 2) `Pen width` (normally specified in millimeters). Generic CADD takes the pen width into account when drawing line widths and fills. If the width is set too wide, gaps appear between the lines; if the width is set too narrow, the lines overlap and the paper may become saturated with ink.

Most plotter pens are labeled with the width of the pen in millimeters. If you do not see a decimal point, assume that the value is tenths of millimeters. Fiber pens typically come in .3mm and .7mm widths. Typical sizes for drafting pens are .15mm, .25mm, .5mm, and .7mm. The pen width normally should be set to allow a very slight overlap to ensure that wide lines and fills appear solid. This may not be necessary for fiber-tip pens, whose tip often flattens out. For technical pens, this means specifying a value a few hundredths less than the rated width of the pen. Roller ball pens often plot much narrower than their rated width, sometimes requiring a pen-width setting 30-50 percent narrower than the pen's official width.

 The pen-width setting is especially important for laser printers in plotter-emulation mode. Laser printers are capable of producing very fine lines, sometimes requiring a pen-width setting as small as .08mm or .07mm.

The value for the third option, 3) `Number of plotter pens`, is set automatically when you configure the plotter. You may need to reset it if you have an optional pen changer installed on the plotter, or if you are using fewer than the maximum number of pens the plotter supports.

This option works in conjunction with the fourth and fifth options: 4) `Pen sort by color` and 5) `Prompt for pen change`.

If the prompts for pen sort and pen change are both set to yes, Generic CADD pauses, after plotting with the last pen available, so that you can change the plotter pens. Generic CADD then plots the next series of colors, pausing again, if necessary, for you to change the pens. If the number of plotter pens is set to 6, for example, Generic CADD prompts you to change the pens after plotting all objects drawn using colors 1-6. It pauses again after plotting all objects drawn using colors 7-12.

If `Prompt for pen change` is set to no or n/a, Generic CADD starts over with the first pen after using the last available pen. If `Number of pens` is set to 8, for example, Generic CADD plots colors 1-8 using pens 1-8, and then uses pen 1 for color 9, pen 2 for color 10, pen 3 for color 11, and so on.

Choose `Pen sort by color` to turn this setting on or off. When `Pen sort by color` is on, Generic CADD plots all objects drawn using color 1, then all objects drawn using color 2, and so forth. Sorting by color decreases plot time by minimizing the number of times the plotter needs to pause to change pens.

If `Pen sort by color` is off, Generic CADD plots objects in the order in which they appear in the drawing database. If you are plotting to an electrostatic or laser printer emulating a plotter, this may reduce plot time slightly because Generic CADD has to process the drawing database once only. Turning off this option also changes `Prompt for pen change` to a setting of n/a, indicating that the choice is not available. Generic CADD prompts for pen changes only when `Pen sort by color` is on.

Choose `Prompt for pen change` to turn this setting on and off. When `Prompt for pen change` is on, Generic CADD prompts you to change pens as described earlier under `Number of pens`.

Import Plotter Command File

When you choose 4) `Import plotter command file`, Generic CADD prompts you for the name of a plotter command file. *Plotter command files* are ASCII files that contain keywords recognized by Generic CADD and plotter commands in the language of the plotter. The keywords tell Generic CADD when to send the plotter commands that follow the keyword. You use plotter command files when you need to send extra command codes to the plotter during initialization (before plotting) and after a plot is finished.

Plotter command files are useful when a roll-feed or sheet-feeding plotter is used, when you need to send a command after plotting to tell the plotter to advance to the next page or plot frame. Refer to the documentation shipped with Generic CADD for a list of the keywords, and to your plotter reference manual for a list of the plotter command codes.

Number of Copies

When you choose 5) Number of copies, Generic CADD prompts you to enter the number of copies you want plotted. This option is useful when you need to generate several identical plots. When you tell Generic CADD to start plotting, it asks whether you need it to pause for paper changes between plots. This prompt occurs only if the number of copies is set to a value greater than one.

If you are using an electrostatic or laser printer, the number of copies often can be set by means of the control panel on the device. Using the control panel to request extra copies is normally a more desirable option because Generic CADD generates additional copies by repeating the entire plot. The devices store the plot data in memory and use the data to make additional copies. Generic CADD creates additional copies by regenerating the plot data for each copy. The Number of copies option should be used only for devices that cannot generate additional copies on their own.

Printer Options

Printing is a relatively simple process. Only two printer options are available on the printer options menu (see fig. 8.12).

```
          ****** GENERIC CADD ******
                 Version  6.0

  Options: Printer

        1) Configure printer
        2) Number of copies 1




     ESC) Return to previous menu

  Enter selection >
```

Figure 8.12:

The options menu for printer output.

Configure New Printer

As you learned earlier, selecting 1) `Configure new printer` enables you to change the model of printer being used.

Number of Copies

When you choose 2) `Number of copies`, Generic CADD prompts you to enter the number of copies you want. This option is most useful when you need to generate several identical prints. With a laser printer, you often can set the number of copies by means of the control panel on the printer. Normally, using the control panel is a more desirable option because, as with plotting, Generic CADD generates additional copies by repeating the entire printing process. It takes Generic CADD much longer to generate the raster data for each plot than it does to have the printer generate additional copies after the plot data is in its memory. The `Number of copies` option should be used only for printers that cannot generate additional copies on their own.

PostScript Options

The PostScript options menu (see fig. 8.13) provides options for setting the line width, greyscale, color, and number of copies.

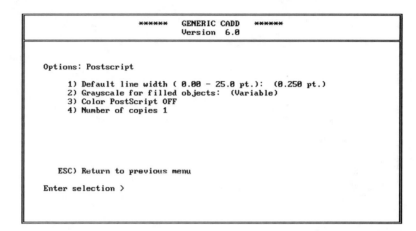

Default Line Width

The PostScript language is based on *points*, a unit of measurement
used in typesetting and page layout. A point is 1/72". The 1)
`Default line width` option sets the base PostScript line width
used when plotting the drawing. Generic CADD line widths of 0
and 1 are plotted using the base line width setting; line width 2 is
plotted using 2 times the base width; line width 3, at 3 times the
base width, and so forth.

When you choose this option, Generic CADD prompts you for a
new default line width. Enter a value from 0 to 25. Note that 25
points is a very wide line, more than one-third of an inch wide. If
you enter a value of 0.00, the PostScript printer draws the thin-
nest possible lines. With 300dpi printers such as the Apple
LaserWriter, this can result in quality output. With PostScript
devices such as Linotronic typesetters, this results in a line so fine
that it is almost impossible to see. If you are plotting to a high
resolution (greater than 300dpi) printer, values from .1 to .3 points
are recommended.

Greyscale for Filled Objects

When using black-and-white PostScript for output, Generic
CADD enables options for printing fills. Fills may be printed
using variable greyscaling based on the color number of the fill,

where color 1 gives the darkest fill and color 15 the lightest. The other option is for all fills to be printed using the same greyscale level.

When you choose the 2) Greyscale for filled objects option, Generic CADD switches between a variable and a number indicating the greyscale level between 0 (darkest) and 1 (lightest). Typically, you would enter a decimal value such as .5 or .75.

If the Color PostScript option is activated, Greyscale for filled objects is changed automatically to read Color PostScript as well. When this option is active, Generic CADD plots fills in their screen colors.

Color PostScript

Choose 3) Color PostScript to turn this option on or off. When Color PostScript is off, Generic CADD prints all lines in black; fills are printed according to the setting of greyscale for filled objects. When Color PostScript is on, Generic CADD prints all objects in color. The effect of this setting varies according to whether you are printing on a black-and-white or color PostScript printer.

If you have a color PostScript printer, the objects in the drawing print according to their screen colors. Some colors, such as 6 and 7, may not print well on some printers. To see what works best with your printer, make a test plot with lines of different colors at various angles. Depending on your printer, as many as 256 colors may be printed. Generic CADD sets the PostScript color palette to match the standard VGA hue and saturation palette. This may not match the default palette on some of the more advanced video cards.

If you have a black-and-white PostScript printer, the objects in the drawing print using greyscales. The greyscales attempt to represent the brightness of the screen color; color numbers such as 1, 5, 8, and 9 are in a fairly dark greyscale, whereas colors such as 3, 7, 11, and 14 are represented by relatively light grey values. Color 15 (white) is printed as solid black rather than white, which would be invisible on white paper. All color values greater than 15 print as solid black.

Because PostScript printers print greyscales using a dither pattern, some fine lines may drop out entirely on black-and-white printers. This effect is worse on 300dpi printers, such as the Apple LaserWriter, than on the much higher resolution Linotronic printers. When printing color PostScript on a black-and-white printer, increase the default line width. PostScript line widths of .5 to 1.5 points work relatively well on 300dpi printers.

Number of Copies

When you choose 4) `Number of copies`, Generic CADD prompts you to enter the number of copies you want plotted. This option is most useful when you need to generate several identical prints. As of this writing, Generic CADD generates additional copies by repeating the entire printing process. Because each copy takes as long to print as the first copy, and you simply may want to use a photocopier to make extra copies. Some day, Generic CADD may generate extra copies by means of the PostScript command that tells the printer the number of copies to print.

Generic CADD also asks whether you want the print sequence to pause between prints. This is of value if you are using the hand-feed option of your PostScript printer to print to legal-size paper.

Plotting to a File

Generic CADD can direct plotting and printing output to a file on disk. Several reasons for directing output to a file follow:

- Exporting drawing data to a word processor or desktop publishing program via HPGL or EPS files

- Printing or plotting drawings when the output device is off site or attached to another computer

- Printing or plotting multiple copies of a drawing without tying up CADD

- Exporting drawing data to another drawing program that can read plotter files or PostScript code

The file that is created on disk contains all the data that normally would be sent to the output device. The file can be used to print or plot independently of Generic CADD by simply using the DOS Copy command to copy the file to the proper output port. This can be very useful for printing or plotting tasks that take a long time to complete. The file can be carried on a floppy disk to another computer, and that system can be used to plot the drawing. A less powerful computer with a high density disk drive, for example, can be used as a plot server in offices where several people share a plotter.

To plot to a file, select 2) Port (COM1, COM2, LPT1, LPT2, LPT3, File):. Generic CADD prompts you to select an output port or file. Select the option for file and, at the prompt, enter a name for the file. Generic CADD suggests the name of the current drawing, followed by an extension indicating the type of file. Type a name for the plot file, or simply press Enter to accept the suggested name. Generic CADD uses the following extensions to denote file types:

Extension	File
DPF	Disk Plotted File (a plotter file)
PRF	PRinter File
DEV	PostScript DEVice file
EPS	Encapsulated PostScript file

If the configurations have been set for PostScript output, Generic CADD offers you a choice of two files: DEV and EPS. A device (DEV) file contains PostScript code, just as it would be sent to the PostScript printer. It can be copied directly to a PostScript device to plot a drawing. An Encapsulated PostScript file (EPS—often called "EPSF" on Macintosh systems) is a special type of Post-Script file, designed to be imported into another document which is then printed to a PostScript printer. Encapsulated PostScript files are an excellent way to import Generic CADD graphics into a word processor or page-layout program (such as PageMaker or Ventura Publisher), provided that the final output is printed on a PostScript printer.

Plotter files in Hewlett Packard Graphics Language (HPGL) also are used frequently to import Generic CADD drawings into a word processor or page-layout program. This option is used routinely when the final document is not printed with a PostScript printer. To create an HPGL file, you should first configure for an HP plotter, preferably the HP model 7475. Some programs expect plot files to have the extension PLT; if this is the case, you can either tell Generic CADD to save the file with this extension or use the DOS Rename command to change the name of the file, if necessary.

To plot or print a file from disk, use the DOS Copy command. If the device is connected to a serial port, you first need to use the DOS Mode command to set the serial port to the proper baud rate, parity, and so on (refer to your DOS manual for details on using the Mode command). To copy a file to a printer or plotter, use the following command:

```
COPY filename port /B
```

Filename is the name of the file, such as HOUSE.DPF, and *port* is the DOS device name for the port to which the printer or plotter is connected. DOS uses the following device names for the following output ports:

Device	Output ports
COM1	Serial Communications Port 1
COM2	Serial Communications Port 2
LPT1	Parallel (printer) Port 1
LPT2	Parallel (printer) Port 2
LPT3	Parallel (printer) Port 3

To send a printer file called PIECHART.PRF to Parallel Port 1, for example, you would type

```
COPY PIECHART.PRF LPT1 /B
```

The /B parameter tells DOS that the file contains binary codes. Although this parameter may not be needed with PostScript or some plotter files, it usually is mandatory with printer files.

Printer files may contain values DOS could interpret as an end-of-file (EOF) mark, which could cause DOS to copy only a portion of the file to the printer. The /B parameter, which tells DOS to ignore any EOF values it may encounter in the middle of the file, should always be included.

Plotting Part of a Drawing

Occasionally, you may want to plot only some of the entities in the drawing—specific layers, for example. Generic CADD offers two ways to do this.

If the objects you want to plot happen to be on one or more layers, the Drawing Plot (DP) command is the easiest to use. First use the layer commands to set the Current Layer (YC), then apply the Hide (YH) or Display (YD) layer commands until the plotted drawing looks the way you want it. Use the Zoom All (ZA) command to be sure everything is correct, and then enter the DP command. DP plots only the layers displayed in the drawing screen when you issued the command. Then set up the page size options and select Page setup to preview the plot.

If the objects you want to plot are not segregated by layers, you can use the Selection Plot (PL) command. This command, as the name implies, selects the parts of the drawing you want to plot. You can select a variety of objects using several methods, including the Entity Filter command. (Generic CADD's standard selection interface is described in Chapter 10.) After you have selected the objects you want plotted, press Enter to confirm your choices and proceed with plotting as usual.

Using Colors in Plotted Drawings

If you are using a plotter, the colors of the objects in the drawing can be plotted in a number of ways. The most obvious is to plot the drawing with different colors, which results in an appealing drawing that is easy to read. Most drafting-style plotter pens are available in a minimum of four colors (black, red, green, and blue), and fiber-tip pens come in a wider range of colors.

You also can use color to control the width of objects. Most plotter pens come in several widths, or *line weights*. Many users overlook this feature and plot entire drawings using different pen colors of the same line weight.

Generic CADD associates color numbers with pen numbers when it plots. Generic CADD does not know whether you insert a .7mm pen in one pen holder and a .25mm pen in another. Because pen width matters to Generic CADD only when it draws fills or line widths, you can choose any configuration of colors and pen widths. All you need to know is that Generic CADD draws all objects drawn with color 1 using pen 1. This enables you to change the colors and line weights used for the plot simply by rearranging the pens.

After the last available pen is used, Generic CADD can either prompt you to install a new set of pens or automatically start using the pens again in order. You can easily determine which pen numbers are used for which color numbers; just remember that whenever Generic CADD runs out of pen numbers, it starts over with pen 1. If you have a 6-pen plotter and 15 colors in the drawing, for example, it works out as follows:

Pen #	Color #
1	1, 7, 13
2	2, 8, 14
3	3, 9, 15
4	4, 10
5	5, 11
6	6, 12

With most black-and-white plotters (such as electrostatic plotters and laser printers in plotter-emulation mode) you can assign different width pens to different logical pen numbers. If all the colors are black, for example, pens with different numbers can plot in different line weights.

Using color numbers to control line widths has two primary advantages: plotting speed increases and the plotter draws cleaner corners between wide lines.

Generic CADD plots a wide line by drawing several parallel lines. When output is to a plotter, Generic CADD always uses an odd number of strokes, offset evenly from the center of the line (with the X,Y coordinates denoting the ends of the line). Figure 8.14 shows wide lines made by stroking a .25mm pen three times, as opposed to a single line drawn with a .7mm pen.

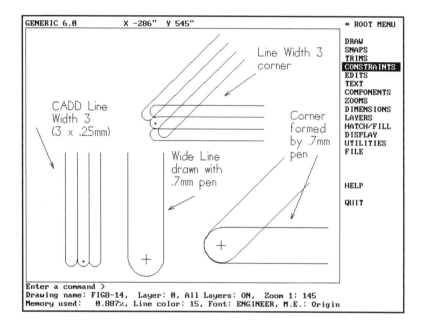

Figure 8.14:

Wide lines drawn using Line Width (LW).

If you plot heavier line weights by using a particular color with a wider pen in the appropriate pen holder, the plots are finished faster because Generic CADD does not have to draw as many lines. You also can plot faster by using wider pens for fills so that the fills may be formed with fewer plotter strokes. Remember to use the plotter options menu to set the pen width accordingly.

Speed is important, but appearance is paramount for many users. Wide lines create a notch when they meet at a corner. A wide pen, however, makes a clean corner because of the pen's round shape. Using colors mapped to pen weights results in a cleaner and sharper plot than using Generic CADD's line-widths feature.

Some users eschew the use of Generic CADD's line widths altogether. These users take full advantage of the 15 line colors offered on most display systems, using specific colors for wider lines and placing heavier line weight pens in the corresponding pen holders in the device. Generic CADD's Solid Double Lines option can be used for particularly bold lines, such as borders. Specific colors can be used for fills, which again are associated with a wider pen. This approach requires planning but results in cleaner, more readable drawings that also plot faster.

Your choice of pens and media greatly influence the appearance of a finished plot. The best plotter in the world cannot overcome cheap pens and rough, inconsistent paper. You can get surprisingly good output with inexpensive plotters if you use quality materials, however. And Generic CADD can produce plots that rival those of far more expensive systems if a quality plotter and quality materials are used.

Summary

The end result of any drawing usually is a finished plot. Generic CADD permits a variety of plotting methods, from quick plots of what appears on-screen to output accurately scaled to hundredths of an inch. Regardless of the output device you use, Generic CADD uses the same interface for setting up and previewing the plotted drawing.

As you have seen in this chapter, Generic CADD's output menu provides all the functions needed for plotting or printing a drawing. You access CADD's output menu by using either the Plot (PL) command (which uses the selection interface) or the Drawing Plot (DP) command. You also can access the output menu by means of three macros on the FILE menu.

Plotting a drawing normally involves six steps: choosing the output device and port, changing the paper size, setting plot options, choosing the type of plot, previewing the plot, and starting to plot.

You also have seen how the various plot options are used to control the appearance of the finished plot and how colors on the screen can be related to pen widths as well as colors.

In the next chapter, you take a look at the many ways to edit your drawings in Generic CADD.

Editing Individual Objects

Some dyed-in-the-wool manual drafters take their first suspicious look at a CADD system and sniff with indignation that they can draw faster than "that machine." Even if they are correct, these folks are missing the point. Perhaps an experienced draftsperson can lay down the original lines as fast as someone using a CADD program, but what happens at revision time? The CADD system can make changes to a drawing much faster than someone restricted to a drafting table.

Editing—the processes of erasing lines or changing their length, moving an end point, copying lines or other objects, filleting or chamfering corners, and much more—is easily accomplished on the CADD screen. When you use CADD for editing as well as drawing, the end result is not a sheet filled with poor erasures, and you do not need a vacuum cleaner to remove the crumbs of rubber from the table.

No matter what the specific application, the one thing common to all professions that rely on the use of scale drawings is that changes occur. Using Generic CADD is a crucial step toward ensuring that the process of change through editing is rapid.

Learning Basic Editing Tools

When you look at Generic CADD's ROOT menu, you see not just the menus but also a logical division of CADD commands. The ROOT menu is organized to complement the way most people work. Three menus—SNAPS, TRIMS, and EDITS—have a direct bearing on the editing process, but most of the other menus contain commands that apply to editing as well.

In Generic CADD, two basic types of editing are possible. The first type of editing occurs as part of the drawing process, by means of editing commands that not only add detail but also ensure precision and eliminate unnecessary construction lines. The second type of editing occurs when you revise a "finished" drawing to accommodate changes to the original design.

The editing commands in this chapter apply to single objects you draw. Chapter 10 covers editing commands that operate on groups of objects simultaneously. Single-object editing commands are used most frequently for adding detail and precision while constructing the drawing. Multiple-object editing commands more often are used for revising a drawing. Stay with Chapter 9 to learn about the editing commands necessary to create a drawing, and turn to the next chapter when you are ready to revise your efforts.

Several of the commands covered in this chapter are in the SHORTCUTS menu. (SHORTCUTS is listed in the EDITS menu, not in the ROOT menu.) Until the release of version 5.0, these single-object editing commands were the only ones in the program. Instead of eliminating the single-object editing commands, the designers of Generic CADD retained them for continuity with older versions of CADD. These single-object editing commands can be used when you do not need the power of multiple-object editing. Although dividing the commands between single- and multiple-object editing was not part of the plan, it has worked out that way. Some of the SHORTCUTS commands are discussed here; others are discussed in Chapter 10, which also covers the newer multiple-object editing commands.

To help you understand the editing commands, you need a drawing to work on. Start Generic CADD and follow the steps below to begin a drawing. The object to be drawn vaguely resembles something a mechanical engineer might draw; if it is not what you normally would draw, do not worry. The skills you learn are what matters.

First, before starting to draw, take care of the necessary environment settings.

Setting Up the Environment

Prompt	Input	Description
Command	LS	Starts the Set Limits command
Change height limit	24	Sets new height limits to 24"
Change width limit	36	Sets new width limits to 36"
Command	ZL	Starts Zoom Limits command
Command	GS	Starts Grid Size command
Change Grid Size X	1"	Sets grid width to 1"
Change Grid Size Y	1"	Sets grid height to 1"
Command	MO	Starts Manual Entry Origin command
Command	GO	Sets Grid Origin
Enter new origin	0,0	Ensures that your grid matches this one
Command	UNI	Sets units to inches
Command	NF	Gives numeric display

continues

Prompt	Input	Description
...Linear (Decimal) **D**ecimal Value (3)	Set Linear to Decimal and Decimal Value to 3	Sets these settings to match figure 9.1
Command	**SG**	Sets Snap to Grid on

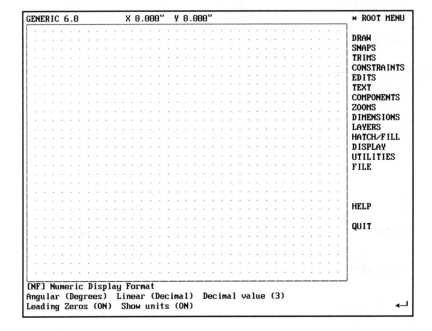

Figure 9.1:

Settings for the Numeric Display Format command.

Now that your environment is ready, make a rough outline of an object to edit.

Drawing Circles

Prompt	Input	Description
Command	**C2**	Starts a two-point circle
Enter center of circle	Move cursor to X 16" Y 16" and click	Sets the center of circle

Prompt	Input	Description
Enter a point on the circle	Move cursor up a nudge and type **5**	Uses direct distance command to set length of radius and draw circle
Command	Press spacebar	Repeats last command (C2)
Enter center of circle	Move cursor to center of circle and click third mouse button or type **NP**	Uses Snap to Nearest Point to identify center of existing circle as start point of a new circle
Enter a point on the circle	Move cursor up a nudge and type **4**	Uses direct distance command to set length of radius and draw second circle
Command	Press spacebar	Repeats last command (C2)
Enter center of circle	Move cursor toward center of existing circles and type **NP** or click third mouse button	Sets center of new circle
Enter a point on the circle	Nudge the cursor in any direction and type **1"**	Sets radius of new circle at 1"
Command	**ZA**	Zooms for a better view

When you add a third circle, the center point of all three circles is the same and can be snapped to by using Snap to Nearest Point (NP) or the third mouse button (see fig. 9.2).

Use the Line Type (LT) command to change to line type 5, the dot-dash pattern. Then put two center lines on the circles drawn so far.

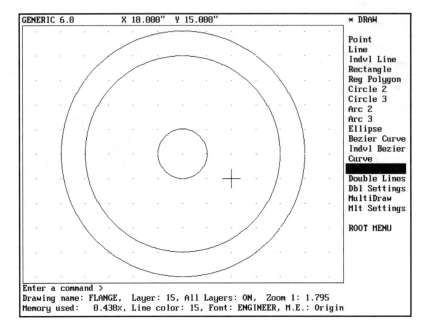

Figure 9.2:

Three circles drawn with Two-point Circle command.

Drawing Center Lines

Prompt	Input	Description
Command	**LT5**	Sets line type to dot-dash pattern
Command	**OR** (Be sure status line reads `Ortho Mode is on`)	Turns on Ortho Mode
Command	Move cursor to center of circles, press third mouse button	Starts a new line
Command	Nudge cursor up and type **6**	Draws construction line from the center up (see fig. 9.3)
Command	Press Esc	Disconnects cursor from the line
Command	**ZA**	Redraws screen to get a complete view of all objects

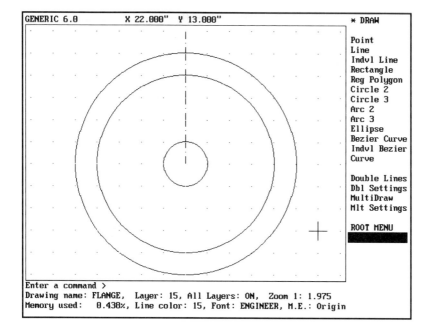

Figure 9.3:

Draw a construction line up from the center of the circles.

Object Copy (OC)

All the activity in this chapter so far has been to create objects on which to use editing commands. Copying objects is a crucial activity in CADD, and the next exercise has you copy the construction line with the Object Copy command. When you type **OC** or select Object Copy from the SHORTCUTS menu, CADD asks for the object to be copied. Select it by clicking anywhere on it. Using Snap to Nearest Point is often a good way to select an object. But the process is not over yet.

Next, CADD asks for a reference point. CADD uses this reference point as the "from" location. The reference point can be anywhere on-screen; usually, but not always, the reference point is on the object you are copying. After you select the reference point, CADD asks for an offset. This is the "to" location. In essence, you are telling CADD, "Take the object I have selected and draw a new copy of it. Space the new copy the same distance from the original as the spacing between the reference point and the offset." As you move the cursor to set the offset, a dotted-line image of the

273

object to be copied moves along with the cursor. This helps you see how the copy of the object fits its new location.

After you have selected the offset, CADD prompts you for the number of copies you need. If you ask for more than one copy, each additional copy is placed the same distance from the previous copy as the first copy is from the original. You may select from one to 99 copies.

Using the Object Copy Command

Prompt	Input	Description
Command	**OC**	Starts the Object Copy command
Pick object	Move the cursor to anywhere on the line; click	Selects line as the object to be copied
Enter a reference point	Move cursor to X 16" Y 22" and press third mouse button	Uses Snap to Nearest Point to select top of line as reference point
Enter new reference point or offset	Move cursor to bottom of original line (X 16" Y 16") and press third mouse button	Sets distance for Object Copy command
Enter number of copies (1-99)	**1**	Makes one copy of line (see fig. 9.4)
Command	**ZA**	Redraws screen for a complete view of all objects

Next, add one more circle to the object. It will fit between the two larger circles.

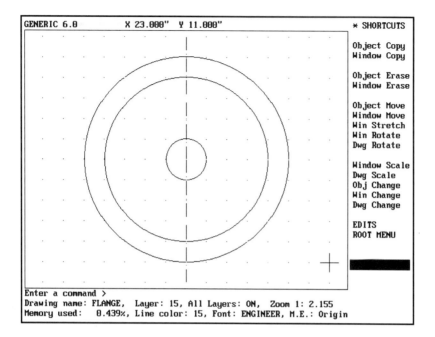

Figure 9.4:

The first line has been copied to extend its length.

Adding Another Circle

Prompt	Input	Description
Command	**LT0**	Changes line type back to zero, a solid line
Command	**GS**	Starts Grid Size command
Change Grid Size X (1.000)	**.5**	Sets new grid width to .5"
Change Grid Size Y (0.500)	Press Enter	Accepts .5" as new grid height
Command	**ZW**	Redraws screen for a close-up view of top of largest circle
Place Window	Move cursor to X 14" Y 21.5" and click; move cursor to X 18" Y 19.5" and click	Draws window to change the view

continues

275

Prompt	Input	Description
Command	Move cursor to X 16" Y 20.5"	Moves to center of new circle
Command	C2 and press Enter	Places center of new circle
Enter a point on the circle	Move cursor to X 16" Y 21" and press Enter	Finishes circle (see fig. 9.5)
Command	RD	Redraws the screen

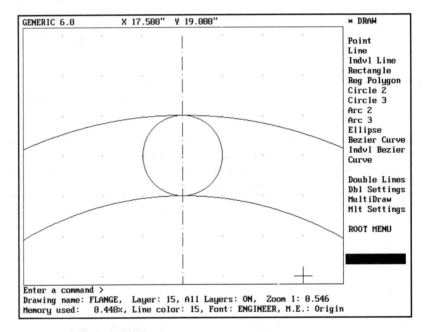

Figure 9.5:

A fourth, smaller circle has been added to the drawing.

Object Break (OB)

In the next exercise, you remove the construction line from inside the smallest circle. To avoid removing the entire line, which happens when you erase an object, you use the SHORTCUT menu's Object Break command to break away a specific part of the line. In fact, use Object Break whenever you need to cut away the middle section of a line but leave the rest in place. In the next exercise, Snap to Grid helps identify the beginning and end points of the section to be removed.

Using the Object Break Command

Prompt	Input	Description
Command	Move cursor to X 16" Y 20.5"	Moves to destination
Command	**OB**	Starts Object Break command
Enter a point on the object to break	Press Enter or click	Selects line as object to be broken
Enter first break point	Move cursor to X 16" Y 21"; press Enter or click	Starts gap in the line at this point
Enter second break point	Move cursor down to X 16" Y 20"; press Enter or click	Sets length of gap

Figure 9.6 shows the smallest circle after you use Object Break to cut away the construction line. As you can see, the line no longer intersects the circle.

Trim (RM) and Extend (XT)

Sometimes a line extends too far or does not extend far enough. Trim and Extend, a useful pair of commands from the TRIMS menu, ensure that lines are always just the right length.

Both commands work in a similar fashion. First you identify the line to be shortened or extended; then click on a line or another object that represents the correct length. The first line is extended to (Extend) or cut off at the second line (Trim).

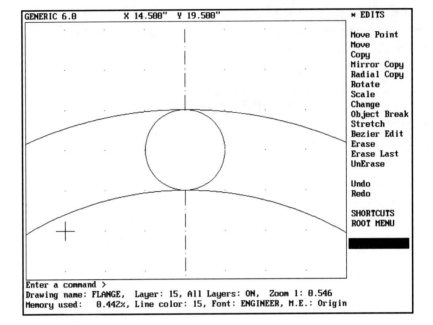

Figure 9.6:

Object Break has cut away the line.

Follow the steps in the next exercise to draw two lines flanking the small circle. Because Snap to Grid is still on, the lines you draw are initially too short. Use Extend to remedy this problem.

Using Trim and Extend

Prompt	Input	Description
Command	Move cursor to X 15.5" Y 20.5"; press Enter or click	Starts a line
Command	Move cursor to X 15.5" Y 20"; press Enter or click	Sets opposite end of line
Command	Press Esc or click on blank line in menu bar	Ends Line command

Prompt	Input	Description
Command	**SG**	Turns off Snap to Grid
Command	**XT**	Extends line to touch circle
Object to extend	Move cursor to any point on line just drawn and click	Identifies line to be extended
Extend to	Move cursor down to the circle just beyond end of line and click	Identifies object to which line extends (see fig. 9.7)
Command	**SG**	Turns on Snap to Grid
Command	**OC**	Copies line to other side of circle
Pick object	Make sure cursor is at X 15.5" Y 20"; press Enter or click	Identifies object to be copied
Enter a reference point	Press Enter	Identifies point at which copying starts
Enter new reference point or offset	Move cursor right to X 16.5" Y Y 20"; press Enter or click	Identifies point to which copying will move
Enter number of copies (1-99)	**1**	Copies line once to flank both sides of circle

In figure 9.8, the line has been copied to the other side of the small circle. Note that both lines extend down to the larger circle.

Now try the same command on a circle.

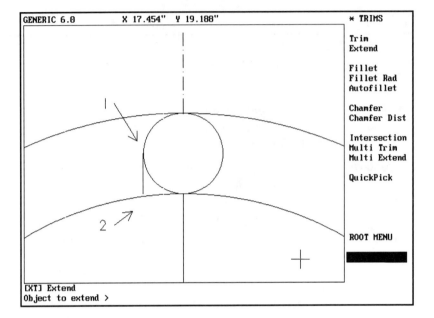

Figure 9.7:

Identify line to extend (1) and distance to extend (2).

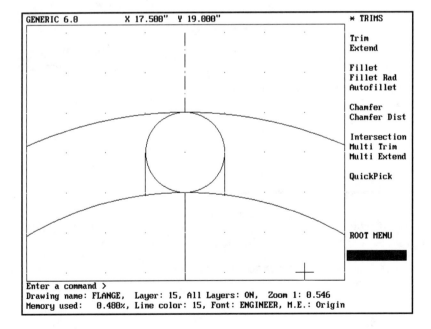

Figure 9.8:

The copied line.

Breaking Up a Circle

Prompt	Input	Description
Command	**SG**	Turns off Snap to Grid
Command	**OB**	Starts Object Break command
Enter a point on the object to break	Move cursor to a point on the circle	Identifies circle as the object to break

Make sure that the cursor is not close enough to any other object to mistakenly select the wrong item. When so directed, click to identify the circle.

Prompt	Input	Description
Enter first break point	**SG**	Turns on Snap to Grid
Enter first break point	Move cursor to X 15.5" Y 20.5" press Enter or click	Starts gap in the circle at this point
Enter the end of the arc	Move the cursor to X 16.5" Y 20.5"; press Enter or click	Sets length of gap along circumference of circle (see fig. 9.9)
Command	**ZA**	Redraws screen for complete view
Command	**SA**	Starts the Save command
...**D**rawing	**D**	Selects Drawing
Save File As	**FLANGE**	Saves drawing as FLANGE.GCD

Keep this drawing. You are finished with it for now, but will use it in Chapter 10.

In the next exercise, you erase the drawing you just made and start a drawing that represents a simple floor plan.

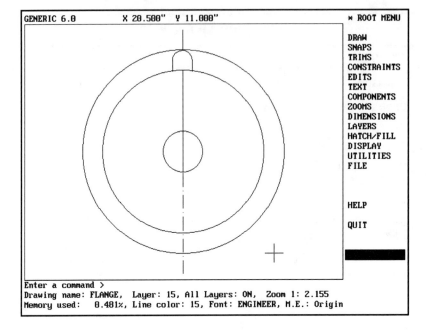

```
GENERIC 6.0          X 20.500"  Y 11.000"              * ROOT MENU

                                                        DRAW
                                                        SNAPS
                                                        TRIMS
                                                        CONSTRAINTS
                                                        EDITS
                                                        TEXT
                                                        COMPONENTS
                                                        ZOOMS
                                                        DIMENSIONS
                                                        LAYERS
                                                        HATCH/FILL
                                                        DISPLAY
                                                        UTILITIES
                                                        FILE


                                                        HELP

                                                        QUIT



Enter a command >
Drawing name: FLANGE,  Layer: 15, All Layers: ON,  Zoom 1: 2.155
Memory used:    0.481%, Line color: 15, Font: ENGINEER, M.E.: Origin
```

Figure 9.9:

The small circle has been broken, using Object Break.

Drawing the walls is faster if you use the Double Line (L2) command. To set the distance between the two lines, use Double Line Offset (TH). Also, set the units to feet and inches.

Drawing a Floor Plan

Prompt	Input	Description
Command	**DXY** (if you still have FLANGE.GCD on screen)	Erases drawing
Command	**LS**	Sets new limits
Change height limit (24)	**48'**	Sets new height limit to 48 feet
Change width limit (36)	**72'**	Sets new width limit to 72 feet
Command	**ZL**	Starts Zoom Limits command

Prompt	Input	Description
Command	**GS**	Starts Grid Size command
Change Grid Size X (.5)	**6"**	Sets grid height to 6"
Change Grid Size Y (6)	Press Enter to accept 6" for Y size	Sets grid width to 6"
Command	**TH**	Sets Double Line Offset
Change Left Offset	**6"**	Left side of double line is 6" from point placed
Change Right Offset	**0**	Right side of double line is at point placed
Command	**UNF**	Sets Display Units to Feet/Inches
Command	**RE**	Starts Rectangle command
Enter one corner of the rectangle	Type **1',1'** or move cursor to X 1'Y 1' and click	Sets first corner of rectangle
Enter opposite corner	Move cursor to X 70' Y 36' and click or type **70',36'**	Finishes rectangle
Command	Press Spacebar	Starts another rectangle
Enter one corner of the rectangle	**1'6", 1'6"**	Sets first corner of rectangle
Enter opposite corner	**69'6", 35'6"**	Finishes rectangle
Command	**ZA**	Redraws screen (see fig. 9.10)

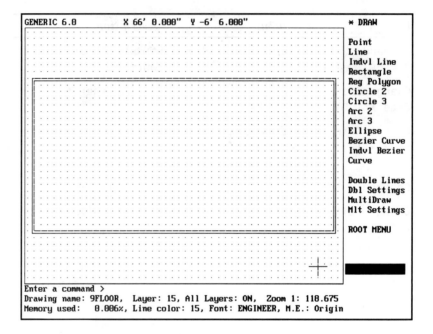

Figure 9.10:

The outline of a basic floor plan.

Tracking (TK)

Although not strictly an editing command, Tracking—found on the CONSTRAINTS menu—is useful when editing. Tracking can be used whenever Generic CADD requests the location of a point. Use it to place components, to locate the first point of an object break, or to start drawing a new object. Tracking also makes it possible to place objects a specified distance from an existing location.

In the next exercise, you use Tracking and Double Line to draw a room in the lower left corner of the floor plan (see fig. 9.11). The wall starts 10 feet up from the floor plan's lower left corner.

Using Tracking To Draw an Interior Wall

Prompt	Input	Description
Command	L2	Starts Double Line to draw interior walls
Enter start point	TK	Starts Tracking command

Prompt	Input	Description
Enter point to start tracking from	Move cursor near inside lower left corner of floor plan and click third mouse button	Starts tracking from inside lower left corner
You are now tracking - type PU to end tracking	Move cursor up and type **10'**	Moves cursor up wall 10 feet
...type PU to end tracking	**PU**	Ends tracking and returns to Double Line command
Double Line: Enter next point	Move cursor right and type **12'**	Draws a wall 12 feet long moving to the right
Enter next point	Move cursor down and type **10'**	Draws a wall 10 feet long moving down the screen
Enter next point	**PU**	Ends Double Line mode

Before going on to the next step, stop and take a moment to get a close-up view of some lines that must be removed from the room you just drew.

Zooming in for a Close-Up View

Prompt	Input	Description
Command	**ZW**	Starts Zoom Window command
Place window	Move cursor above and to the left of the room just drawn (about X 0 Y 13'6") and click	Starts the zoom window

continues

285

Prompt	Input	Description
Place window	Move cursor below and to the right of the room (about X 17' Y -2') and click	Finishes window and redraws screen with new view (see fig. 9.12)

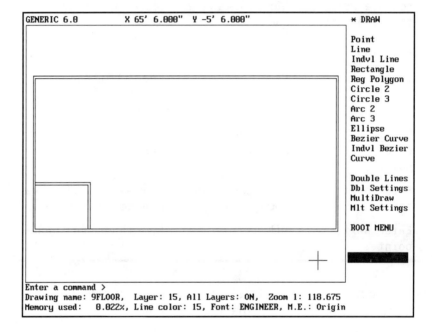

Figure 9.11:

The room drawn with Tracking and Double Line.

Intersection Trim (IT)

The intersections of the floor plan walls shown in figure 9.12 need to be trimmed. If Object Break were the only tool available, it could be used here. But a special editing command exists just for situations like this. Intersection Trim can open up the intersections of sets of lines. Use it whenever you need to trim all the lines coming into an intersection, provided that the sets of lines are parallel or near-parallel. Given a set of intersecting line pairs, Intersection Trim can create an X-shaped, T-shaped, or L-shaped intersection.

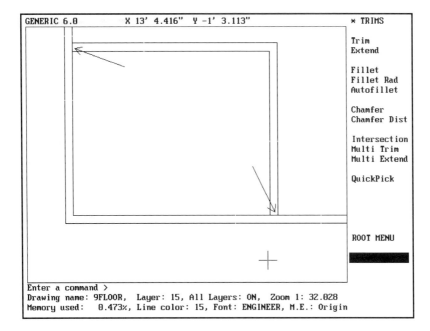

Figure 9.12:

Close-up view of the room, showing lines to be removed.

Intersection Trim can create three possible intersections from the same set of intersecting lines (see fig. 9.13). Using Intersection Trim requires clicking twice; the arrows show where to click to create each type of intersection.

To use Intersection Trim, you must click once inside the intersection to identify it for Generic CADD. The next click shows the program how you want the intersection to be cleaned. When you use the command, notice that the possible trims appear on-screen as you move the cursor. When the intersection is the way you want it, click to complete the trim.

In figure 9.14, the two corners of the interior walls intersecting the outside walls have been trimmed using Intersection Trim. Follow the steps in the next exercise to trim the two intersections in the floor plan.

287

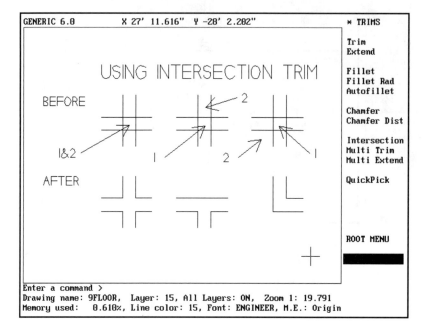

Figure 9.13:

Using Intersection Trim.

Trimming an Intersection

Prompt	Input	Description
Command	**SG**	Turns off Snap to Grid
Command	**IT**	Starts Intersection Trim
Enter a point inside the intersection	Move the cursor to about X 1'3" Y 11'9" and click	Identifies inside of intersection to trim
Enter a point outside corner	Move the cursor straight left to about X 0'6", Y 11'9" and click	Finishes trimming the intersection
Command	Press spacebar	Repeats the Intersection Trim command
Enter a point inside the intersection	Move cursor to about X 13'9" Y 1'2" and click	Identifies inside of intersection to be trimmed

Prompt	Input	Description
Enter a point outside corner	Move the cursor straight down to X 13'9" Y 0'6" and click	Finishes trimming the intersection

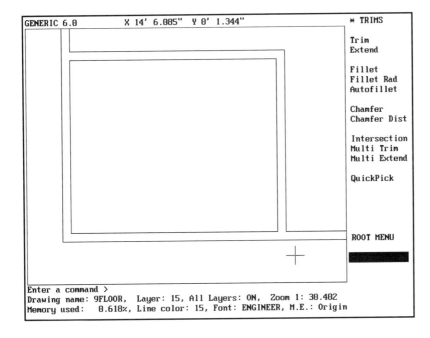

Figure 9.14:

Two corners trimmed with Intersection Trim.

Fillet (FI) and Chamfer (CH)

Fillet and Chamfer, both on the TRIMS menu, are similar to each other in that they trim corners. Fillet cuts away the corner and replaces it with an arc, whereas chamfer replaces the corner with a beveled edge. The size of both the arc and the bevel is predetermined by Fillet Radius (FR) and Chamfer Distance (CA).

To use either command, simply click on each line of the intersection. Generic CADD then finds the intersection and replaces the corner as appropriate. The lines to be filleted or chamfered can either terminate or overlap at their intersection.

Figure 9.15 shows filleted and chamfered corners made from overlapping lines and from lines that terminate at the intersection. Fillet replaces the corner with an arc, and Chamfer replaces the corner with a beveled edge.

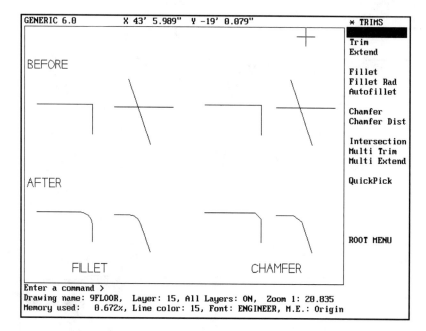

Figure 9.15:

Filleted and chamfered corners.

Fillet Radius (FR)

The size of the arc used by Fillet is set by the Fillet Radius (FR) command, also found on the TRIMS menu. The default setting for Fillet Radius is 0. You may set it to any size; experiment with it in your own CADD work to find the most useful settings.

If you use Fillet on an intersecting set of lines with Fillet Radius set to zero, Fillet cuts off the overlapping lines and leaves a clean intersection. Thus, you can use Fillet (and Chamfer, described soon) as a "corner clean" command for single sets of intersecting lines in the same way you use Intersection Trim for double sets of intersecting lines.

Autofillet (AF)

Autofillet is a toggle command on the TRIMS menu. When
Autofillet is on, any lines drawn as continuous lines (LI or L2)
are filleted automatically as you draw them. (To have Autofillet
work with single lines, you must start by typing **LI**; just moving
the cursor and clicking does not cause Autofillet to take effect.)
When Autofillet is off (the default mode), corners created when
you use LI or L2 to draw continuous lines are at the angle you
draw them, without a radius inserted.

Chamfer Distances (CA)

When Chamfer trims a corner, a line is inserted and the corner
redrawn to create a beveled edge. The Chamfer Distances command provides Chamfer with the information necessary to create
a beveled edge.

Chamfer Distances holds two values. Each value is the distance
from one corner to the point at which the beveled edge connects
with one existing line. Normally, you set both values of Chamfer
Distances to the same number to create an even edge. For a special
effect, set the two values to differing numbers.

If both Chamfer Distance values are set to zero, Chamfer also can
be used to trim single pairs of intersecting lines (see the earlier
explanation for Fillet).

The interior walls of the room just drawn are chamfered and
filleted in the next exercise.

Filleting the Walls

Prompt	Input	Description
Command	**FR**	Starts Fillet Radius command
Change Fillet Radius	**5"**	Sets Fillet Radius to 5"

continues

Prompt	Input	Description
Command	CA	Starts Chamfer Distances command
Change chamfer distance 1"	3"	Sets first distance to 3"
Change chamfer distance 2"	3"	Sets second distance to 3"
Command	FI	Starts Fillet command
Enter a point on the object to fillet	Move cursor to top inside line, at about X 12'0" Y 12'0", and click to identify line	Identifies first line for the Fillet command
Enter second object	Move cursor down to outside right line, at about X 14'0" Y 10'0" and click	Identifies second line for Fillet command, completing the sequence
Command	Press spacebar	Repeats Fillet command
Enter a point on the object to fillet	Move cursor to lower line of the top interior wall at about X 12'0" Y 11'6" and click	Identifies the first line for the Fillet command
Enter second object	Move cursor to intersecting line, at about X 13'6" Y 10'0" and click	Inserts arc at the intersection of the two lines (see fig. 9.16)

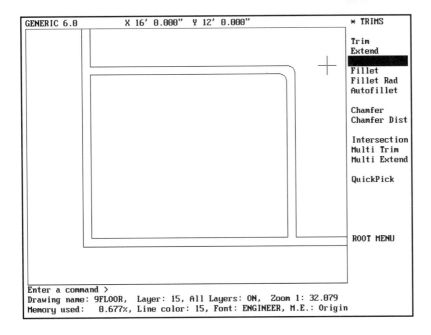

Figure 9.16:

The room's upper right corner has been filleted.

Now try chamfering each line of the intersection between the right interior wall and the bottom exterior wall. The results are shown in figure 9.17.

Chamfering the Walls

Prompt	Input	Description
Command	**CH**	Starts Chamfer command
Enter a point on first object to be chamfered	Move cursor to inside line of right wall, at about X 13'6" Y 3'0" and click	Identifies first line for the Chamfer command
Second object	Move cursor to inside line of bottom wall, at about X 12'0" Y 1'6" and click	Inserts a beveled edge at the intersection

continues

Prompt	Input	Description
Command	Press spacebar	Repeats Chamfer command
Enter a point on first object to chamfer	Move cursor to about X 14'0" Y 2'0" and click	Identifies first line
Second object	Move cursor to about X 15'0" Y 1'6" and click	Inserts a beveled edge at the intersection

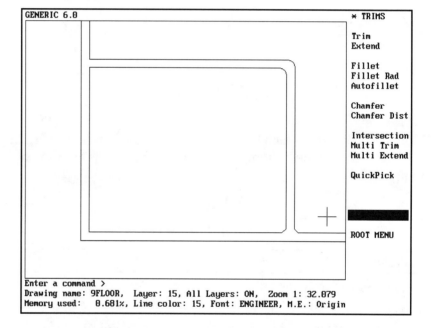

Figure 9.17:

Lines at inter-section have been chamfered.

To draw a series of lines that will be used to explain additional editing commands, follow these steps:

Continuing the Floor Plan

Prompt	Input	Description
Command	**ZA**	Redraws screen for complete view
Command	Move cursor and click to draw lines inside floor plan (see fig. 9.18)	Exact lengths are not important; press Esc to end; Ortho Mode should still be on

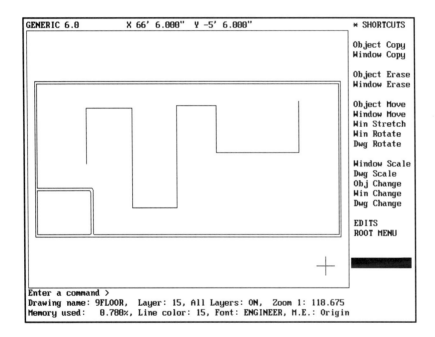

Figure 9.18:

Draw the pattern of lines shown inside the floor plan.

Object Erase (OE)

Erasing is the most common editing need. A few objects always seem just not to belong. If the line or other object you need to erase is the last one drawn, you can use Erase Last (EL). But if the object was drawn earlier, you can send it to oblivion by using Object Erase on the SHORTCUTS menu.

Using Object Erase is simple; type **OE** or select the command from the menu. Generic CADD prompts you to identify the line; when you click on it, it is erased immediately. If you goof and click on the wrong object, you can bring it back immediately with either Unerase (UE) or Undo (OO).

Erasing Objects

Prompt	Input	Description
Command	**OE**	Starts Object Erase command
Pick object	Move cursor to first vertical line in pattern just drawn; click on it to erase	Erases the first vertical line
Command	Press Spacebar	Repeats Object Erase
Pick object	Repeat Object Erase as needed to erase all vertical lines in pattern	Erases vertical lines (see fig. 9.19)

Object Change (OG)

You frequently need to change the width, type, or color of a line. If you want to change only one object, using Object Change, from the SHORTCUTS menu, is faster than using the more powerful Change (CG) command. You can use Object Change to change any or all of these attributes: layer, color, type, or width.

Try using the Object Change command in the following exercise. As shown in figure 9.20, the top left horizontal line has been changed to Line Type 9, Line Width 6.

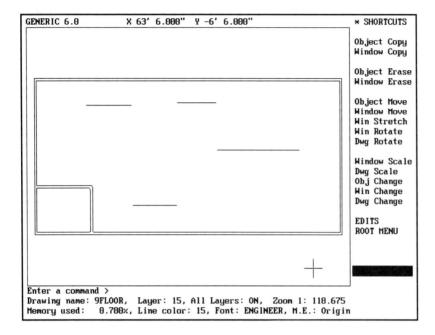

Figure 9.19:

All vertical lines in pattern were erased, one by one.

Changing Objects

Prompt	Input	Description
Command	**OG**	Starts Object Change command
Pick object	Move cursor to first horizontal line on left and click	Selects horizontal line on the left as the object to be changed
Line Width (0)	**LW**	Starts Line Width command
Enter Line width	6	Changes to line width 6
...Limits: 0 to 255	**LT**	Changes line type of object
Enter Line type	9	Changes to line type 9
...Limits: 0 to 255	Press Enter	Accepts the setting; changes the selected object

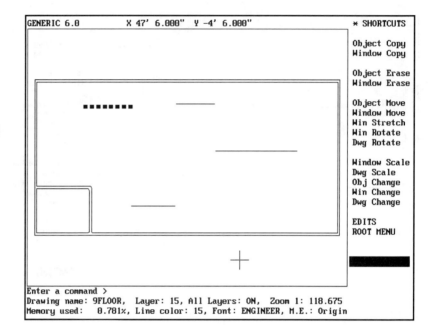

Figure 9.20:

The upper left horizontal line was changed with Object Change.

Object Move (OM)

Object Move, on the SHORTCUTS menu, works very much like Object Copy, except that it moves the original (rather than the first copy) to a new reference point. When the object for the Object Move command is selected, Generic CADD asks for a first reference point, then for a new reference point or offset. As soon as the new reference point is selected, the object is moved to its new location. In the program's eyes, the point identified as the reference is moved to the new reference point, and the rest of the object connected to that point moves with it.

You may want to practice using Object Move on your own, moving the other vertical lines inside the floor plan.

Reshaping Entities

Three of the trim commands used earlier in the chapter (Trim, Fillet, and Chamfer) can change the shape of an object by cutting off portions of its lines. Extend changes the shape of a line by lengthening it. Two other editing commands can reshape an object without cutting it: Move Point (MP) and Bézier Edit (BE).

Move Point (MP)

As you learned earlier, Generic CADD's Object Move command moves the reference point to a new location, and the rest of the object moves also. When Move Point (found on the EDITS menu) is used, the effect is slightly different. The point moves to the new location, but the rest of the object remains rooted in place. It may stretch, contract, or rotate as the point is moved, but it does not become completely detached from its original location.

Except for a standard point, every object in Generic CADD has at least two construction points. When Move Point is used, one of these points shifts to the new location and the other construction points in the object stay still. The parts of the object that connect between points (the vectors) are redrawn to connect the construction points when the selected point reaches its destination. Exactly what happens depends on the object. If Move Point moves the construction point on the circumference of a circle, the size of the circle is changed but the center point remains the same. If the center point is moved with Move Point, the construction point on the circumference stays rooted, changing both the size and relative placement of the circle.

Bézier Edit (BE)

Bézier Edit, found on the EDITS menu, is strictly for changing the shape of Bézier curves. Like Bézier Curve, this command takes a little getting used to. If you use Bézier curves regularly, you eventually gain an intuitive understanding of how they behave, making it easy to draw and edit these special curves.

To use the Bézier Edit command on a series of connected Bézier curves, type **BE** or select Bézier Edit from the EDITS menu. Responding to Generic CADD's prompts, click on two segments you want to reshape. When you select each curve segment, the control points for that curve become visible. CADD then prompts you to select a point to be moved. This point can be a construction point on one of the curve segments you have selected, a control point, or even a construction point on a third Bézier curve segment. The point selected can make a big difference in the nature of the reshaping; you may need to press Esc and try again if the combination you have selected does not enable you to bend the lines the way you want.

Try drawing a series of Bézier curves (BV, on the DRAW menu) and then practice reshaping the curves with Bézier Edit, using various combinations of construction points and control points. There is no one right way to achieve the end result.

Figure 9.21 shows two curves selected for Bézier Edit. The control points extend out from the curves as dotted lines. The arrows point to the curve segments selected for the edit.

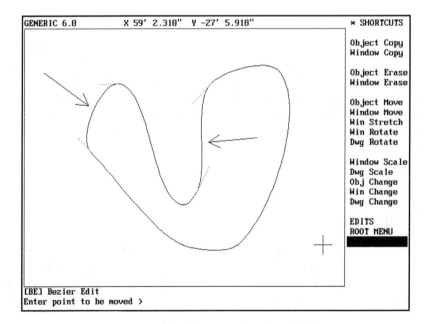

Figure 9.21:

Two curves selected for Bézier Edit.

Measuring Entities

It is not uncommon while drawing with Generic CADD to need to know the exact length of an object or perhaps the angle at which two objects meet, yet not need to dimension the object. The Measure (ME) command is for such situations. It enables you to use the information available in the drawing.

To invoke the Measure command, type **ME** at the prompt or select Measure from the UTILITIES menu. The four options available when you use Measure—Distance, Area, Two-point angle, and Three-point angle—are covered in the sections that follow.

Measure Distance

To measure the length of a line, select the Distance option of Measure by pressing **D** after starting the command. Move the crosshairs to the beginning of the line and snap to the end point; then move to the other end and snap again. After you select the two points, CADD displays the distance between them in the prompt lines at the bottom of the screen.

This command can be used to measure the total length of several objects, or to measure the perimeter. Just keep clicking on end points. The cumulative distance as well as the last distance measured appear in the status line.

Measure Area

To measure the area of a closed figure made of straight line segments, select the Area option of Measure by pressing **A** after starting the command. Move the crosshairs to the beginning of the first line that defines the figure and snap to the end point; then move from point to point until you have returned again to the starting point. When you press Esc, CADD displays the area of the object at the bottom of the screen.

Measure Two-point Angle

The option to measure a 2-point angle actually measures the *heading* of a line. As discussed earlier, every line in Generic CADD has a heading; this is the direction it points away from the 0,0 origin point of the coordinate plane. The 2-point angle option of the Measure command tells you, in degrees, where a line is pointing.

When you use this option (type **2** from the Measure prompt), click on the base of the line. CADD assumes that this end of the line is at 0,0. Next click on the opposite end. CADD assumes that this end of the line identifies the direction of the line, and calculates the precise heading of the line. Any line in CADD can have two possible headings, depending on which end is identified as the base.

Measure Three-point Angle

The 3-point angle option measures the distance in degrees between two lines that meet at a common point. To use this command correctly, remember that CADD always calculates angles in a *counterclockwise* direction. To use this option, type **3** from the Measure prompt. Click on the base of the angle, the point at which the two lines meet. Next, click on the end point of the first line (or use Snap Object to click anywhere along the line's length if the end is off-screen). Then click on the second line that defines the angle. The width of the angle is displayed at the bottom of the screen.

Examining CADD Mimicry

The whole idea behind using a CADD program to draw working plans is to give someone a pattern to follow when creating an object. It is one thing to ask someone to manufacture a nickel-plated widget, but quite another to give him a set of pictorial instructions in the form of a CADD drawing, detailing the size and characteristics of the widget. For the experienced widget machinist, reading the drawing becomes a form of mimicry. The machinist can take the ideas in the drawing and create an object just like the one pictured.

The CADD user can take advantage of a little self-induced mimicry to be more productive while drawing. The information already available in the drawing, including such things as line type or width, color, and size, can be used as a reference for drawing new objects.

Three commands in Generic CADD enable you to copy information; only one has a two-letter command and a place in the menu. All three commands—the Like command, Show By Example, and Match Parameters (MH)—can be used at various times, when you feel the urge to mutter, "I want it just like *that* one."

The Like Command (=)

The Like command, which enables you to copy an object that has the characteristics you need, generally is used with information that can be typed from the keyboard. Using Like, you can specify attributes such as width, color, layer, and length of a line.

To use the Like command when you want to copy something already on-screen, press the equals (=) key when you are prompted for a value or a name. One practical use for the Like command is when you need to set the size of text but do not know exactly what size to use. If you can see what size is correct, draw a line segment as long as the height you need the text to be. Then summon the Text Size command, and when you are prompted for a new size, press the equals key. When Generic CADD asks what object you are referring to, click on the line. The program then sets the size of the text to the length of the line. (Do not forget to erase the line after you use the Like command on it.)

Try the examples that follow to see how the Like command works.

Using the Like Command

Prompt	Input	Description
Command	**ZA**	Redraws screen
Command	**OR**	Turns off Ortho Mode

continues

Prompt	Input	Description
Command	Draw a line on the screen to represent the size text you want	
Command	**TZ**	Starts Text Size command
Text (1.0")...	**T**	Sets size of regular text
Change Text Size	Press =	Summons the Like command
Like what object	Click on the line just drawn	Generic CADD measures the line and uses the value as the new size for text
Text (1.0)"	Press Enter	

It is possible to take advantage of Like in ways you might not think of at first. For example, you can set text size by "liking" an arc. Generic CADD measures the radius of the arc and uses that distance to set the text size. You can use the color of any object to set the color of any other object, and you can specify a scale reduction by "liking" something that has a specified scale—a component, for example. If you need to match the rotation of something in a drawing, use Like when asked for the rotation. CADD measures the angle at which the object sits and uses that value to set the rotation of the new object. Setting the rotation of text equal to other rotated objects in a drawing becomes an easy task when you use the Like command.

TIP You can even use Like to specify a name when you select a font, a component, or a specific attribute. If the item you need already exists in the drawing, click on it using Like. Generic CADD takes the name of the object and uses it to finish the task at hand.

Show by Example

Show By Example is a limited version of the Like command. Show By Example is available only for setting distances (Show Distance) or angles (Show Angle).

Show Distance

Whenever Generic CADD requires a distance, you can use Show Distance to identify an existing object. Instead of typing in the value, type **D**. Generic CADD asks you to enter two points. It then calculates the distance and uses that value as the distance requested when you typed D. The most precise way to select the two points is to use Snap to Nearest Point (NP or the third mouse button) to select each end of the object.

Show Distance is useful only for setting straight distances when a value (not a coordinate) is requested. You cannot use it to draw a circle or even a line using C2 or LI, for example, because these commands require coordinate locations rather than distance values. Do not try to use Show Distance to set scale factors, either. Valid situations in which to use Show Distance include Text Size, Double Line settings, Grid Size, Text Spacing, and Dimension settings. If you use Show Distance to provide a value for a command that needs an angle, the length is translated as an angle. (This may be a useless bit of information, but at least you have been warned.)

Show Angle

Use the Show Angle commands whenever you are prompted for an angle, as when setting the angle of rotation for a component. Instead of typing in the value, type **A** or **V**. Option A gives a two-point angle, otherwise known as a *heading*. If you select this option, CADD prompts you for two points and measures the heading of the line between the two points, starting with the first point you place and moving toward the second point. CADD uses the heading of this "line" as the value needed to complete the command.

Use the V option when you want a three-point angle. In Chapter 10, you use the V option with Radial Copy to bisect one angle into two equal angles.

Match Parameters (MH)

Match Parameters (MH), introduced in version 5.0, is a powerful editing feature. Located on the UTILITIES menu, Match Parameters is similar to the Like command, except that it can return *all* the values related to an object.

The following is a typical scenario that makes good use of Match Parameters. Imagine that most of the lines in a drawing are width 0, type 0, but one line is obviously wider and of a different line type—and you need to draw a circle using those characteristics. You could use Screen Flip (SF) to find the line and read what line type and line width it uses, or you could use Match Parameters. Follow the steps in the exercise to try it out. In a previous exercise, line width and line type were changed from zero to other values; now they are reset to zero, using Match Parameters.

Using Match Parameters to Choose Line Width and Line Type

Prompt	Input	Description
Command	**C2**	Starts a circle
Enter center of circle	Move cursor to an open area on-screen and click	Sets center of circle
Enter a point on the circle	**MH**	Uses Match Parameters to set characteristics of the circle
Select object to match	Click cursor on any line of width 0, type 0	CADD responds "line matched"
Enter a point on the circle	Move cursor to set size of circle and click	Draws circle using line type 0, line width 0

After you finish reading about components and dimensioning in Chapters 11 and 13, come back to this discussion of match parameters.

If you know that you regularly will use more than one set of options for dimensioning, save an example of each type as a component. When you need to dimension a drawing, place the component that holds the dimensioning style you need. Explode the component, then use Match Parameters on the sample dimension; all the dimensioning settings change to match the characteristics of the sample.

Placing components is another situation in which Match Parameters comes in handy. If you are placing components in a variety of scale factors and rotations, use Match Parameter to identify a component placed using the same rotation and scale factors you need for the next component to be placed.

Match Parameters also can save time when you place text (use MH to match the font, size, and rotation of text already on-screen); when you use hatch patterns (select the pattern and the scale); and when you use attributes (match the settings of attributes already in the drawing).

Summary

In writing, editing means to modify the text to improve clarity and accuracy; it means the same thing in Generic CADD. Some editing commands help to clarify the message of the drawing by eliminating unnecessary objects (or parts of objects). Commands like Erase Last, Object Erase, and Object Break are used to improve clarity. Some editing commands help improve accuracy by modifying existing objects. Included in this group are Trim, Extend, Intersection Trim, Fillet, Chamfer, Move Point, and Bézier Edit. The Object Move and Object Copy editing commands improve accuracy and increase clarity by moving or copying objects.

Several commands make it easier to find locations and adjust settings while editing. These include Tracking, Show By Example, the Like command, Measure, and Match Parameters.

The commands in this chapter, for the most part, work on only one object. They are useful when you need to make quick small changes. In the next chapter, you become familiar with the more powerful multiple-object editing commands. After you have learned how to use the entire range of editing commands, you will have mastered much of what gives Generic CADD the edge over manual drafting. After all, how fast *can* you erase?

Editing Groups of Objects

C hapter 9 introduced the use of single-object editing commands. While these commands are quick and handy, they are limited in their effectiveness. The editing commands covered in this chapter are more robust, thanks to two processes: selection and filtering.

As you work through the exercises in this chapter, think of selection and filtering as the lever and pulley of CADD. Simple tools, perhaps, but they make it easy to amplify your efforts, achieving maximum productivity from minimum effort. Instead of moving one object, move 12 objects with only one or two extra keystrokes. Use selection and filtering to pick and choose objects that match specific criteria (all red circles of line width 3 on layers 14 and 38, for example). Selection and filtering can be used to identify objects as well as to edit them, making it possible to correctly identify the nature of objects (such as line width, color, layer).

Selection and Filtering

To understand the difference between the single-object editing commands in Chapter 9 and the multiple-object editing commands in this chapter, consider Object Copy (OC) and its counterpart Copy (CO). Object Copy enables you to select and copy one object. Copy enables you to select several objects, gathering them together, and then copy this group all at once. You can select by using a window, by clicking on objects one at time, by identifying a layer, or even by selecting every object in the drawing. If you goof while selecting objects, you can deselect members of the group before executing the Copy command. Using filtering, you can even specify that only the objects matching certain criteria are to be selected for the Copy command.

In Generic CADD, multiple objects can be selected by one of three methods: *active selection*, used as part of the editing commands covered here (as well as with other commands in other chapters); *passive selection*, used only to select objects—not edit them; and *entity filtering*, which selects entities according to a set of user-defined parameters.

Active Selection within Editing Commands

All multiple-object editing commands share the same active selection methods and display the same options. When a command is chosen, a list of options appears in the prompt line (see fig. 10.1). Items may be chosen for the edit using one or all of the following:

```
Window  Object  laYer  Drawing  Crossing  Last  Filter
```

To copy the two circles on the left in figure 10.1, you can type **O** for Object, click on one of the circles to select it, type **O** again, click on the second circle, and then copy both. Or you can type **W** for Window and draw a selection window around the two circles. Only objects completely inside the window are selected. In figure 10.2, only the circles are selected; the arc and the polygon are not.

A second window-type selection tool is listed in the prompt as Crossing. To use Crossing, type **C** and draw a window. The difference between Crossing and Window is that Crossing selects not only any objects inside the window but every object that is intersected by the window, as well. Crossing makes easy work of selecting objects in a crowded field. In figure 10.2, if Crossing were used rather than Copy, the arc and one line of the polygon would be selected as well as the two circles.

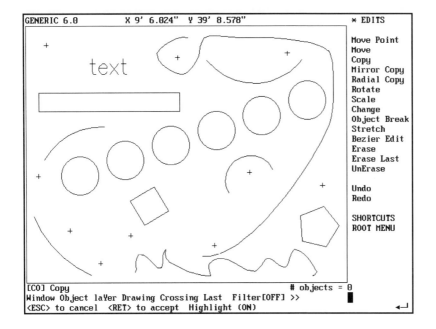

Figure 10.1:

Multiple-object editing options.

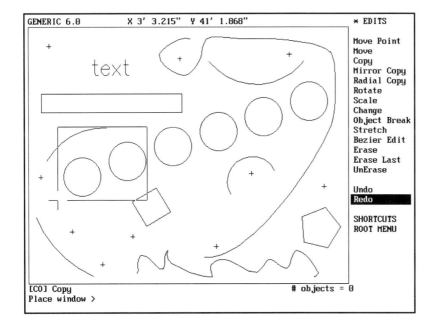

Figure 10.2:

A selection window around two circles.

Although CADD takes longer to identify objects when using Crossing than when using Window, the wait is worthwhile if it saves extra steps.

The number of objects you select is recorded on the lower right portion of the screen, just below the drawing window. When you select the two circles, Generic CADD shows two objects (# objects = 2). Because figure 10.2 illustrates the act of selecting the circles, # objects is still =0.

A component is counted as one item, even if it contains 100 or more lines. Each line of text placed with the Text Line Placement command is counted as one object for each line; characters placed using the Text Character Placement command are counted as one for each character. A Bézier curve is made of individual segments; to select a complete curve, you must select each segment. A complex curve is considered to be one item, however. In figure 10.3, six objects have been selected: the two circles, one complex curve (the squiggly line at the bottom of the drawing), one section of the Bézier curve (highlighted at the bottom of the screen), the line of text at top left, and one standard point (at the right corner of the diamond).

Figure 10.3:

Six items selected using active selection.

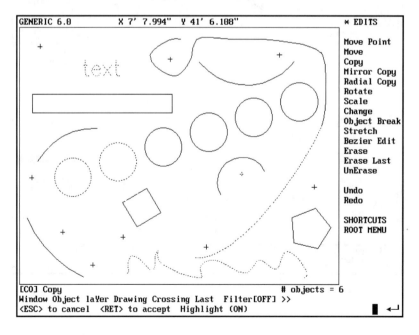

All the zoom and redraw commands are available while you use an active selection option, which makes it easier to zero in on what you select. It may be difficult to draw a window around the objects you need when the screen displays a Zoom All view, but the same objects can be selected easily with a window by using Zoom In to get up close first. If you are using Multiple Viewports, the selection tools are active in all viewports at all times, regardless of the status of Active Viewport.

When all the objects to be edited have been selected, press Enter or click on the statement <RET> to accept in the status line. What happens after that depends on which editing command you are using.

If your computer is slow, you may want to turn off the Highlight option while you use editing commands. The extra time it takes to redraw selected objects extends an editing sequence by several seconds on slow computers. To turn off Highlight, click on it in the status line or type **H** whenever the Active Selection options appear. Highlight is a toggle and can be set by typing **HI** whenever CADD accepts a two-letter command from the keyboard. If the Highlight option is on when you are using multiple viewports, selected objects appear highlighted in the active viewport only. If no viewport is currently active, highlighting appears in all viewports. Having to draw four or more sets of highlights slows down the computer; you probably should make sure that an active viewport is selected when you use a selection command with multiple viewports.

The All Layers Active (AL) command affects which items can be selected. If AL is off, only the items on the current layer can be selected (unless you use the Drawing selection option, which overrides AL, or the Layer command, which selects all items on the specified layer regardless of whether AL is on or off).

Generic CADD remembers which objects you selected (unless they have been erased) until you select new objects with another command that relies on active selection. The Last selection option lets you take advantage of CADD's memory. If you want to rescale, rotate, and change the color of the six objects you are about to copy, for example, you can select them with one keystroke each time you perform an editing operation by using the

Last selection option. But be forewarned: when you copy objects, both the originals *and* the copies are remembered and selected by the Last selection option. (If you want to rescale, rotate, change, and copy the same items, copy them last).

Passive Selection (SE)

You can use the Last selection option after you use the Selection command on the UTILITIES menu. Although this command uses the same selection methods as the active selection editing commands, it only selects objects (it does not edit them).

The value of passive selection is that commands such as Selection Save Batch (BS) and Selection Save Drawing (SV) can refer to the items identified using Selection. The Selection command also can be used for selecting items to be edited more than once, using Last selection. Items that can be retrieved using Last selection can be combined with other items, using any of the other selection devices. To use Selection in other ways, you can combine it with the Entity Filter (EF), Object Info (OI), or Screen Flip (SF) commands, as explained in the following sections.

Entity Filter (EF) Selection

Selecting by entity filter is the third way to select multiple objects in Generic CADD. The Entity Filter command is on the UTILITIES menu. The Generic CADD manuals refer to it only as Filter (or *the* Filter), but calling it Entity Filter makes it easier to remember its two-letter command and better describes its purpose.

As stated earlier in this chapter, you can be very selective about which items are to be edited. The Entity Filter command makes this possible. It can select every entity that can be drawn in CADD, as you can see from the status lines and prompts at the bottom of figure 10.4. Because rectangles and regular polygons are stored in the CADD database as lines only, they are not mentioned by name. Ellipses created with the Construction option are stored in the CADD database as arcs; they show up as arcs in the Entity Filter command. Ellipses created with the True option are listed as ellipses in the CADD database and may be filtered as such.

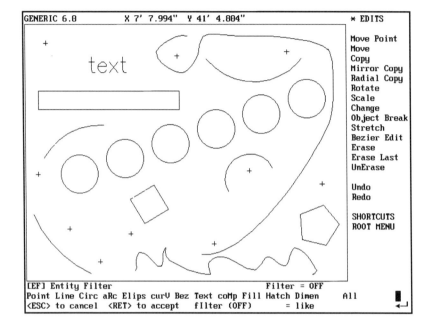

GENERIC 6.0   X 7' 7.994"   Y 41' 4.804"   * EDITS

                                                            Move Point
                                                            Move
                                                            Copy
                                                            Mirror Copy
                                                            Radial Copy
                                                            Rotate
                                                            Scale
                                                            Change
                                                            Object Break
                                                            Stretch
                                                            Bezier Edit
                                                            Erase
                                                            Erase Last
                                                            UnErase

                                                            Undo
                                                            Redo

                                                            SHORTCUTS
                                                            ROOT MENU

[EF] Entity Filter   Filter = OFF
Point Line Circ aRc Elips curV Bez Text coMp Fill Hatch Dimen   All
<ESC> to cancel <RET> to accept   fIlter (OFF)   = like

Figure 10.4:

Selecting entities with the Entity Filter command.

When the Entity Filter command is started, the top status line, just below the drawing screen displays Filter = OFF. This lets you know that no objects (entities) have been chosen for the filter. When you select an entity type, the filter status changes to show the name of that entity.

The drawing used as an example in this chapter includes several standard points. Imagine that each point represents an outcropping of rocks in a field. You want to know how many such outcroppings have been recorded in the drawing, and you want to move these markers to their own layer. This drawing has only a few outcroppings, and counting them manually would be relatively easy. But what if the drawing contained 50 outcroppings, or 500? The Entity Filter command can count them for you.

Take a few minutes to re-create the drawing shown here. (If you have the optional disk, the drawing, called CH10.GCD, is on it.) The exact placement of items is not important, but be sure to include 10 standard points, a long Bézier curve (the exact number of sections is not important), a complex curve, 6 circles, 4 arcs, a line of text placed using the Text Line Placement (TL) command, and 13 line segments. Use Line Type 0, Line Width 0, and Line Color 15 (unless you must use a different color on your monitor). The placement method is up to you. (In the drawing shown in figure 10.4, all the line segments were placed using the Rectangle and Regular Polygon commands.) After you have created the drawing on your screen, follow the steps in the exercise to become more familiar with the Entity Filter command.

Using the Entity Filter Command

Prompt	Input	Description
Command	**EF**	Starts the Entity Filter command
Point...	Type **P** and then press Enter	Selects Points as the entity type
Select characteristics to filter	**A**	Selects all characteristics
Select characteristics to filter	Press Enter, or click on <RET> in the status lines	Selects points of all colors, widths, layers; ends command

The Entity Filter command ends abruptly after you have made your choices. Because the information is stored in CADD's memory and no further action is required, it returns to the command prompt. But the next time you use a selection command, Generic CADD limits its search to the entities that match the description you gave when using the Entity Filter command. The following exercise displays that knowledge by using the Selection command to find only the objects that match the definition given to Entity Filter.

Using the Selection Command

Prompt	Input	Description
Command	SE	Starts the Selection command
...Drawing...	D	Selects all objects in the drawing that match the filter's criteria

In figure 10.5, the Selection command has been used to select all objects in the drawing that match the criteria set by the Entity Filter command. (The top status line shows # objects = 10.) If all you need to know is how many points are in the drawing, using the Selection command after you set the Entity Filter gives you the answer. If you want even more information, however, use the Screen Flip command.

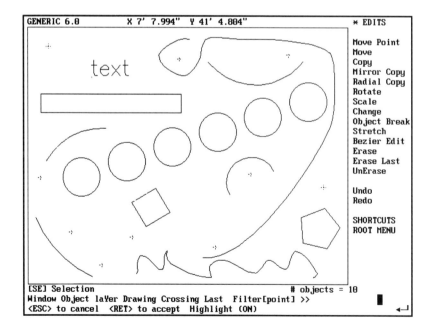

Figure 10.5:

The Selection (SE) command selects 10 points as specified.

Checking the Database

There may be times when you need to know some of the information stored in Generic CADD's database. The Screen Flip and Object Info commands, found on the UTILITIES menu, give you access to this information. Screen Flip also provides a convenient one-stop view of all program settings.

Screen Flip (SF)

This command is named Screen Flip because the screen "flips," changing from a graphics screen to a text-only screen. (The File Selection screen is a text screen also.) When you type **SF** or select Screen Flip from the UTILITIES menu, the options shown in figure 10.6 are displayed.

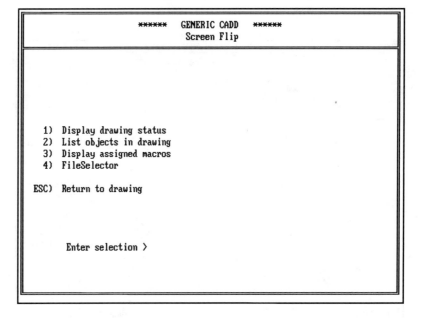

Figure 10.6:

The Screen Flip command options.

```
******    GENERIC CADD    ******
                Screen Flip




     1)  Display drawing status
     2)  List objects in drawing
     3)  Display assigned macros
     4)  FileSelector

  ESC)  Return to drawing



         Enter selection >
```

The first item on the text screen, Drawing Status, shows a summary of settings and reports on memory usage when selected. If you are curious about the internal workings of your computer, this information should interest you. The technical support people at Autodesk Retail Products often ask their callers to use this screen to report on the status of their memory, disk space, and other possible problem areas. Figure 10.7 shows an example of the Drawing Status screen. If you need to create a large drawing, looking at the Drawing Status screen may help you decide whether you need to make room on your hard drive or switch virtual memory to another drive.

```
******  GENERIC CADD  ******
          Drawing Status

Drawing name: CH10GCD
Drawing extents min: 0.0 , 0.0 "  max: 0.0 , 0.0 "

Point records: 204 , Entities: 52 , Definitions: 3
Memory available: 3,861,330 Mem used: 2,840 Mem remaining: 3,858,490
Basepoint: 0.0 , 0.0 " from drawing origin.

Database unit: Inches     Display unit: Feet & Inches
Disk space: C:\ 13,443,072  D:\ 2,142,208
Current drive & directory:  C:\CADD6\
Virtual memory drive: C:\      Shell drive: C:\

Tolerance: 0.250          Current layer:   15
Trace mode: OFF,  Ortho mode: OFF
Grid size: 6.0 , 6.0 " , Grid display: OFF, Grid snap: OFF

Menu Size: Video (4178)   Digitizer (0)

Press any key or click a pointer button to continue >
```

Figure 10.7:
The Drawing Status screen.

Try out the Screen Flip command's second option, List objects in drawing, in the following exercise:

Listing Objects in a Drawing

Prompt	Input	Description
Command	**SF**	Starts the Screen Flip command
...2) List objects in drawing..	**2**	Selects List objects in drawing option

continues

Prompt	Input	Description
List objects in current: ... View Drawing Selected_List	S	Displays the previously selected objects

After you type **S** for Selected_list, the display on your screen should look like the one shown in figure 10.8. To see the rest of the list, press PgDn or click on Next Page with the first pointer button. Every item in this list matches the criteria set by the Entity Filter command and was logged in Generic CADD's memory by the Selection command. You already knew the drawing included 10 points, but now you can see all the characteristics of each point. If the points were assigned different colors or layers, you could see that as well. (Basalt rock outcroppings, for example, could be in Color 14 on Layer 14 and limestone rock outcroppings could be in Color 6 on Layer 6. Please, no letters from geologists saying that the two rocks would not be found near each other.) If the points were assigned such characteristics, you could use the Entity Filter and Selection commands to further refine your list.

Figure 10.8:

The list of items selected, as displayed by Screen Flip.

```
Object: point      ID#: 100      Data Points: 1
Color: 15      Layer: 15      Ltype: 0      Width: 0
Pt1: X 71.677 Y 531.141

Object: point      ID#: 102      Data Points: 1
Color: 15      Layer: 15      Ltype: 0      Width: 0
Pt1: X 100.531 Y 532.296

Object: point      ID#: 217      Data Points: 1
Color: 15      Layer: 15      Ltype: 0      Width: 0
Pt1: X 34.698 Y 499.979

Object: point      ID#: 219      Data Points: 1
Color: 15      Layer: 15      Ltype: 0      Width: 0
Pt1: X 90.540 Y 500.939

Object: point      ID#: 221      Data Points: 1
Color: 15      Layer: 15      Ltype: 0      Width: 0
Pt1: X 42.942 Y 485.572

Object: point      ID#: 223      Data Points: 1
Color: 15      Layer: 15      Ltype: 0      Width: 0

<PgDn> Next Pg  <PgUp> Previous pg  <G>oto  <Home/End>  <ESC> to exit >
```

The third Screen Flip option, Display Assigned Macros, is discussed in Chapter 15.

Object Info (OI)

With Screen Flip, looking at information about objects in the current drawing is one of several options. With Object Info, it is the command's only purpose. If you need to examine the database, the difference between the two commands is the selection process. Passive selection is necessary when you want to examine the database with Screen Flip. The objects to be analyzed must have been selected earlier, unless you want to see information about every object in the drawing or only what currently is visible on-screen.

Object Info uses active selection to let you decide what objects to review. Pressing **OI** or selecting Object Info from the UTILITIES menu causes the set of tools for object selection to appear, just as they do for Copy, Scale, or any of the other multiple-object editing commands. After you select the objects you want to analyze, press Enter. The screen shifts, displaying a text screen with data on the items you selected. Use PgUp and PgDn to move through the data.

Options for Editing Groups of Objects

The selection process enables you to use a variety of editing commands. As you explore them here, one by one, use the current drawing to experiment with some of them.

Stretch (SS)

The Stretch command, located in the EDITS menu, is used to reshape objects by moving their construction points. Stretch is the multiple-object counterpart of the Move Point command. As with Move Point, construction points (not the objects drawn using them) are the key. New users may be confused by the Stretch command until they understand the difference. The lines on the screen connect construction points. When you move one of the construction points in an object, the object changes shape.

The first step of the Selection process is to identify the *objects* to be affected (selection does not acknowledge construction points). After the objects have been selected, the Stretch command prompts the user to draw a window to show which *construction points* are to be moved. If you want to stretch a line, for example, and have selected it, you would draw the window only around the construction point on the end of the line to be stretched; the construction point on the other end of the line would not be included in the window.

Then a reference point is chosen and moved to a new location. All the construction points inside the previous selection window move along with the reference point, and the objects are redrawn to correspond with the construction points in the drawing.

Follow the steps in this exercise to stretch the pentagon in the lower right corner of the drawing. (If you drew something else, follow along as best you can. Be sure that your selection window completely includes the object you plan to stretch.)

Stretching the Pentagon

Prompt	Input	Description
Command	SS	Starts the Stretch command
Window...	W	Selects Window option
Place Window	Draw selection window around entire pentagon, selecting each line (see fig. 10.9)	Encircles the pentagon
Window...	Press Enter	Completes selection

Prompt	Input	Description
Place window around points to be moved	Draw window around top two lines of pentagon; bottom window line should intersect the two lower lines of pentagon (see fig. 10.10)	Moves all the points on the top two lines
Enter a reference point	Move cursor to top corner of pentagon; type **NP** or click third mouse button	Uses Snap to Nearest Point to select the pentagon as the reference point
Enter new location of reference point	Move cursor slightly upward, stretching pentagon out of shape (see fig. 10.11)	Moves the construction points upward as the reference points move; connecting objects stretch as points move
Enter new location of reference point	Move cursor to new reference point and press Enter	Completes the stretch

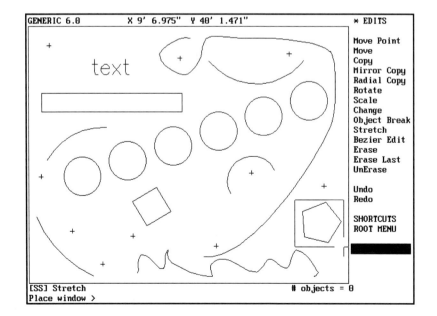

Figure 10.9:

Drawing a selection window around the pentagon.

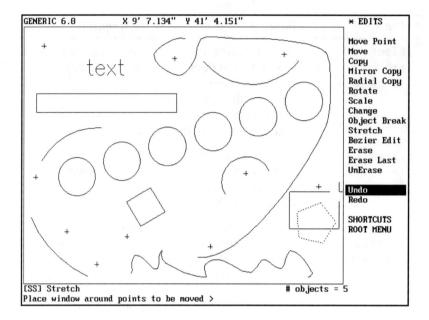

Figure 10.10:

Selecting the pentagon's top two lines.

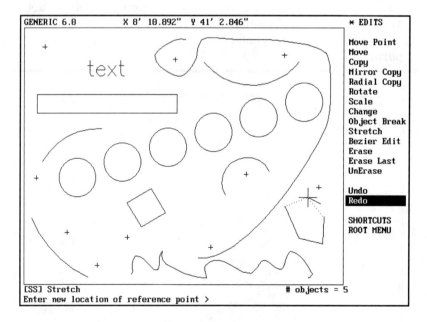

Figure 10.11:

Moving the reference points stretches the objects attached to them.

The Stretch command is often used to change the dimensions of a floor plan or the dimensions of a room in a floor plan. You can use the Tracking, Direct Distance, or Manual Entry Relative commands to select the new location of the reference point.

Scale (SZ)

The Scale command, found on the EDITS menu, changes the size of selected objects by a percentage of their original size. If you selected several objects and set the scale of change to 1 for both the X direction and the Y direction, you would be telling CADD to redraw them at 100 percent of their original size. In other words, their size would remain the same. A scale of 2 is 200 percent; a scale of .5 is 50 percent.

In some CADD programs, you cannot set the width and height separately as you can in Generic CADD. Normally, you maintain the original shape of an object, changing only its size. But in Generic CADD it is possible to change the proportions of objects by setting different values for X and Y.

Positive or negative numbers can be used to change the scale. Setting either the X scale (width) or Y scale (height) to -1, and the other to 1, causes the object to stay the same size but redraws it as a mirror image of itself.

Follow the steps in the exercise to resize the rectangle near the top of the drawing. Place the reference point for rescaling at the center of the rectangle, using the Snap to Midpoint and Tracking commands to make sure that all sides of the rectangle are drawn evenly.

Resizing the Rectangle

Prompt	Input	Description
Command	**SZ** or select Scale from EDITS menu	Starts the Scale command
Window...	**W**	Starts Window selection

continues

Prompt	Input	Description
`Place window`	Draw selection window around rectangle; other objects may be intersected (but are selected only if completely inside the window)	Selects the rectangle
`# objects = 4`	Press Enter	Completes Window selection; the four lines of the rectangle are highlighted in the drawing (see fig. 10.12)
`Enter a reference point`	**TK**	Finds the center of the rectangle
`Enter point to start tracking from`	Move cursor to top line of rectangle, and type **SM**	Establishes the first point for tracking
`Midpoint of`	Click on top line of rectangle	Cursor snaps to midpoint of the top line
`You are now tracking`	**OR** (Make sure that ortho mode is on; if prompt indicates that ortho mode is off, type **OR** again)	Constricts the movement of the tracking line
`You are now tracking`	Move cursor to center of rectangle, and then to left	Moves toward the next temporary point

Figure 10.13 shows a close-up view of the rectangle. The tracking line points straight down, but the cursor is free to move toward the left side of the rectangle. Snap to Midpoint is used to find the midpoint of the left side, placing the end of the tracking line in the exact center of the rectangle.

Prompt	Input	Description
You are now tracking	**SM**	Starts the Snap to Midpoint command
Midpoint of	Move cursor onto left side of rectangle and click	Executes the Snap to Midpoint command
You are now tracking	**PU**	Ends the Tracking command; the last point identified becomes the reference point for the Scale command
Enter new X scale	**.5**	Reduces width by one-half
Enter new Y scale	**.5**	Reduces height by one-half; redraws rectangle (see fig. 10.14)

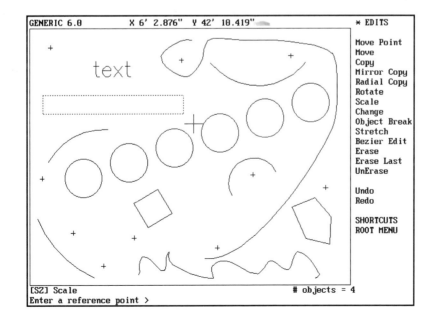

Figure 10.12:

The lines of the selected rectangle appear dotted (highlighted).

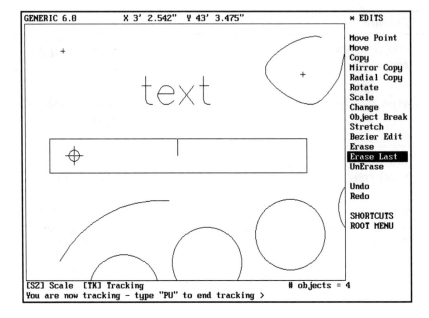

A close-up view of the rectangle.

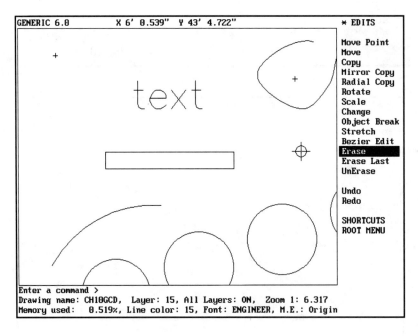

Figure 10.14:

The rectangle redrawn at one-half original size.

Move (MV)

Even the most carefully prepared plans sometimes need to be changed. Fortunately, Generic CADD has a Move command, which relocates objects in a drawing. You select the objects, set a reference point, and move the point to a new location. All the selected objects move as a unit with the reference point.

In the following exercise, you move three of the selected circles down and to the left, away from the other three. To keep all six circles in line, take advantage of existing geometry when choosing the reference point and its new location.

Moving Circles

Prompt	Input	Description
Command	**MV**	Starts the Move command
Window...	**W**, or click on Window	Selects the Window option
Place window	Draw selection window around lower three circles	Selects the three lower circles

If your drawing matches the one in fig. 10.15, a line from the four-sided polygon also is inside the selection window. To make the selection window large enough to contain all three circles at once, the line also is included (# objects = 4, rather than the desired three).

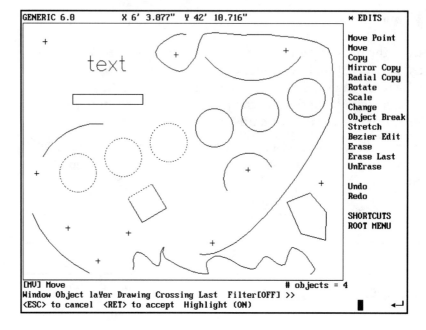

Figure 10.15:

Selecting the lower three circles.

Prompt	Input	Description
Window...	Press Ctrl and type **O**	Uses the object selection to *deselect* the line
Select object	Click on previously selected line; press Enter	Eliminates the line from the selection group (three objects should remain); then selects objects
Enter a reference point	Move cursor to to center of uppermost circle in drawing (not the ones to be moved); type **NP** or press third mouse button	Uses Snap to Nearest Point to select center of the uppermost circle as location of the reference point

Prompt	Input	Description
Enter new location of reference point	Move cursor to center of the next circle in row and press third mouse button	Selects the center of the next circle as the new location of the reference point (see fig. 10.16)

When you complete the preceding sequence, the selected circles are moved a distance equal to the distance between the center points of the top two circles. Note the images of the three circles being moved in figure 10.16 as dotted-line versions of the originals.

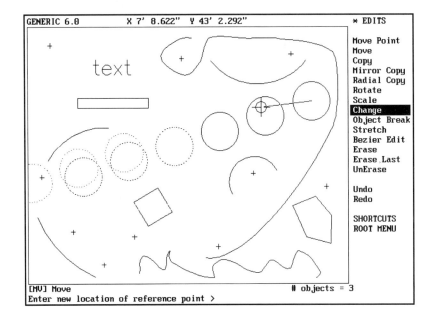

Figure 10.16:

Setting the reference point's new location.

If Quick Pick (QP) is on (a circle overlays the cursor, as in fig. 10.16), you may not be able to snap to the center point of the circle with your first attempt, unless you are aiming carefully at the center of the circle. When Quick Pick is on, only points inside the circle are considered when a point is requested. Quick Pick can be shut off whenever you can enter a two-letter command; it works as a nested command.

The preceding sequence showed how to take advantage of existing geometry to help you as you draw. The goal was to move three of the circles while keeping them in line with the other three. Using the Show By Example Angle command was not possible because it cannot be used when you specify coordinate locations.

Copy (CO)

The Copy command, located in the EDITS menu, is simply a more flexible version of the Object Copy (OC) or Window Copy (WC) commands. You use it in the following exercise to add a circle to the row, placing the new copy in the gap created when the others moved.

Using the Copy Command

Prompt	Input	Description
Command	CO	Starts the Copy command
...Object...	O	Selects Object option
Pick object	Move cursor to circle just below gap created by the Move command; click anywhere on circle and press Enter	Selects circle to be copied
Enter a reference point	Move cursor to center of circle below circle being copied; type **NP** or press third mouse button	Selects new reference point (see fig. 10.17)

Prompt	Input	Description
Enter new reference point	Move cursor up toward center of item being copied; press third mouse button or type **NP**	Selects new location of the reference point (see fig. 10.18)
Enter number of copies	1	Makes one copy of circle

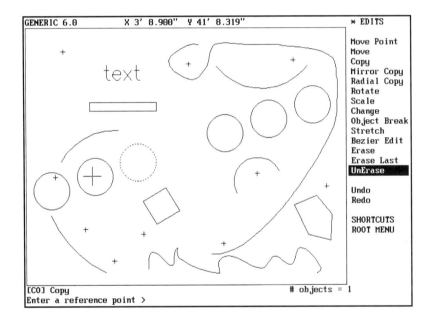

Figure 10.17:

Using the center point as the reference point.

Change (CG)

All the objects now in the drawing use Line Type 0, Line Width 0, and Line Color 15, and they all reside on Layer 15 (your layer number may be different). In the following exercise, you use the Change command, found in the EDITS menu, to make a few changes.

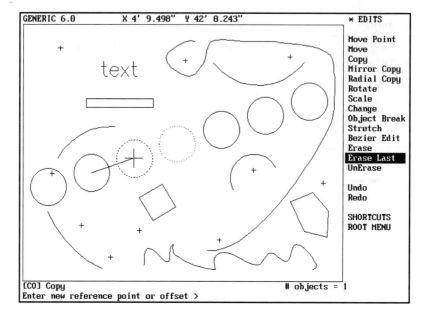

Figure 10.18:

Selecting another reference point.

The Entity Filter command, described earlier in the chapter as a separate command (not an editing command, per se), also is available during the selection process. You can use it to select quickly the items you want. All circles, arcs, and Bézier curves are selected in the following steps. The filter is used at times to speed the selection process.

Using the Change Command

Prompt	Input	Description
Command	**CG**	Starts the Change command
...Filter[OFF]	**F,** or move cursor to Filter and click	Starts the Entity Filter command
Select entity to filter	Move cursor to Bez and click	Selects Bézier curves
Select entity to filter	Press Enter, or move cursor to arrow at far right and click	Ends Entity selection

Prompt	Input	Description
`Select characteristic to filter`	**A**, or move prompt-line cursor to All and click or press Enter	Sets filter to select all Bézier curves
`...Drawing...`	**D**	Selects all objects that match the filter's criteria; highlights all segments of the Bézier curve
`...FILTER[OFF]`	**F**	Resets the filter
`Select entity to filter`	**C** and press Enter	Selects circles as the entity to filter
`Select characteristics to filter`	**A** and press Enter	Sets filter to select all circles
`...Drawing...`	**D**	Selects all objects that match the filter's criteria; highlights all circles
`...FILTER[OFF]`	**F**	Resets the filter
`Select entity to filter`	**R** and press Enter	Selects arcs as the entity to filter
`Select characteristics to filter`	**A** and press Enter	Sets filter to select all arcs
`...Drawing...`	**D**	Selects all objects matching filter's criteria; highlights all arcs
`Window...`	Press Enter	Ends selection process
`Change objects to`	**T**	Changes the Line Type

continues

335

Prompt	Input	Description
Enter Line Type	**2**, or move menu bar to Line Type 2 and press second mouse button	Selects Line Type 2
Change objects to	**W**	Changes the Line Width
Enter Line width	**3**, or move menu bar to Line Width 3 and press second mouse button	Selects Line Width 3
Change objects to	Press Enter	Redraws objects with new characteristics (see fig. 10.19)

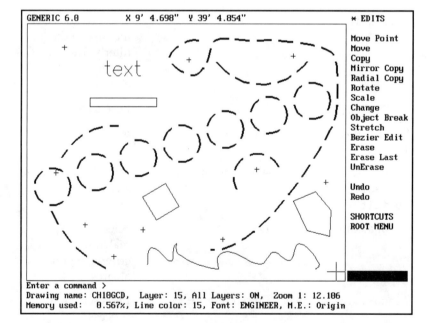

Figure 10.19:

The curves, arcs, and circles after being redrawn.

Rotate (RO)

The Rotate command, found on the EDITS menu, sounds simple. It just rotates objects around a reference point, right? Well, yes, but as you probably have figured out by now, the location of that reference point is extremely important. With the Rotate command, you can place the reference point so that the object spins in place or shifts to a new portion of the drawing. Take a look at the following illustrations, and then try the Rotate command on your own.

The diamond in the following figures is rotated 60 degrees, in two different ways.

The arrow in figure 10.20 displays the reference point for the first rotation; figure 10.21 shows the resulting rotation of the object, using a point of rotation inside the diamond. The diamond stays in the same portion of the drawing. The arrow appears again in figure 10.22, to show where the reference point will be placed for the second rotation; figure 10.23 shows the resulting rotation, using a point of rotation located away from the diamond. The diamond's new location in the drawing is dramatically different.

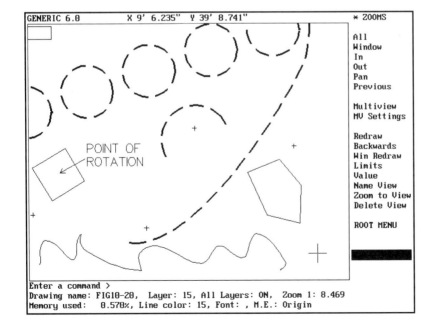

Figure 10.20:

The first point of rotation for the diamond.

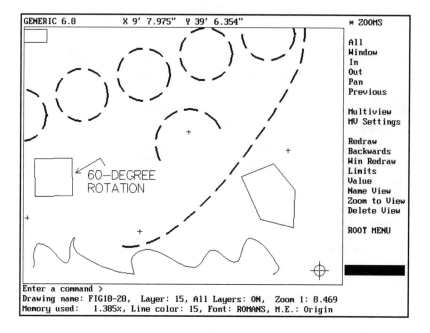

Figure 10.21:

Rotating the diamond with an internal point of rotation.

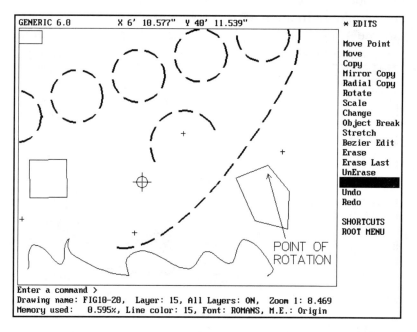

Figure 10.22:

The second point of rotation.

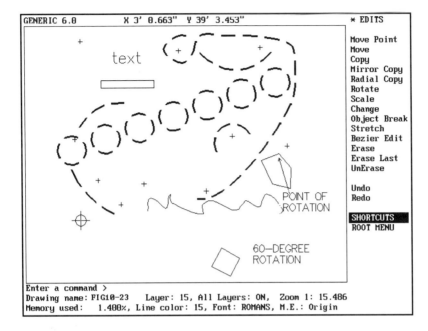

Figure 10.23:

Rotating the diamond with an external point of rotation.

The Rotate command is a good candidate for the use of Show By Example. If you want to rotate an object so that it sits at the same rotation in the drawing as another object, type **A** (for two-point angle) when CADD prompts for the angle of rotation. Click to show the base of the angle, then click again to show the heading. CADD rotates the selected object(s) to match the rotation of the object used for the Show By Example command.

Mirror Copy (MI)

The Copy command makes from one to 99 exact copies of the objects you select. The Mirror Copy command, found on the EDITS menu, makes one *mirror-image* copy of the selected objects. If you are designing a symmetrical object, draw only half the object and then use the Mirror Copy command to create the other half.

Take care when using the Mirror Copy command with text. If the text was placed using the Text Character Placement (TP) command, the result of the Mirror Copy command is that each *character* is inverted. If the text was placed using the Text Line Placement (TL) command, the result is that each *line* of text is mirrored; the individual characters remain readable as a line, although they are upside down. The Mirror Copy command treats lines of text (placed with TL) and individual characters of text (placed with TP) differently, as you can see from figure 10.24. (The dotted line in the figure shows the axis used for the mirror command.)

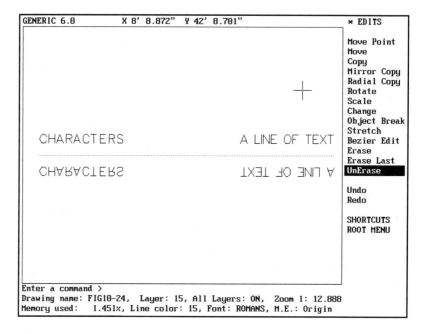

Figure 10.24:

The Mirror Copy command treats characters and lines of text differently.

To use the Mirror Copy command, select the object as you would for any other multiple-object editing command. When you have made your selection, Generic CADD prompts you to draw an axis line. This is the location of the imaginary "mirror" CADD uses. As with the Rotate command, your placement of this line determines the location of the mirrored copy. You may even place a mirror copy of an item on top of the original by drawing the axis line through the original object.

You no longer need the drawing you have used so far in this chapter. You may erase it if you like.

Multi-Trim (MT)

The Trim (RM) command, introduced in Chapter 9, has a multiple-object sibling in Multi-Trim (MT), found on the TRIMS menu. The Multi-Trim command uses the same selection process as the editing commands covered so far, but then trims the objects selected to line up with another line. The command works only with lines, arcs, and circles, not with Bézier curves or true ellipses.

Follow these steps to set up a situation, and then try the Multi-Trim command.

Using the Multi-Trim Command

Prompt	Input	Description
Command	**DXY**	Erases the current drawing
Command	Draw one vertical line on left side of screen; use Ortho Mode command or press Ctrl	Draws a vertical line
Command	**OC**	Initiates Object Copy command
Pick object	Move cursor to the line; click on it with first mouse button	Selects the line as the object to be copied
Enter a reference point	Move cursor near top of line; type **NP** or press third mouse button	Selects the top of the line as the reference point for the copy
Enter new reference point or offset	Move cursor to right about 1/2" and click; use Ortho Mode to move reference point to right	Moves the image of the original to set the distance for the Copy command

continues

Prompt	Input	Description
Enter number of copies	**10**	Makes 10 copies of the original line
Command	**A3**	Initiates a 3-point Arc command
Enter start of arc	Move cursor to bottom of first line; type **NP** or press third mouse button	Places start of the arc at bottom of first line
Enter a point on the arc	Move cursor to top of sixth line; type **NP** or press third mouse button	Places the mid point of the arc on top of the middle line
Enter the end of the arc	Move cursor to bottom of last line; type **NP** or press third mouse button	Places the end of the arc at bottom of last line (see fig. 10.25)

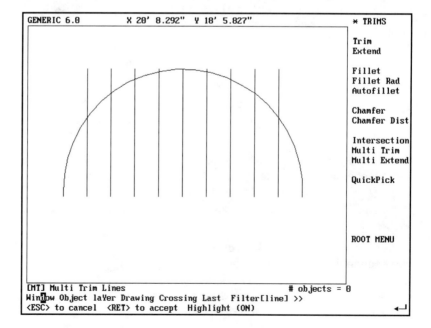

Figure 10.25:

Nine lines inter-sected by an arc.

Multi-Trim with Lines

Prompt	Input	Description
`Command`	**OE**	Starts the Object Erase command
`Pick object`	Move cursor to last line and click on it	Erases the last line
`Command`	Press spacebar	Repeats the Object Erase command
`Pick object`	Move cursor to first line and click on it	Erases the first line
`Command`	**MT**	Starts the Multi-Trim Lines command
`...Drawing...`	**D**	Selects all lines in the drawing and completes the selection process
`Trim to`	Move cursor to arc and click anywhere on it	Selects the arc as the object to which the lines will be trimmed
`Enter sides to keep`	Move cursor inside span of arc and and click	Displays images of the lines to show you how the lines will be trimmed; selects side of arc to trim lines on (see fig. 10.26)

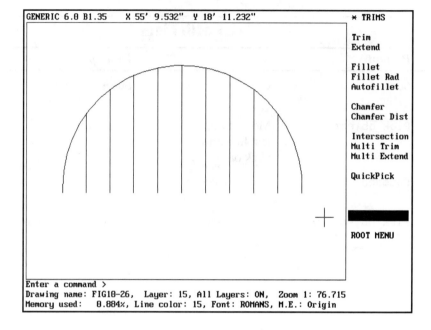

Figure 10.26:

The lines after being trimmed to the arc.

Multi-Extend (MX)

Extend, like Trim, has a multiple-object sibling—Multi-Extend. The command works exactly like Multi-Trim, except that the goal is to extend lines to another object rather than to trim them at the object.

Multi-Extend extends straight lines to intersect with any arc, line, or circle. If one of the lines to be extended would never intersect the destination object, no matter how far it was extended, Multi-Extend does not change it.

As with the other trim and extend commands, Multi-Extend does not work if the target object is a curve or true ellipse.

Radial Copy (RC)

Two copy commands have been introduced in this chapter: Copy (CO) can create from one to 99 exact copies in a straight line, and Mirror Copy (MI) can draw one mirror-image copy. A third multiple-object copy command, Radial Copy (RC), is located in the EDITS menu. The Radial Copy command copies objects in a circular (radial) pattern around an axis. The number of items and the angular span of the copies are adjustable.

To practice this command, load the drawing created in Chapter 9. It looks as though it might have been created for a machine shop; you may have called it FLANGE.GCD. If you did not create and save the drawing, draw it now (use fig. 10.27 as a guide).

To use the Radial Copy command, select the objects to be copied and then select an axis point. The objects you selected are copied around this point. Next, select the degrees of the span. A positive number copies in a counterclockwise direction; a negative number, in a clockwise direction. The final step is to specify the total number of items in the copy. This number includes the original—be careful to provide the correct number.

Follow the steps in the exercise to copy the hole near the edge of the flange around the circle, made from an arc and two lines.

Using the Radial Copy Command

Prompt	Input	Description
Command	**RC**	Starts the Radial Copy command
Window...	**W**	Draws a window
Place window	Draw selection window around arc and 2 lines at top of object (see fig. 10.27)	Selects the hole to be copied (# objects = 3)
Window...	Press Enter	Ends selection of objects to be copied

continues

Prompt	Input	Description
Enter an axis point	Move cursor to small circle in center of flange; type **NP** or click with third mouse button	Identifies the center of the small circle as the axis
Enter total degrees to span	360	Determines placement of items to be copied
Enter total number of items in span	6	Places six holes around the circle, distributed evenly (see fig. 10.28)

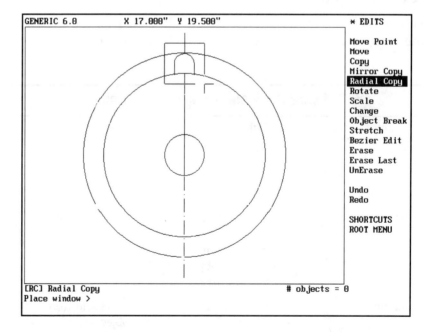

Figure 10.27:

Using window selection for Radial Copy.

You may use the Object Break command to remove the construction line from the bottom hole, bringing balance to the object in the drawing. Save the changes to the drawing just completed, if you like, and clear the screen.

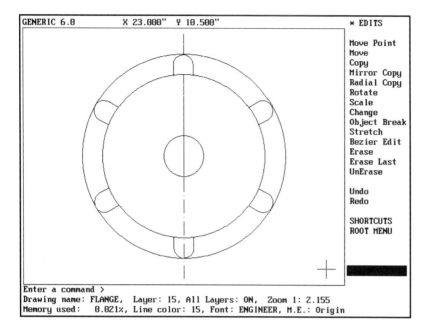

Figure 10.28:

*Radial Copy makes
five additional copies
of the hole.*

Next, bisect an angle, using the Show By Example and Radial Copy commands. To form the angle to bisect, draw two lines that come together at a common point (see fig. 10.29). The steps that follow start with the assumption that you have drawn the lines.

Although you can bisect an angle automatically, without the Radial Copy and Show By Example commands, doing so involves additional steps: First you use Measure 3-point Angle to measure the angle between the two lines. Then you use Measure 2-point Angle to determine the exact heading of one of the lines. Next, using a direct distance command, you draw a line out from the intersection of the two lines at a heading that bisects the existing angle. The method you are about to use is much simpler.

The following procedure creates an extra line; the last step is to erase the extra line and redraw the screen. The angle between the two original lines is bisected, using the Radial Copy and Show By Example-Vector commands.

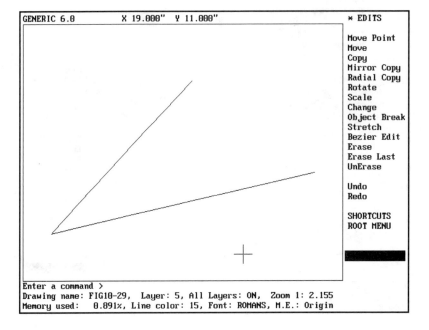

Figure 10.29:

Two lines that meet at a common point.

Bisecting an Angle

Prompt	Input	Description
Command	**RC**	Starts the Radial Copy command
...**O**bject...	**O**	Selects Object option
Pick object	Move cursor to lower line and click; press Enter	Selects the bottom line to be copied
Enter an axis point	Move cursor to base of angle; type **NP** or click with third mouse button	Selects base of the angle as axis for copy function
Enter total degrees to span	**V**	Show By Example-Vector determines the number of degrees to span

Prompt	Input	Description
`Enter base of angle` `Show vertex by example (3 pts)`	Move cursor to base of angle; type **NP** or click with third mouse button	Selects the base of the angle
`Enter a point on the ray`	Move cursor to end point of bottom line; type **NP** or click with third mouse button	Selects the first line of the angle
`Enter next point`	Move cursor to end point of top line; type **NP** or click with third mouse button	Selects the second line of the angle (lines must be selected in counterclockwise fashion)
`Enter total number of items in span`	**3**	Places line evenly between the beginning and the end of span

If you input 2 instead of 3 at the preceding prompt, the program puts one line at the beginning and one at the end of the angle.

`Command`	**ELRD**	Erases the last item and redraws screen (see fig. 10.30).

Explode (EX)

One multiple-object command (Explode) is not an editing command; it is a utility that sometimes must be used to edit objects. The Explode command, found on the UTILITIES menu, causes linked objects to revert to the individual pieces from which they were made. You have yet to learn about the entities (other than text) that can be exploded in Generic CADD: dimensions, components, and attributes. Remember this section on exploding text when you read the later sections on the other entity types.

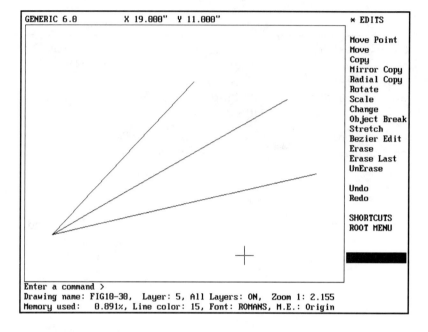

Figure 10.30:

The completed bisection.

You might explode text for two reasons: to move individual characters placed using the Text Line Placement (TL) command, and to change the shape of characters for a special look.

When a line of text placed with the Text Line Placement command is exploded, it reverts to individual characters, as though it had been placed with the Text Character Placement command. When individual characters are exploded, they revert to lines, arcs, curves and so on; then they can be edited like any other graphic object in the drawing. After erasing the angle on your screen, use the steps in the following exercises to place a line of text on-screen and then explode it twice.

Placing a Line of Text

Prompt	Input	Description
Command	**TL**	Starts the Text Line Placement command

Prompt	Input	Description
`Enter starting point`	Move cursor to left side of screen and click	Sets the starting for a line of text
`>`	Type **Generic CADD**; press Enter and Esc	Places a line of text (see fig. 10.31)
`Command`	**ZA**	Starts the Zoom All command
`Command`	**PR**; if the prompt says reference points are off, type **PR** again	Turns on reference points
`Command`	**RD**	Redraws the screen

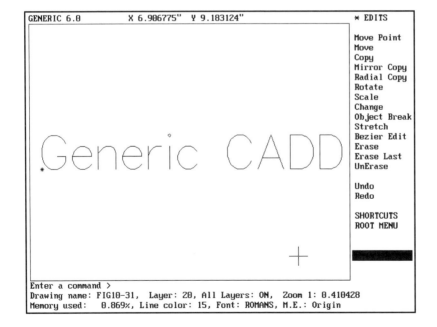

Figure 10.31:

The text "Generic CADD" placed by Text Line Placement.

Exploding the Text Line

Prompt	Input	Description
Command	**EX**	Starts the Explode command
...**D**rawing...	**D** and press Enter	Selects the entire drawing; explodes line of text into individual characters (see fig. 10.32)
Command	Press spacebar	Repeats the last command (Explode)
...**D**rawing...	**D,** and press Enter	Selects the entire drawing; explodes each text character
Command	**PCRD**	Starts the Construction Point and Redraw commands (see fig. 10.33)
Command	**SS**	Starts the Stretch command
Window...	**W**	Starts a window
Place window	Draw window around the word CADD; press Enter	Selects the word CADD
Place window around points to be moved	Draw window around bottom half of the word CADD; include crossbar of the letter A in window	Identifies the section to be stretched (see fig. 10.34)

Prompt	Input	Description
Enter a reference point	Move cursor to top of the A in CADD and click with third mouse button	Selects the top of the A as the reference point
Enter new location of reference point	Press Ctrl and move cursor straight down until satisfied with amount of stretch; click	Stretches the word CADD (see fig. 10.35)

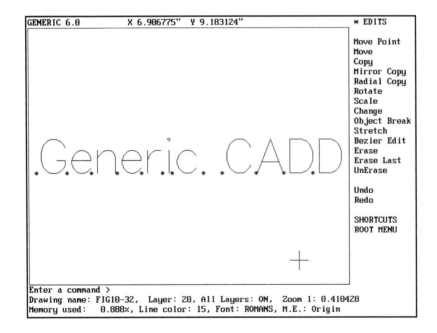

Figure 10.32:

Text is now individual characters, with individual reference points.

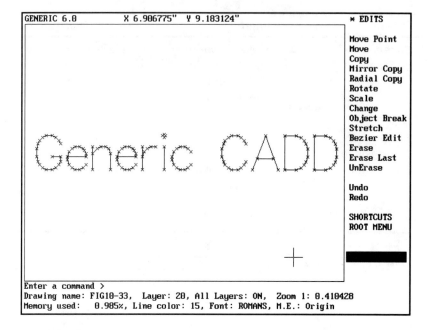

Figure 10.33:

Text reduced to individual objects.

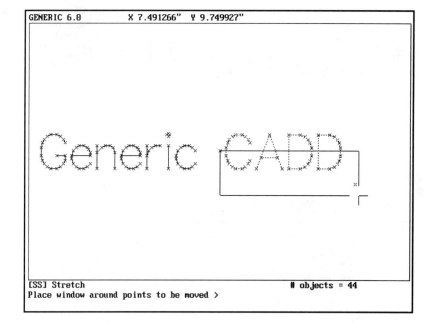

Figure 10.34:

Selecting the construction points for the Stretch command.

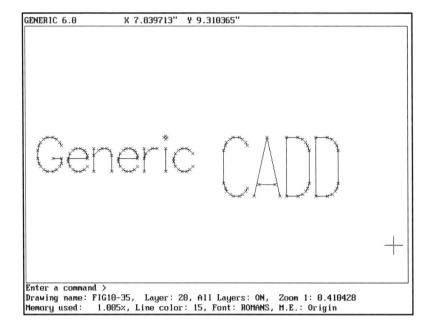

Figure 10.35:
The word "CADD" after being stretched.

Multiple-Object and Single-Selection Editing

Now that you have studied both the single-selection editing commands (in Chapter 9) and the multiple-object selection commands (in this chapter), you can understand the use of the many editing commands that fall somewhere between the two categories. Some editing commands provide one chance to choose what is to be edited, yet enable you to select more than one object. These editing commands select either one window, one layer, or the entire drawing. They do not use the selection process, and the filter and highlighting are not available.

The following commands are on the SHORTCUTS menu:

Window Copy (WC)

Window Scale (WZ)

Window Erase (WE)

Window Move (WM)

Window Rotate (WR)

Drawing Rotate (DR)

Drawing Change (DG)

The following commands are on the LAYERS menu:

Layer Scale (YZ)

Layer Erase (YE)

Layer Rotate (YR)

Layer Change (YG)

Because the methods are the same as for their single-object and multiple-object counterparts, a detailed description of each is not provided. Practice using them, if you like, on the exploded line of text used earlier.

Summary

With only a few keystrokes, the multiple-object editing commands provide a virtually unlimited number of ways to select objects for editing. Commands like Copy (CO), Move (MV), Scale (SZ), and Radial Copy (RC) are not limited to acting on only one object. They can be used to perform a single action simultaneously on many objects.

Selection and filtering are at the heart of the multiple-object editing commands. Selection enables you to pick and choose which objects should be edited, and filtering fine-tunes the selection process by providing a precise definition of what kinds of objects can be selected.

Some of the multiple-object editing commands, including Copy and Move, compare to what one might do if using manual drafting. But other editing commands have no direct manual equivalent unless one invests in a fast electric eraser (Stretch, Rotate, and Multi-Trim are examples). The power of automation is obvious when you use Screen Flip, which makes it possible to examine the nature of the drawing file as it resides in memory, and Explode, which reduces linked objects to their individual pieces.

The selection and filtering technology used by the multiple-object editing commands turns up elsewhere in Generic CADD, in commands like Explode (EX), Selection Save (SV), and Selection Save Batch (BS).

Another way to speed up your work with Generic CADD is to use components. The next chapter introduces you to the basics of working with components in Generic CADD.

Components

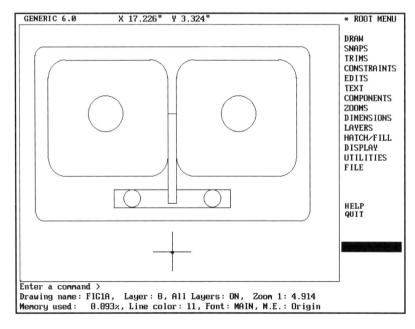

I n CADD, a *component* is a special object made of one or more primitive entities (lines, arcs, circles, and so on). Here is a simple example: using lines and circles, you draw a sink (see fig. 11.1); you can save that sink as a component and use it repeatedly in other drawings. CADD enables you to save components on disk (separate from drawings), in the same way that fonts and hatch patterns (yet to come) are saved on disk, ready to be used at any time.

Figure 11.1:

This sample component is a sink used in house plans.

When a component is created, it is given a name and a reference point. This reference point, which is used to place the component in the drawing, also is known as the *insertion point*. When placed in a drawing, a component acts like a single object, not several objects. If you select a component, using a selection command, the number of objects selected show as one (# objects = 1), no matter how many lines are inside the component. If you need to move a component, simply select the reference point; the entire component moves.

Components are a key to fulfilling one of the great laws of CADD: never draw anything more than once. In manual drafting, the drafting technician draws every line, arc, and circle from scratch. In CADD, inserting components helps you construct the final drawing faster. After you have used CADD for a while, individual objects make up only a portion of each drawing you create; components make up the rest. A variety of commands enables you to edit and manipulate components, so that you get more mileage from your components.

As discussed in Chapter 10, the potential speed of computer-aided drafting versus manual drafting probably became evident to you. Now comes the component, which helps you develop drawings quickly on-screen. This is what CADD is all about.

Because a component is drawn once and used many times, you can afford to put more effort and artistry into each one. The kitchen range top shown in figure 11.2 could have been left as just basic lines and circles. But the addition of hatching and fills gives a distinctive look to an otherwise humdrum component.

Components improve the accuracy of a drawing. In manual drafting, the little details develop subtle differences over time. Perhaps a line is drawn a little longer, the text is slightly different or, worst of all, a critical portion of the detail is forgotten. This cannot happen with components. Once a component exists, it is exactly the same whether it is used once or a million times.

Components may be either *current* or *permanent*. Current components are those used only while a drawing (or set of drawings) is under development, such as the components you construct for this chapter. Because they are not used later, you can delete them when the exercise is completed, saving space on your hard drive. Permanent components are those that are used many times. The kitchen sink in figure 11.1 or the range top in figure 11.2 could be permanent components for someone who designs houses, for example. Components can be saved to disk and reused as many times as you want. Remember CADD's golden rule: Never draw the same thing twice.

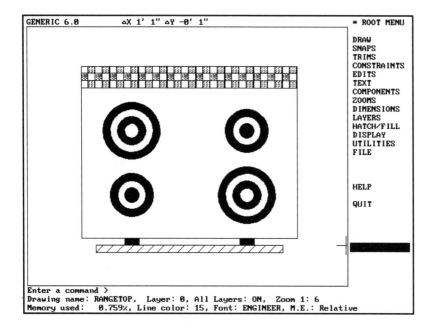

Figure 11.2:
A kitchen range-top component.

Some components develop as specifically created parts; others are taken from larger drawings. In either event, Generic CADD makes creating components easy. A dozen or so commands control the entire powerful process.

Creating Components

Two commands are used to create components. The first is Window Component Create (CW), a one-shot approach to identifying the contents of a component. The other command is Component Create (CC), which uses the selection options in the same way that

Copy or Explode enables you to select or deselect items to be included in the command. The first step in creating a component, however, is not deciding which of these two easy commands to use, but thinking through a plan of consistent style.

Nothing sours the use and effectiveness of components more quickly than random insert points, random rotation, random naming conventions, and the lost or forgotten parts that result. Read and consider the following guidelines; then write down a simple policy for the components you want to make. Attach this policy to the side of your monitor and follow it every time you create a component.

Picking Insert Points

The type of drawing you do probably influences how you pick an insert point (see fig. 11.3). An electronic drafter, for example, may always pick the top left pin, or pin number one, as an insert point for components. Flow chart users may select the center of each component. Architects and contractors may have two insert points, depending on the type of component drawn. Floor plan components that are never rotated, such as the symbol for a light or a smoke detector, would have a centered insert point. Window and door elevation symbols could have an insert point located on a centered point 6'8" above the floor line.

In certain situations, you may not want an insert point that is located on the component itself. Such an insert point is called an *offset insert point*. A lavatory bowl, for example, should be located a certain distance from a wall to place it at a consistent distance from the front edge of a countertop. Depending on the size of the lavatory component, the insert point may be located two, three, or four inches from the back edge of the bowl.

In this instance, you locate the insert point by drawing a line from the midpoint of the back of the bowl to a point two, three, or four inches away from the bowl. Be careful not to select this line when you create the component. When the screen prompt asks for the insert point, type **SC**, for Snap to Closest Point, and pick the far end of the line. Because the insert point is several inches away, you can pick the wall line rather than guess the location of the bowl in the countertop. See figure 11.4 for a graphic representation.

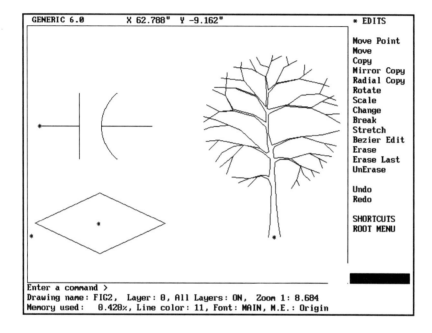

Figure 11.3:

Typical insert points.

Rotating Components

In some drafting situations, a component can be correctly inserted in only one way. An example is the decision symbol used in flow charting. In other drafting situations, only two rotations, 0 degrees and 90 degrees, are used 99 percent of the time. Most of the time, a capacitor is shown as horizontal or vertical. In architectural drafting, the symbol for a switch or outlet can be shown in any of 360 different degrees of rotation, but generally is shown as 0, 90, 180, or 270 degrees of rotation (see fig. 11.5).

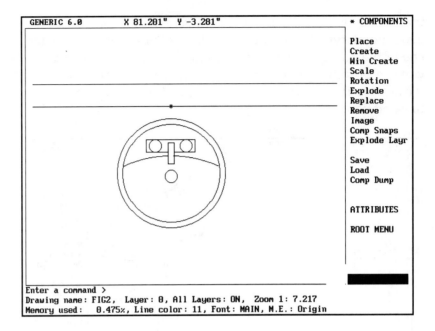

Figure 11.4:

Using an offset insert point to place a lavatory bowl.

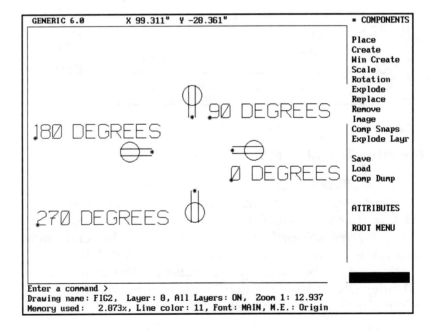

Figure 11.5:

Sample symbol rotation.

Suppose that you drew the switch component pointing toward zero degrees and the outlet pointing to 90 degrees. Then you created a door bell button pointing toward 270 degrees and added a chime symbol rotated at another angle. As you add components, it becomes increasingly difficult to remember how much rotation to give each symbol.

This problem has a logical solution. If a symbol normally sits in a certain position, draw it that way. Door-front elevations and electronic components are examples; door fronts stand up and electronic components usually are horizontal. If a symbol typically is rotated in a variety of positions, however—the plan-view switch symbol in architectural drafting is an example—create the component pointing toward zero rotation (see fig. 11.6). When you insert the symbol later and want it to point up, you can rotate it 90 degrees.

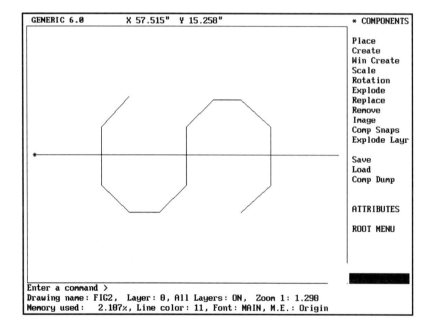

Figure 11.6:

Suggested drawing rotation of the switch symbol.

Naming Components

Component names can be up to eight characters long. (Generic CADD can display 12-character names on the menu, but when you save the component, DOS uses only the first 8 characters for the name.) Be careful to avoid bland or erratic names. Naming a collection of chair components CHAIR1, CHAIR2, and so on (see fig. 11.7) may seem logical but can lead to confusion later. Giving the chairs specific names, such as ARMCHAIR, ROCKER, or LOUNGE, is a better idea.

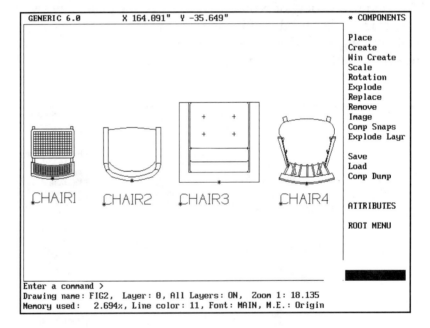

Figure 11.7:

Components with bland names.

Using subtly different names or picking names at random can wreak havoc also. Suppose that you have developed a collection of door elevation components and given them a variety of names (see fig. 11.8). This is worse than using bland names. If you forget what a particular door is called, you lose the use of that component. Remember that over time you are likely to create hundreds of different components. You do not want to have to search through this multitude of names to find a door whose name you forgot.

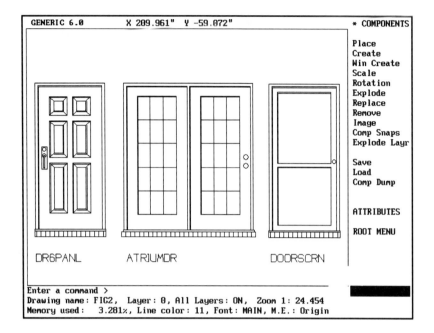

Similar components with a wide variety of names.

Here is a possible solution to the problem. First, decide whether the newly created component is going to be a current component or a permanent component. If it is a current component, use JUNK as the first four letters of the name, followed by as many as four more letters to describe the component. Some examples are JUNKOUTL, JUNKSINK, JUNKWALL, and JUNKROOM. Days, weeks, or months from now, when you decide to "houseclean" your disk, you can issue the command **DEL JUNK*.*.** Because you were careful not to begin the name of a permanent component with JUNK as the first four letters, you would be deleting only unnecessary files. Or you could use any prefix to denote components for a certain project, and archive them when finished using the prefix to identify the relevant components.

Permanent components can be named by type. All light components, for example, could have LIT as the first three letters of the name. Doors could start with DR, windows with WDW, and so on. This reduces the time spent looking for a particular component.

If size is important, by all means use it in the title. A collection of single-hung window components could be named SH2030, SH2040, SH2050, and SH2060 (see fig. 11.9). By grouping them by type and then by size, you can remember them easily.

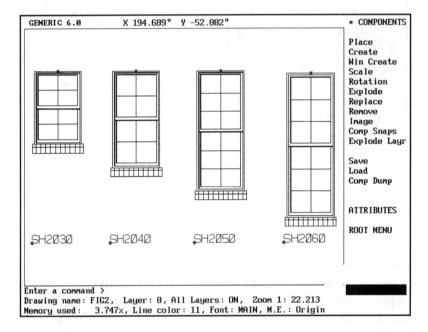

Figure 11.9:

Single-hung window components.

No matter what you name them, remembering the names of hundreds of components is extremely difficult. For now, write down the name of every component you create. A better solution—the use of special menus—is presented in Chapter 16.

Using the Component-Creation Commands

Having planned how to insert, rotate, and name the components, you are ready to draw them. The next section covers the component-creation commands.

Window Create (CW)

This two-letter command defines a portion of a drawing as a component. Place a window around the lines, arcs, circles, and

other elements that make up the component you want to create. A
screen prompt asks for the component name and requests an
insert point. It is that simple.

Remember that a component can be created from anything on the
screen, as long as it is visible and on the active layer. If some of the
entities may be on different layers, turn on the All Layers (AL)
command.

In the following exercise, you create the component shown in
figure 11.10. Later, you bring it back into a drawing and use the
different component-edit commands on it.

Creating a Component

Prompt	Input	Description
Command	**SG**	Turns on Snap to Grid command
Command	**OR**	Turns off Ortho command
Command	**PR**	Turns on Display Reference Points
Command	Type **LI**; draw a line 4" down the screen and then 10" to the right, then draw the line back at an angle to finish where you started	Starts the Line command
Command	**CW**	Starts the Window Component Create command
Place window	Place window around drawing	Identifies component
Enter component name	**JUNKSTUF**	Names component

continues

369

Prompt	Input	Description
Enter component reference point	**SM**	Snaps to midpoint (see fig. 11.11)
Midpoint of	Pick vertical line	Sets reference point
<RET> to complete	Press Enter	Finishes command

Now, to check whether or not the component was really defined, select the Component Place command from the component menu. Do you see JUNKSTUF in the list of components that appears on the side menu? You have created a component that points to zero rotation. As you will see, this makes insertion rotation simple.

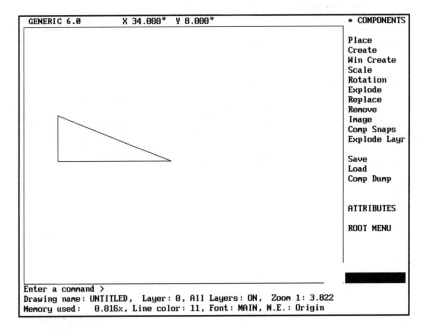

Figure 11.10:

JUNKSTUF component.

Component Create (CC)

This command is almost identical to the Window Component Create (CW) command; the only difference is the way objects are selected. With Window Component Create (CW), you can select only one window's worth of objects. This method is fast but also limiting.

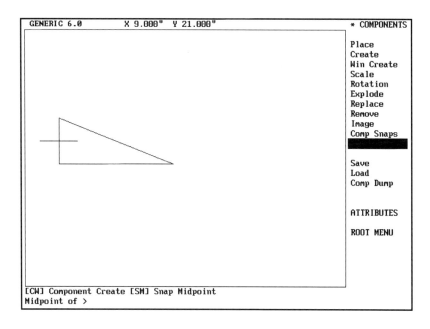

```
GENERIC 6.0        X 9.000"  Y 21.000"              * COMPONENTS

                                                    Place
                                                    Create
                                                    Win Create
                                                    Scale
                                                    Rotation
                                                    Explode
                                                    Replace
                                                    Remove
                                                    Image
                                                    Comp Snaps
                                                    ▮▮▮▮▮▮▮▮▮▮

                                                    Save
                                                    Load
                                                    Comp Dump


                                                    ATTRIBUTES

                                                    ROOT MENU



[CW] Component Create [SM] Snap Midpoint
Midpoint of >
```

Figure 11.11:

Snapping to midpoint of JUNKSTUF.

The Component Create (CC) command enables you to select entities in different ways. After you select the Component Create command from the COMPONENTS menu, or type **CC**, you can select the objects you want to use in a component by typing the appropriate letter, as follows:

Window	Places window around entities for a component
Object	Picks entities for a component
la**Y**er	Picks entities for a component by layer
Drawing	Entire drawing becomes a component
Crossing	Selects all entities inside or touching the window
Last	Last selection becomes part of a component
Filter	Selection is initiated by characteristics

You can deselect entities by pressing Ctrl and typing any of the preceding boldface letters.

You can use any combination of selection and deselection devices. When you are satisfied with what is shown on-screen, press Enter. The entire selection is ready to be a component; all you need to add is a component name and an insert point.

Saving Components

Do not assume that completing the Create Component Window (CW) command or the Component Create (CC) command causes the new component to be installed on the hard drive. The component is stored in the current drawing—that is all. If you quit the drawing without saving, the component is lost. Even current components need to be saved to the hard drive if they are to be used in another drawing.

Near the bottom of the COMPONENTS menu you see Save (SA,C). After Save is selected, the prompt is

```
Select component from side menu
```

Use the second mouse button to pick the component JUNKSTUF from the side menu. Next, Generic CADD offers a default path and name to accept or alter. This prompt is as follows:

```
Save file as >> C:\CADD6\CMP\JUNKSTUF
```

Press Enter to accept this line. Now the component is stored on the hard drive for future use.

The other way to save components is to wait until the end of the drawing session and save all the new components to the hard disk at one time. Although this method is efficient, if you forget to do this, you lose all your work. The command to save all the components is Component Dump (CD). This command calls up the new components one-by-one so that you can choose whether or not to save each one.

Working with Components

Now that you have made a component, it is time to work with it. You can place, scale, and rotate a component. Components can be treated as individual entities by using the Component Image, Component Explode, Explode Object, and Component Snap commands.

Placing Components

Generic CADD inserts a component with the Component Place (CP) command. After you pick this command from the COMPONENT menu or type it in, a prompt asks you for the component name. You can type the name or pick it from the side menu. If the component is in another subdirectory and not listed on the side menu, pick the Look On Disk option to find the subdirectory and then the component name. The final prompt you need to answer concerns the insert point. This location can be picked on-screen or typed as coordinates from the keyboard.

Sometimes accurately picking a spot on-screen to locate a component is easy. At other times, doing so amounts to a stab in the dark because you cannot accurately place what you cannot see, especially if you cannot remember the location of the insert point. To solve this problem, Generic CADD has the Object Drag (OD) command. When this command is turned on, an outline of the component appears on-screen with the cursor locked on the component's insert point. As you move the cursor across the screen, the component drags with it. This enables you to see exactly where you want to place the component. When the component is properly positioned, pick that point on-screen.

Inserting a Component

Prompt	Input	Description
Command	**OD**	Turns on Object Drag
Command	**CP**	Starts the Component Place command
Select component from side menu	**JUNKSTUF**	Picks a component to place
Enter placement location	Drag in JUNKSTUF	Drags in a component (see fig. 11.12)
Type [IP] to change insert point	**IP**	Changes insert point (see fig. 11.13)
Temporarily place component	Pick a point on the screen	Parks the component temporarily while you change the insert point
Enter new location of reference point	**SC**	Snaps to closest point
Closest point to	Pick top of vertical line	Sets temporary reference point
Enter placement location	**SC**	Snaps to closest point
Closest point to	Pick right end of line in original drawing	Places component (see fig. 11.14)

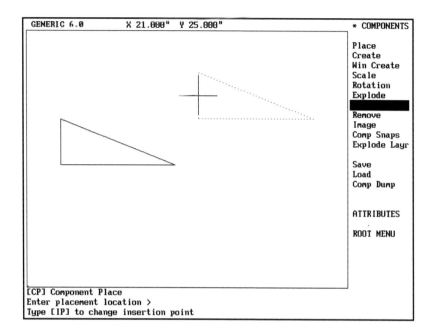

Figure 11.12:

Dragging in JUNKSTUF.

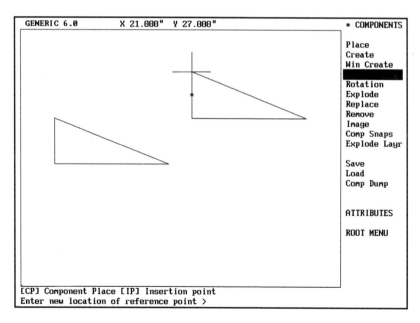

Figure 11.13:

Changing insert point.

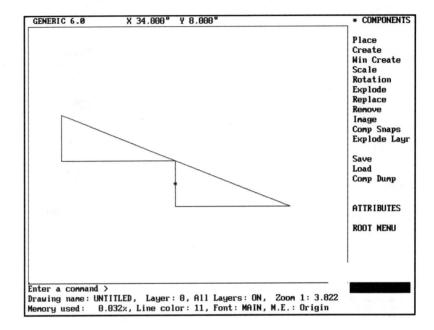

Figure 11.14:

Your screen should look like this.

Component Load (LO)

This command loads components stored on the hard drive into the current drawing. If you want to load certain components or all the components in a particular subdirectory, you can tag multiple components in the File Selector, to be loaded into CADD.

You start the Component Load command by selecting Load from the COMPONENTS menu, or by typing **LO**. You can pick the component to load from the side menu or by typing it in.

From a practical standpoint, this command is not useful if you need to bring a component into the drawing—using the disk-search option of the Component Place (CP) command makes more sense. Component Place works in two instances: in a macro file that quickly loads needed components into a drawing, or to put the components needed in a certain drawing into their own subdirectory. You can then use Component Place to load all of those components at once, if you use the File Selector.

Component Scale (CZ)

With this command, components can be displayed either larger or smaller than the original component. The command has a powerful additional dimension: X (horizontal) and Y (vertical) scaling can be changed, thereby altering the appearance of a component.

The Component Scale (CZ) command has many applications. If you drew 1" widgets but now need 1 1/4" widgets, you would use this command. After placing the stretched widget, you explode it and make a new component. Suppose, for example, that you have a plan view 1-foot wide window as a component in an architectural drawing, and that the next application requires a 3-foot wide window. Type **CZ** and, at the prompt for X scaling, enter **3**. At the prompt for Y scaling, enter **1**. Then type **CP** and place the window. It is now rescaled to three feet wide.

The Scale command can be selected from the COMPONENTS side menu or by typing **CZ**. The first prompt asks for an X scaling factor. The second prompt asks for a Y scaling factor, using the newly entered X scaling factor as the default. You can accept the default by pressing Enter, or enter another value.

Several rules should be remembered about this command. If you rescale a component oddly by giving it different X and Y factors, interesting things happen when you explode that component. Circles and arcs that were stretched to ellipses return to normal circles and arcs, whereas stretched lines remain stretched. This command must be used before you place a component you want to alter. It does not work after the fact by rescaling a component that already exists in the drawing. Scaling factors always apply to the original component size. If you use negative numbers, you get a mirror image of the original component.

The following exercise takes you through the Component Scale (CZ) command. Refer to figure 11.15 if you doubt the outcome of what you got in your version of the drawing.

Using the Component Scale Command

Prompt	Input	Description
Command	Select Scale from COMPO- NENTS menu	Displays the component scale
Enter new X scale	2	Doubles the X scaling (1.000)
Enter new Y scale	.5	Halves the Y scaling (2.000)

The Y scaling default matches the X scaling factor you input.

Prompt	Input	Description
Command	From side menu, pick Place	
Select component from side menu JUNKSTUF	Press Enter	Selects JUNKSTUF
Enter placement location	Pick a point in drawing (see fig. 11.15)	Places component

Notice how radically different the component looks now. After issuing the Undo command, you may want to repeat this exercise several times. Try using negative numbers and combinations of negative and positive numbers. When you finish experimenting, remember to reset the X and Y factors to 1.

Prompt	Input	Description
Command	OO	Undoes the last command
Command	CZ	Resets the scale command
Enter new X scale (2.000)	1	Resets X to normal
Enter new Y scale (1.000)	Press Enter	Accepts new default value

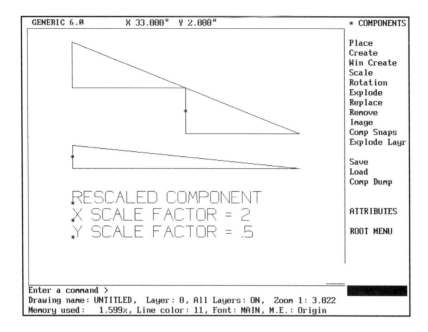

Figure 11.15:

JUNKSTUF with changed scale factors.

Component Rotation (CR)

This command rotates a component around the insert point. Use it before selecting the Component Place (CP) command. After a value is set, all future placements of components have this rotation until the angle of rotation is changed again. Changing the rotation back to zero restores the original rotation.

The Component Rotation command is on the COMPONENTS menu. The prompt asks for a change in component rotation. Rotation limits are from negative 360 degrees to positive 360 degrees. Negative numbers rotate the component clockwise, whereas positive numbers rotate it counterclockwise.

If you want to change the rotation of a component that already exists in the drawing, you have two choices: either use the Rotate (RO) command on the EDITS menu or erase the component, use the Component Rotation command, and then reinsert the component.

In the following exercise, JUNKSTUF is rotated.

379

Using the Component Rotate Command

Prompt	Input	Description
`Command`	From COMP-NENTS side menu, pick Rotation	Displays the Component command
`Change component rotation (0.000) Limits-360.000 to 360.000`	**90**	This rotates JUNKSTUF 90 degrees
`Command`	From COMPO-NENTS, side menu, pick Place	Places a component
`Select component from side menu >> JUNKSTUF`	Press Enter	Selects JUNKSTUF
`Enter placement location`	Pick a point in drawing (see fig. 11.16)	Places component
`Command`	**OO**	Undoes last command
`Command`	**CR**	Resets the rotation command
`Change component rotation (0.000) Limits-360.000 to 360.000`	**0**	Restores JUNKSTUF to its original orientation

Treating Component Parts as Individual Entities

Exploding components has both good and bad effects. The individual entities that make up the component can be edited. Exploded components, however, take up more memory than nonexploded components and cannot be globally edited. This is demonstrated later in the chapter.

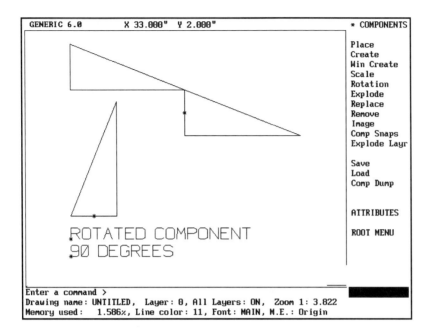

Figure 11.16:

JUNKSTUF with 90-degree rotation.

Three commands can be used to explode a component from a single entity into individual entities: Component Image (CI), Component Explode (CE), and Explode (EX). Another command, Component Explode Layer (XY), controls which layer exploded components go to. The Component Snaps command allows a component to be snapped to as if it were exploded. That is, the points on all objects inside the component may be selected by any snap command.

Component Image (CI)

The Component Image command explodes components as they are inserted. No reference point and no attributes exist. The individual entities appear on the layer on which they were created unless you use the Explode Destination Layer (XY) command.

The command is a toggle. If it is on, components come into the drawing already exploded. If it is off, components come into the drawing as whole components. You then select Image from the COMPONENTS menu.

These points are illustrated in the following exercise.

Using the Component Image Command

Prompt	Input	Description
Command	From COMPO-NENTS side menu, pick Image	Starts Component Image command
* [CI] Place component image is ON		Components placed in the drawing from now on are exploded
Command	From COMPO-NENTS side menu, pick Place	
Select component from side menu >> JUNKSTUF	Press Enter	Selects JUNKSTUF
Enter placement location	Pick a point in drawing (see fig. 11.17)	Places component

The component's reference point did not appear on-screen. This indicates that the component is exploded into individual entities. In the next exercise on Component Explode (CE), you test editing exploded and unexploded components. For now, complete the exercise.

Command	**OO**	Undoes the last command
Command	**CI**	Switches off Component Image (CI)

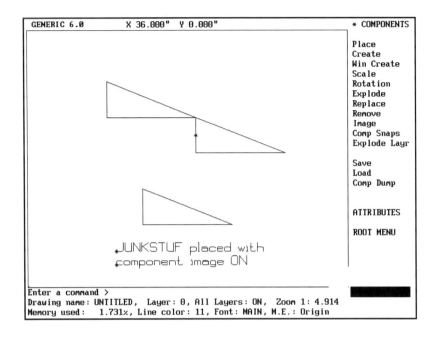

Component Explode (CE)

Use the Component Explode command to change individual
components to individual drawing parts, so that they can be
edited. Either pick Explode from the COMPONENTS menu, or
type **CE**. The prompt asks you to pick the component you want to
explode. The Explode Destination Layer (XY) command helps
control which layer the exploded parts revert to.

In the exercise that follows, you use the Erase command (ER) to
test unexploded and exploded components.

Using the Component Explode Command

Prompt	Input	Description
Command	**ER**	Invokes the erase command
Window, Object...	**O**	Object

continues

Prompt	Input	Description
`Pick object`	Pick JUNKSTUF (see fig. 11.18)	Notice that the entire component is selected
	Press Esc	Cancels the command
`Command`	From Components side menu, pick Explode	Starts the Component Explode command
`Pick object`	Pick JUNKSTUF	Selects the component (see fig. 11.19)

Now the reference point is gone, as you can see from figure 11.19.

`Command`	**ER**	Starts Erase command
`Window, Object...`	**O**	Object
`Pick object`	Pick JUNKSTUF	Selects the component (see fig. 11.20)

As you can see from figure 11.21, only one line has been selected.

`Window, Object...`	Press Esc	Cancels the command

Explode Object (EX)

The Explode Object command is found on the UTILITIES menu, or can be initiated by typing **EX**. It functions the same as the Component Explode (CE) command, with two differences: it explodes attributes, dimensions, text lines, and text characters in addition to components, and you can select components using the options shown in the next paragraph.

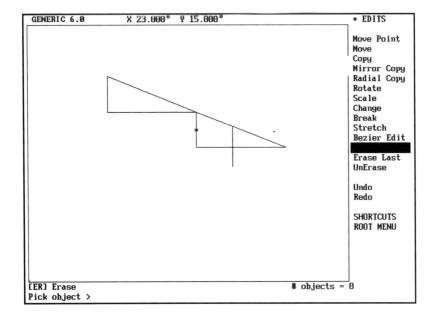

Figure 11.18:

Getting ready to pick a line on JUNKSTUF.

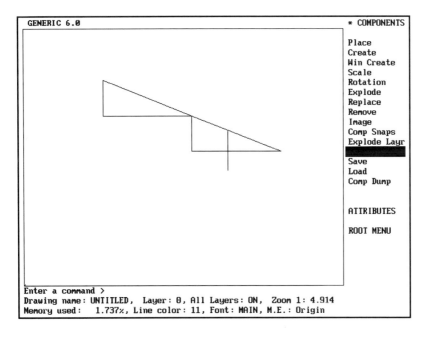

Figure 11.19:

Picking an object to erase.

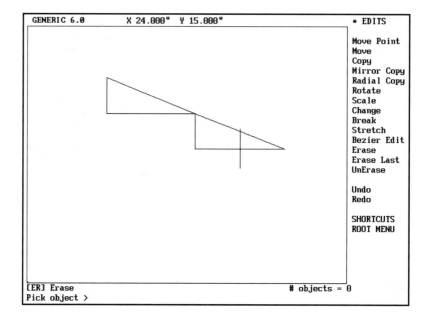

Figure 11.20:

The reference point is gone.

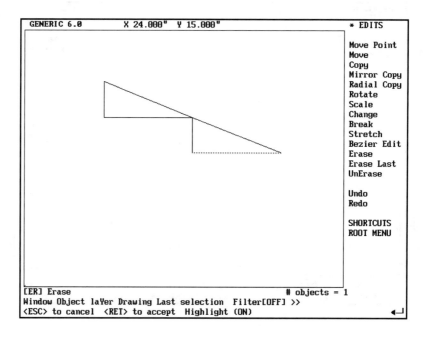

Figure 11.21:

Only one line of JUNKSTUF was selected.

After starting the Explode Object command from the UTILITIES menu or by typing **EX**, select the components you want to explode by typing the appropriate letters, as follows:

Window	Places window around component(s) to explode
Object	Picks individual components
la**Y**er	Picks components by layer
Drawing	Explodes everything listed in the preceding paragraph
Crossing	Selects all entities inside or touching the window
Last	Last selection is exploded
Filter	Selection is initiated by characteristics

Press Ctrl and any of the preceding letters to deselect entities.

You may use any combination of selection devices and deselection devices. When you are satisfied with what is on-screen, press Enter. The entire selection is exploded.

Component Snap (GC)

Normally, you can snap only to the reference point of a component. This can be a distinct disadvantage. To avoid exploding a component, Generic CADD offers another option—the Component Snap command.

This toggle command is listed as Comp Snaps on the COMPONENTS menu, or it can be accessed by typing **GC**. When it is turned on, Snap Closest (SC) and Nearest Point (NP) may be used on objects within the component.

The following exercise demonstrates this useful command.

Using the Component Snap Command

Prompt	Input	Description
Command	Pick Place from the COMPONENTS side menu	
Select component from side menu >> JUNKSTUF	Press Enter	Selects JUNKSTUF
Enter placement location	Pick a point in drawing	Places component
Command	**LI**	Starts the Line command
Starting point	**SC**	Snaps to closest point
Closest point to	Pick a point on JUNKSTUF	Tries to use snap (see fig. 11.22)

Notice that no matter where you picked JUNKSTUF, the line jumps to the reference point (see fig. 11.23).

	Press Esc	Stops Line command
Command	From COMPONENTS side menu, pick Comp Snaps	Starts Component Snaps command
* [GC] Component snaps is ON	Press Enter	Components now accept all the object snaps
Command	**LI**	Starts the Line command
Starting point	**SC**	Snaps to closest point
Closest point to	Pick a point on JUNKSTUF	Uses the snap (see fig. 11.24)
Enter next point on line	It worked!	Snaps to a point (see fig. 11.25)
	Press Esc	Cancels Line command

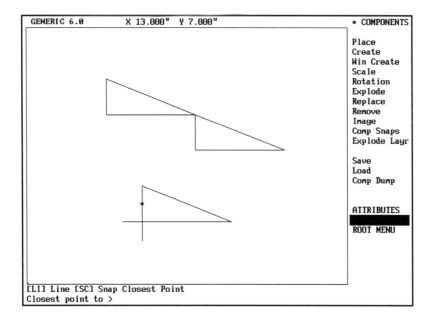

Figure 11.22:

Trying to pick a point on JUNKSTUF.

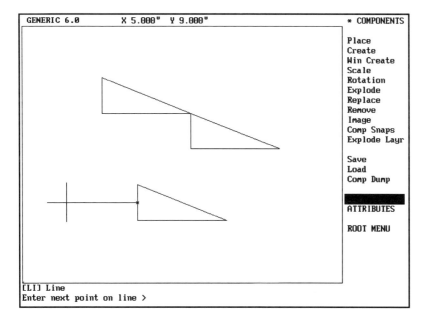

Figure 11.23:

The line has snapped to the reference point.

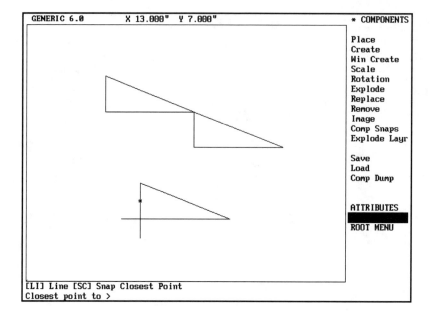

Figure 11.24:

Trying to pick an end point of JUNKSTUF.

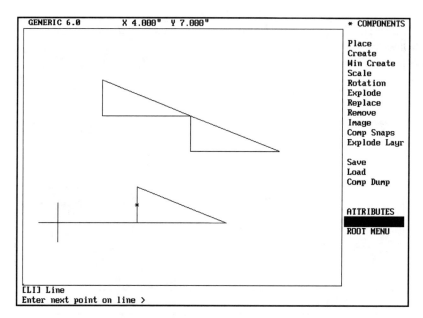

Figure 11.25:

It worked!

Removing Unwanted Components

Generic CADD has a pair of edit commands for removing or replacing components in a drawing. These commands can work globally or by individual selection. The one exception is that these commands do not work with exploded components.

Component Replace (CN)

The Component Replace command replaces one component with another one. The command can select individual components or it can globally select every component of a certain type, thus enabling you to redefine a component, an attribute attached to a component, or both.

You initiate this command by selecting Replace in the COMPONENTS menu or by typing **CN**. The first prompt asks which component you want to replace. The second prompt asks for the name of the replacement component. You now have a choice to replace all the components or a specific one. Selection can be by **W**indow, **O**bject, la**Y**er, **D**rawing, **C**rossing, **L**ast, or **F**ilter. You also can deselect by pressing Ctrl and one of the options listed in the preceding sentence.

The selected components are replaced by the new components at the reference point. The new components take on all the characteristics of rotation, scale, and layer of the old components. The old attributes, however, are replaced by the attributes attached to the new components.

In the following exercise, JUNKSTUF is replaced by a new component called JUNKTOO.

Using the Component Replace Command

Prompt	Input	Description
Command	**LI**	Starts the Line command

Create a square by drawing a line that goes up 5", to the right 5", down 5", to the left 5" and, finally, back to the beginning to complete the square.

Prompt	Input	Description
Command	**CW**	Starts Window Component Create command
Place window	Place window around drawing	Identifies component
Enter component name>	**JUNKTOO**	Names component
Enter component reference point	**SM**	Snaps to midpoint
Midpoint of	Pick left vertical line	Sets reference point
<RET> to complete	Press Enter	Finishes command
Command	**CN**	Starts the Replace command
Select component from side menu	Pick JUNKSTUF	Selects component to be replaced
Select component from side menu	Pick JUNKTOO, replacing JUNKSTUF	Selects replacement component (see fig. 11.26)
<RET>Replace all -S for selection	Press Enter	Accepts replacing all JUNKSTUF components

Your screen should look like figure 11.27. The second JUNKSTUF was not replaced because it was exploded.

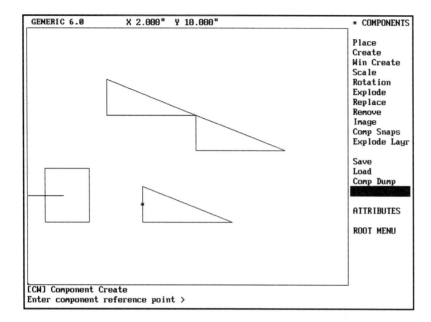

Figure 11.26:

The new component JUNKTOO.

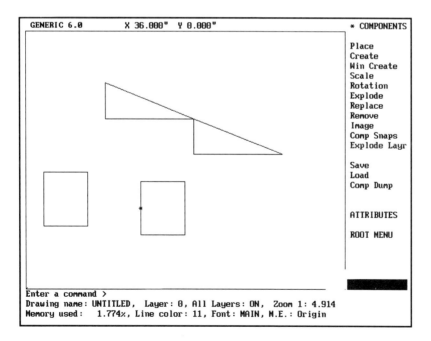

Figure 11.27:

JUNKSTUF replaced with JUNKTOO.

Component Remove (CX)

The Component Remove command erases all the unexploded components, as well as the component definition. No part of the component remains in the drawing, although it still exists on the hard drive if you saved it. The Undo (OO) command, however, brings everything back.

Start the Component Remove command by typing **CX** or selecting Remove from the COMPONENTS menu. The first prompt asks for the name of the component to be removed. You can select it from the side menu or type it in. A warning appears on-screen. You have the option to proceed with the removal by typing **Y** for yes, or cancelling the command by typing **N** for no.

The warning may seem ominous, but it is not. The Undo command brings the component back. In the worst case, you may need to use the Look on Disk option when you want to select the component again with the Component Place (CP) command.

JUNKTOO is removed in the following exercise.

Using the Component Replace Command

Prompt	Input	Description
Command	**CX**	Starts the Component Remove command
Select component from side menu	Pick JUNKTOO	Selects component to be removed
** Warning ** the component "JUNKTOO" will no longer exist! Remove the component? (Y/N)	**Y**	JUNKTOO is removed (see fig. 11.28)

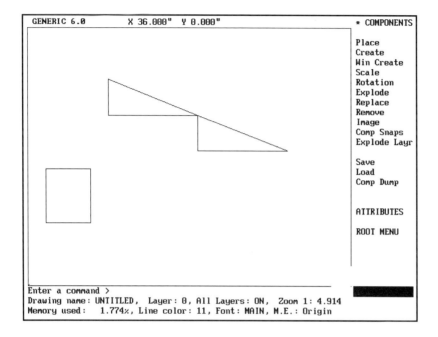

Figure 11.28:
JUNKTOO is removed.

Summary

This chapter covered a great deal of information about CADD's most useful tool—the component. The chapter began by illustrating and explaining what makes a good component and what makes a not-so-good component. With that background, you created a component with the Window Component Create (CW) command.

Scale and rotation can be used a number of ways to produce a variety of effects when you place components in a drawing.

Exploded components have advantages and disadvantages, most of which you explored by tackling special exercises throughout the chapter. You learned about the Remove and Replace commands, and you explored some practical uses for the Component Load (LO) command.

Components are discussed again in Chapter 14, when you learn to supercharge them with attributes. Read that chapter carefully; it enhances what you learned in this chapter.

Drawing Enhancements

T he drawings used so far in this book serve their purpose but will not win any awards for elegance. This chapter shows you two ways to add visual interest to your drawings—by using hatches and fills. *Hatches* are repeating patterns of fine lines; *fills* are blocks of solid color.

Beginning CADD users frequently overlook hatches and fills, considering them an unnecessary waste of time and computer resources. But the experienced CADD user has a different view. The thoughtful use of hatch patterns can provide additional visual clues to the nature of the objects in a drawing. Many professionals learned how to apply hatching manually to a drawing and already know the value of using hatch patterns in their designs.

Using Hatch Patterns

Hatches can be used to define certain objects, to provide shading, or to add interest to a drawing. Adding hatching to a drawing by hand is a tedious task but becomes relatively simple in Generic CADD. Hatching involves only a few rules and limitations.

All the commands for using hatches and fills are found on the HATCH/FILL menu.

Choosing a Hatch Pattern

The 50 hatch patterns supplied with Generic CADD are illustrated in figures 12.1, 12.2, 12.3, and 12.4. In addition, several third-party vendors sell other hatch patterns. You can even design your own, as detailed in the program documentation.

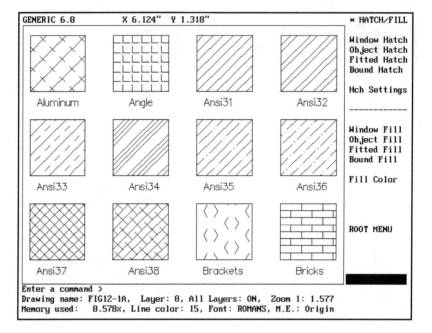

Figure 12.1:

Thirteen of the hatch patterns included with Generic CADD.

Some of the hatch patterns shipped with Generic CADD conform to professional standards (the ANSI hatches, for example). Most of the others represent patterns commonly used in many drafting environments.

Do not worry about which Line Type or Line Width to use for hatching. Generic CADD always uses Line Type and Line Width 0 for hatches. The color is not governed by the Line Color command, but by the Hatch Settings (HS) command, described next. After a hatch pattern is drawn, it is considered one single object. Each hatch pattern placed in a drawing has its own reference point. To edit the hatch pattern (erase, rotate, rescale, and so on), select it by selecting only the reference point, as if it were a component.

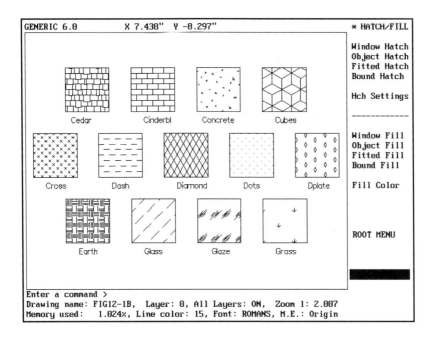

Figure 12.2:

Twelve more of the hatch patterns included with Generic CADD.

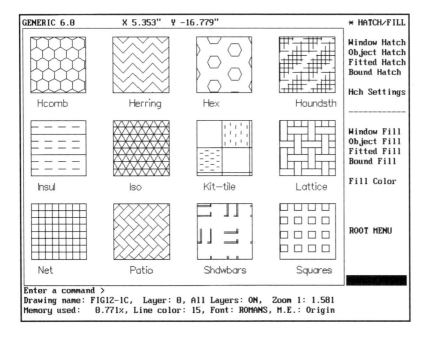

Figure 12.3:

Twelve more of the hatch patterns included with Generic CADD.

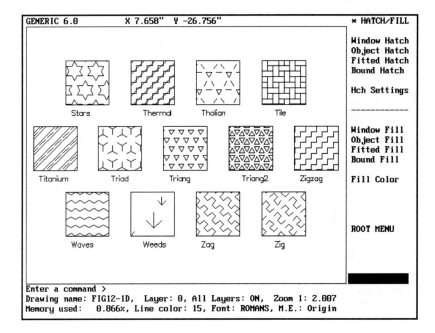

Figure 12.4:

The final 13 hatch patterns included with Generic CADD.

Choosing Hatch Settings (HS)

The Hatch Settings (HS) command is used to adjust all the factors that affect hatches. To use the command, type **HS** at the prompt or select Hatch Settings from the HATCH/FILL menu.

Select Hatch Pattern

The most important option in the Hatch Settings command is the name of the pattern. After selecting Hatch Settings or typing **HS**, type **P** to select a pattern. The list of patterns available appears in the menu on the side of the screen (see fig. 12.6). Either type the name of the pattern or select it with the menu bar.

The first time you configured Generic CADD, a subdirectory was assigned for the storage of hatch patterns. Unless you changed it, that directory is C:/CADD6/HCH. Generic CADD looks in this directory when you select a pattern. If you acquire new hatch patterns, be sure to place them in this directory. If you have not added them to the \HCH, use File Selector to view other directories containing hatch patterns.

Chapter 12

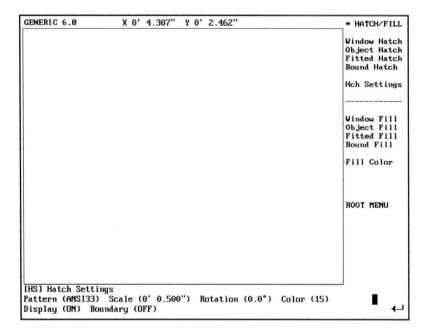

Figure 12.5:
The Hatch Settings command options.

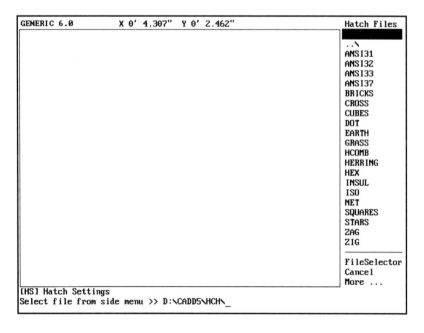

Figure 12.6:
Hatch pattern titles appear in the menu.

Select Hatch Scale

The Scale option controls the size of the individual elements that make up a hatch pattern. When you examine any of the hatched objects shown in this chapter, you can see that all the hatches are made up of repeating line segments arranged in different patterns. Figure 12.7 shows two hatch patterns at four different scale factors. The hatches are inside 1" squares. In these examples, the best choice for a scale factor is 1/4 (.25) because the drawings cover such a small area. The best scale factor for a drawing that covers an acre may be 10 or even 40 or more, depending on the look you need to achieve. Experiment in a drawing by hatching a small area first, to be sure that you like the hatch scale, before using it throughout the drawing.

Figure 12.7:

Scale of hatch patterns determines how they fill an area.

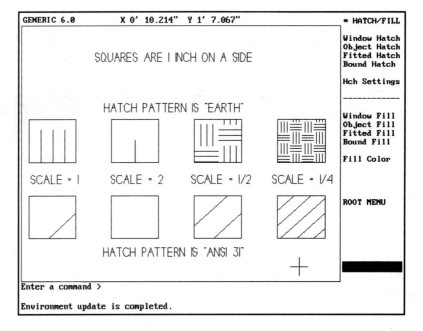

Select Hatch Rotation

The default rotation for hatch patterns is 0 degrees, but the alignment of patterns in a drawing can be changed by using the Rotation option. Figure 12.8 shows four possible rotations for two hatch patterns. A rotation of 0 degrees normally is fine, but the option to change exists if you need it. As with everything else in Generic CADD, positive numbers refer to counterclockwise rotation; negative numbers refer to clockwise rotation.

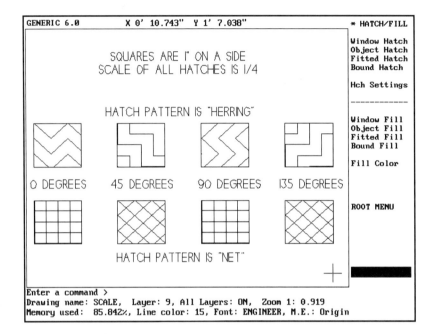

Figure 12.8:

Hatch patterns may be set at any angle of rotation.

Select Hatch Color

To set the color of a hatch pattern, type **C** from the Hatch Settings prompt. You may choose from all the line colors normally available in Generic CADD. For most systems, there are 16 colors; for a few very high performance video systems, 256 colors are available. If you print or plot to a color device, make sure that the color you choose for hatching is one your output device can reproduce.

Select Hatch Display

Hatch patterns take more time to draw and redraw than regular lines; they redraw at about the same speed as text placed with the Text Character Placement (TP) command. If you have a large drawing with several hatch patterns and considerable text, you may want to set Display to off. The hatch pattern is still part of the drawing, and its reference point is still visible if you have reference point display turned on, but the pattern is not visible. The display of hatch patterns also can be set by using the Fast Redraw (FA) command in the UTILITIES menu. If either command is used, the other command recognizes the change.

Select Hatch Boundary

When Generic CADD places a hatch pattern inside a boundary, it draws a line representing the boundary of the pattern. If this line, which is the same color as the hatch pattern, distracts from the drawing, type **B** at the Boundary option of Hatch Settings to shut off the display. This command is a toggle; to turn on the display again, type **B** again.

Choosing a Hatching Method

Generic CADD offers four ways to hatch objects. The method you choose depends on the items to be hatched and their proximity to other objects. The method you choose also depends on whether the objects you select come together to form closed boundaries.

When you draw a box using the Rectangle (RE) command, CADD draws four lines. The end points of each line touch the end points of another line, and the rectangle forms a closed boundary. If, however, you draw a box using four overlapping lines, the intersection of the lines defines a box, but the box is not considered a closed boundary for the purposes of hatching. (Solid color fills, which are discussed later in this chapter, generally follow the same rules.) To place a hatch pattern successfully inside an area defined by "open" boundaries, use the technique described later in the "Fitted Hatch" section.

Some Generic CADD users do not take the time to draw with precision. They "eyeball" the connection of lines, for example. This lack of concern for precision can cause problems when hatching. If the end points of two lines come close but do not connect, Generic CADD may miscalculate the boundary of the object being hatched and do an incomplete job. To be considered a closed boundary, the lines that form an object must meet at the end points (see fig. 12.9). Although adding hatching to "open boundary" objects is possible, the process is more time-consuming, and the likelihood of user error is higher.

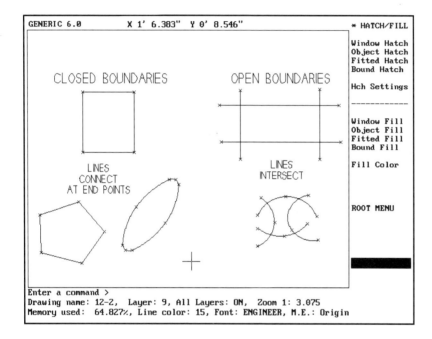

Figure 12.9:

Closed boundaries must meet at the end points.

To be hatched, an object must have been created with straight lines, circles, arcs, or ellipses (either true or construction), as shown in figure 12.10. The Rectangle (RE) and Regular Polygon (RP) commands create objects using straight lines; anything drawn using these commands can be successfully hatched. An ellipse drawn using the construction method also can be hatched, because it is defined using arcs. One exception to the preceding rule is that an object created using Bézier curves can be hatched by using the Window Hatch (WH) command only. The object may be created completely from Bézier curves or from a mix of Bézier curves and other legal lines. The boundaries must be closed (the end points must connect). Under no circumstance can an object made from complex curves (CV) be hatched.

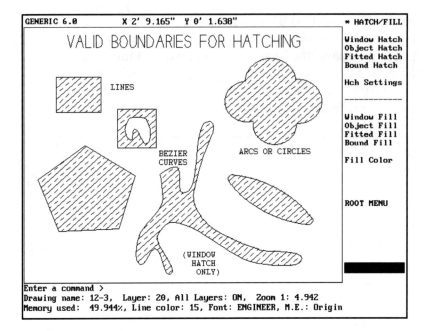

Figure 12.10:

Objects made from lines, circles, arcs, ellipses, and Béziers can be hatched.

Window Hatch (WH)

The Window Hatch command, the most commonly used of the four hatch commands, is the easiest to use. It can be used successfully only when the boundaries of the objects being hatched are closed (the end points of all lines connect).

When the window is drawn around items to be hatched, Generic CADD starts at the window and works its way in, identifying valid boundaries. If a second set of boundaries is found inside the first, hatching stops at the second boundary, which makes it possible to create hatches with open areas inside. This method was used to hatch the square with the Bézier curves inside it in figure 12.10. Figure 12.11 shows how the Window Hatch command can identify several sets of boundaries, stopping and restarting the hatching as it works from the outside in. Window Hatch can identify multiple sets of boundaries if they are nested (each inside the next) and if they are otherwise valid boundaries for hatching.

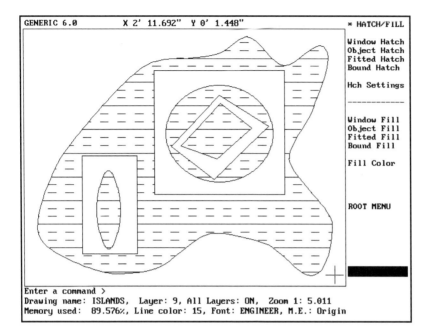

Figure 12.11:

Window Hatch can identify nested sets of boundaries.

Window Hatch is easily confused, however, if the lines are not distinct as well as securely connected to each other. An example would be a series of connecting boxes. Window Hatch would not know where one box ends and another begins. In such a situation, use Fitted Hatch instead.

Object Hatch (OH)

Object Hatch can define an area to be hatched by selecting the lines one by one, instead of having Generic CADD determine the boundaries (as it does when Window Hatch is used). The main difference between this command and Window Hatch is that each line, arc, or other boundary must be selected. The entities used to create the boundaries must still follow the rules. Because the boundaries are selected individually, you can hatch areas that would be left unhatched if Window Hatch were used. The objects in figure 12.12 are the same as those in figure 12.11, but the hatching is different because only the circles, arcs, and Bézier curves (not the straight lines) have been selected as boundaries.

407

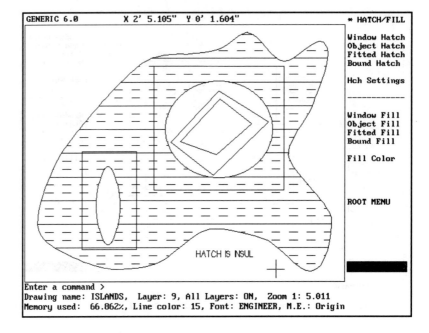

Figure 12.12:

Use Object Hatch to select specific boundaries.

When hatching an area with a variety of valid boundaries, cursor placement is crucial. Notice the location of the cursor in figure 12.13. One side of the crosshairs intersects the object being selected, but the center of the crosshairs does not touch the line. When lines overlap, use this method of selection to ensure that the line closest to the others you are selecting is chosen.

As objects are selected, the counter used in the selection process in editing commands appears. If you know how many lines are in an object, the counter helps you verify that you have selected them all. Another key to selecting all the required lines is to watch the screen for the appearance of construction points. As each line, arc, and so on is selected, its construction points appear (unless construction points are already on display for all objects). Making sure that every segment of a Bézier curve is selected is much easier if you check to see that construction points for every part of the curve are showing as you move along it. Always select the objects for Object Hatch in a circular fashion, from the outside in (see fig. 12.13).

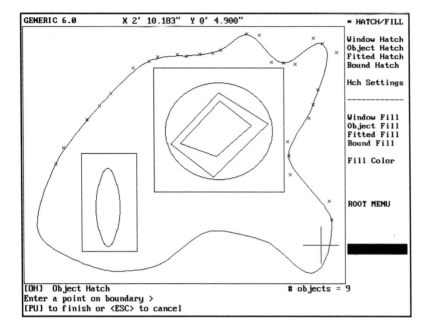

Figure 12.13:

Selecting the boundaries in a circular pattern.

Fitted Hatch (FH)

If you take care as you draw, and create connecting boundaries, Window Hatch and Object Hatch work in most situations. Situations may still arise, however, when you need to hatch an area that is not well-defined. If so, use the Fitted Hatch command.

Fitted Hatch works like Object Hatch. Objects that form the boundary for the hatch are selected one by one. The difference is that Generic CADD looks for intersections as it analyzes the boundaries you have selected, and places the hatch accordingly.

As you select objects for the boundary, place the cursor in the midsection of an object, not near the end point or where one line intersects another. The arrows in figure 12.14 point to where you should click on each line. If you do happen to select an object that you do not want to include in the definition of the boundary, press Ctrl-Backspace to remove the object from the list of selected items. Each time you press Ctrl-Backspace, the last object selected is deselected; you can continue deselecting items back to the start if you like.

409

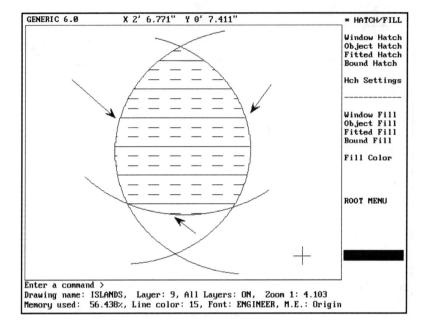

Figure 12.14:

Fitted Hatch hatches objects without valid boundaries.

As with the other hatch commands, only straight lines, circles, and arcs may be used with the Fitted Hatch command. (Remember— Bézier curves are valid boundaries only if Window Hatch or Object Hatch are used.) At least three objects must be selected for the Fitted Hatch command to work. A circle by itself, for example, is ineligible for the Fitted Hatch command. If you need to hatch the space between two intersecting arcs, such as those shown in figure 12.15, use Object Break first to break one of the arcs into two. So that the boundaries are still connected, use the same point for both the first and second selection in the Object Break command.

Boundary Hatch (BH)

If you want to place hatching in an area that is not defined by existing objects, use the Boundary Hatch command. It enables you to create a straight line boundary and hatch it at the same time. You can draw the lines in open space, on top of existing lines, or in any combination. You can use snaps to define the end points of the boundary if necessary. The boundary lines drawn by the

Boundary Hatch command are visible after the hatching is placed only if the Boundary option in the Hatch Settings command is on (as illustrated in fig. 12.16).

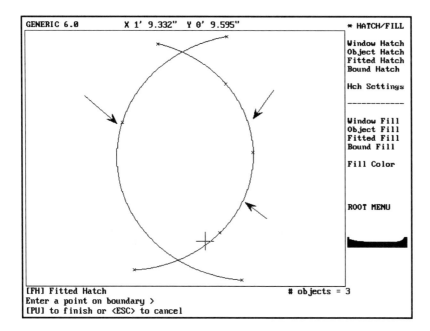

Figure 12.15:

At least three objects must be selected for Fitted Hatch.

Using Solid Color Fills

Solid color fills follow most of the same rules as hatches, except that all basic construction entities are valid fill boundaries. To select the color of the fill, use either the DISPLAY menu's Color Settings (CS) command or the HATCH/FILL menu's Fill Color (FC or FK) command. To save time during redraws, the display of fills may be turned on or off by using the Fill display option of Fast Redraw (FA), on the DISPLAY menu; alternatively, use the two-letter DF command to toggle the display of fills on and off. DF (for *display fills*) is not located on any menu; it is left over from earlier versions of Generic CADD that lacked the Fast Redraw command, and continues to be included primarily for the convenience of experienced users.

411

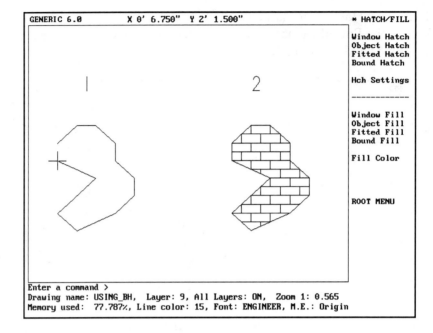

Figure 12.16:

Boundary Hatch can be used to place a hatch pattern.

A solid color fill is considered one object, and each fill has its own reference point. Sometimes, if the fill is complicated, locating the reference point may be difficult. In figure 12.17, for example, one Window Fill command was used to fill all the objects; the reference point is located in the center of the circle at the top of the drawing. If each object had been filled separately, each would have its own reference point. You can make finding the fill and hatch reference points easier by putting fills and hatches on their own layer. This way, the hatches and fills can be erased easily, if necessary, without disturbing other objects. Just set All Layers Edit (AL) to off, switch the current layer to the hatch/fill layer (using Layer Current, YC), and erase the fills or hatches as required, by selecting Layer from the Erase (ER) command.

Using Window Fill (WF)

The Window Fill command works exactly like the Window Hatch command, except that a solid color is placed inside the boundaries selected. If there are nested boundaries, the solid color fill creates islands of filled and unfilled areas, depending on the number of boundaries found. The boundaries must connect at their end points. Figure 12.18 shows an example of using Window Fill with nested boundaries.

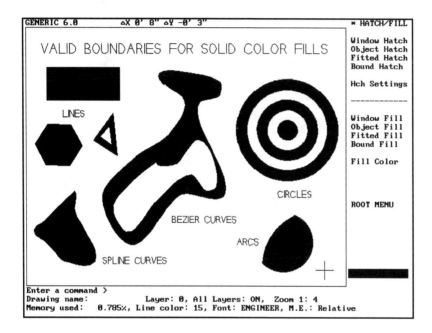

Figure 12.17:

Valid boundaries for solid color fills.

Using Object Fill (OF)

You use the Object Fill command to define an area to be filled with a solid color, selecting the lines one by one instead of having Generic CADD determine the boundaries (as it does when Window Fill is used). The main difference between this command and Window Fill is that each line, arc, or other boundary must be selected. Because the boundaries must be selected individually, you can add solid color fill to areas that would be left uncovered if Window Fill were used. The objects in figure 12.19 are the same as those in figure 12.18, but the shape of the fill is different because only the circles, arcs, and Bézier curves have been selected as boundaries (not the straight lines). Figure 12.19 has been modified to show the location of the straight lines; in normal use, the fill would cover them.

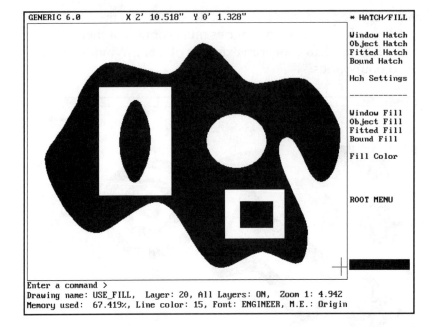

Figure 12.18:

Window Fill can identify nested sets of boundaries.

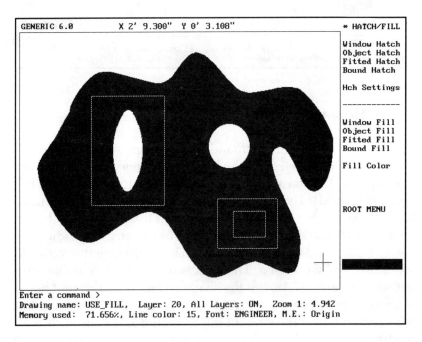

Figure 12.19:

Use Object Fill when the solid color should overwrite objects.

Using Fitted Fill (FF)

If you take care as you draw and create connecting boundaries, Window Fill and Object Fill work in most situations. If you need to hatch an area that is not well-defined, use the Fitted Fill command.

The Fitted Fill command is used the same way as the Object Fill command. Objects that form the boundary for the fill are selected one by one. The difference is that Generic CADD looks for intersections as it analyzes the boundaries you have selected, placing the solid color accordingly.

As you select objects for the boundary, place the cursor on the midsection of an object, not near the end point or where one line intersects another (refer to fig. 12.14, where this technique is used for Fitted Hatch). If you happen to select an object that you do not want to include in the definition of the boundary, press Ctrl-Backspace to remove the object from the list of selected items. Each time you press Ctrl-Backspace, the last object selected is deselected; you can continue deselecting items back to the start if you like.

At least three objects must be selected for the Fitted Fill command to work. This means, for example, that a circle, by itself, is ineligible for the Fitted Fill command. If you need to fill the space between two intersecting arcs, as shown in figure 12.20, use Object Break first to break one of the arcs into two (see fig. 12.21). (Note in the illustration that # objects = 3.) To keep the boundaries connected, use the same point for both the first and second selection in the Object Break command.

Using Boundary Fill (BF)

If you want to place solid color in an area that is not defined by existing objects, use Boundary Fill. It works the same way as Boundary Hatch, allowing you to create a straight-line boundary and fill it at the same time (see fig. 12.22). You can draw the lines in open space, on top of existing lines, or any combination of the two. If necessary, you can use snaps to define the end points of the boundary. Unlike the boundary lines drawn by Boundary Hatch, the boundary lines drawn by the Boundary Fill command are temporary; they do not appear after the fill has been placed in the drawing.

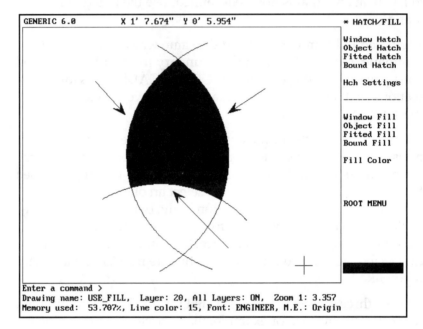

Figure 12.20:

Use Fitted Fill to fill objects without valid boundaries.

Summary

Placing hatches and fills in a drawing is a relatively simple procedure, but certain rules must be followed, and not all objects qualify as valid boundaries for hatches and fills. The wise Generic CADD user is always as precise as possible in placing end points and connecting lines, not only to ensure easy placement of hatches and fills but also to take advantage of the program's capability to draw with precision.

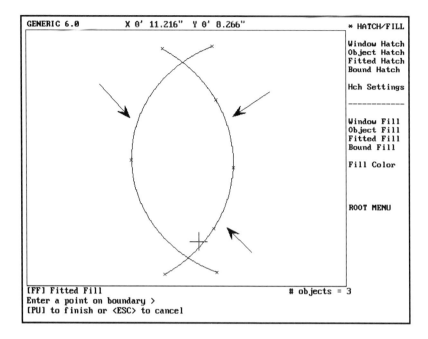

Figure 12.21:

At least three objects must be selected for Fitted Fill.

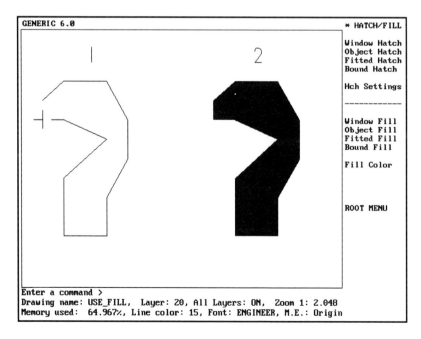

Figure 12.22:

Boundary Fill may be used to place a solid color fill anywhere.

Dimensioning

Drawings convey ideas. In past chapters, you learned how to create drawings with an electronic "drafting machine" called Generic CADD. Contained within the lines, arcs, circles, and other objects is a wealth of information. Layers, colors, line lengths, text starting points, center locations for arcs, and more are part of the drawing on the screen. Some of this data is plain to see, but other information is hidden until it is displayed by a series of keystrokes.

When you print a drawing, much of its information is hard to convey. A line created with an accuracy of .0001" on-screen is impossible to duplicate accurately on a piece of paper. In fact, a printed drawing is itself less exact because it is the product of a conversion of vectors to rasterized dots. These dots are placed on the paper by a printer that can print in a predesignated pattern only. In a plotter, the paper slips and the pens skip.

The solution is to use text to tell the story. Describe the length of the line. Label the location of the center of an arc. In other words, use dimensioning to place measurements in your drawings.

Understanding the Dimensioning Process

All types of objects can be dimensioned—arcs, circles, angles, and lines. Generic CADD offers many options and a wide variety of ways to accomplish dimensioning tasks.

Learning about dimensioning can be challenging. The many terms and variables have only subtle shades of difference. As is frequently the case with technical terms, seeing is understanding.

To understand dimensioning, you need to understand the basic anatomy of a *dimension string*. A dimension string may include an arrowhead, dimension text, a dimension line, and extension lines (see fig. 13.1).

Figure 13.1:

The anatomy of a dimension string.

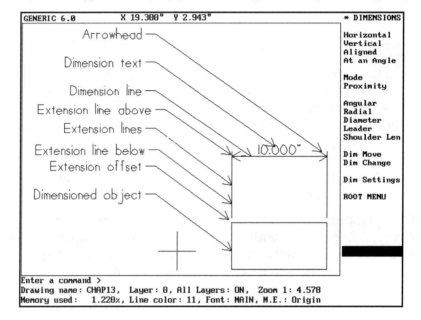

Dimension Text

Dimension text is a crucial part of the dimension string. It specifies the exact size of the dimensioned object, and can specify a tolerance also. Text can be generated automatically or input manually. Generic CADD also enables you to add clarifying text; for example, you might add *Dia* for diameter, or *O.C.* for on center, or supply other text to convey a special meaning to the user.

Dimension Line

The dimensioned text sits above, or in the middle of, a *dimension line* (depending on the type of drafting you do). The line can be horizontal, vertical, angled, or arced. It often lies between extension lines, with particular arrowheads to indicate which extension lines pertain to which dimension text.

Arrowheads

Extension lines, visible when an object is selected, usually end in a wide variety of shapes, referred to as *arrowheads*. These shapes include short open arrows, long filled arrows, filled and unfilled dots, and hash marks. Generic CADD offers a wide choice of options that enable you to indicate related extension lines and text.

Extension Lines

Extension lines define the boundaries of a dimension string. They usually extend from the dimensioned object to the dimension line and beyond. Consisting of three distinct parts—offset, line below, and line above—extension lines can be manipulated by using the dimension settings commands. When you first start dimensioning objects, the results may not be exactly what you expect. Reworking the dimensions so that they match what you are used to seeing involves tapping Generic CADD's extensive library of dimension settings. Using dimension settings is covered later in the chapter.

Dimensioning Methods

Generic CADD gives users a wide range of dimensioning options. You can dimension horizontally, vertically, aligned, at an angle, and with or without tolerancing. You can dimension angles, circles, and arcs, and even add dimension notes.

Linear Dimension (LX)

The basic dimensioning command, Linear Dimension, dimensions the distance between two points. It creates dimension lines, arrowheads, extension lines, and text that indicates size. At the prompt, the user can add text next to the displayed size.

The way you prefer to use Generic CADD determines your approach to placing linear dimensions in a drawing. If you like the two-letter commands, use the two-letter command LX whenever you want to dimension objects. You will need to set the dimensioning directive manually each time (using the choices listed below under Dimension Direction), if you dimension objects at various angles. You can think of using LX as the manual transmission approach to dimensioning straight lines.

If you prefer to use menus, four choices are listed for linear dimensioning: Horizontal, Vertical, Aligned, and At An Angle. When you select one of these four options from the menu, the option you select sets the direction variables for you; all you need to do is place the dimensions. You can think of using menu commands to place linear dimensions as the automatic transmission approach to dimensioning straight lines.

To give you a thorough understanding of linear dimensioning, the material that follows describes a "manual" method of dimensioning. After you understand how to set the variables yourself, the "automatic" method will not seem like some kind of "black box" approach.

To start the Linear Dimension command, either type **LX** or select one of the four types of linear dimensioning listed in the menu. The prompt line displays the current mode: Single, Partitioned, or Cumulative. (More about these modes later.) To begin to dimension, select the first point (snap commands make this easy) and then the end point for the dimension. The prompt then displays the distance and pauses so that you can add more text. At this point, you have several options: you can press Enter to accept the text; use the Backspace key to erase the "#" sign and replace the given text value with another value; or add additional text. To finish the command, enter the location of the dimension line. Generic CADD uses this information to construct the dimension.

The command is affected by the dimension variable commands, Dimension Direction (UD) and Dim Mode (UM). As you may guess from the command name, Dimension Direction dimensions in different directions or orientations. Dim Mode enables you to dimension objects one at a time or in a string.

Dimension Direction

Dimension Direction (UD) controls the direction of dimensions placed in the drawing. Dimension Direction may be set using the two-letter command UD, or by selecting Dimensions Settings (US), then pressing D for Dim-Line, N for Direction, and pressing the letter of the style you need. (The four choices are A for Aligned, H for Horizontal, V for Vertical, and E for at an anglE.)

Of the four, only Aligned enables you to get a correct dimensioning of any straight line at any angle. If you select Horizontal, Vertical, or At An Angle, only straight distances that match the setting will be dimensioned. If you use Linear Dimension to try to dimension a vertical line, and Dimension Direction is set to Horizontal, for example, the dimensioning command tells you that the object is 0" long, because the horizontal distance of the object really is zero. Only when Aligned is used can the Linear Dimensioning command give the true distance of any line.

The advantage of limiting Linear Dimension to either a Horizontal, Vertical, or an At An Angle option comes when you add dimensions to complicated drawings. Choosing to dimension only vertically, then only horizontally, can help you develop a rhythm to your work. Looking for all the items of each orientation helps to focus your attention, resulting in a more systematic and thorough use of CADD.

In the following exercise, which demonstrates the use of the Linear Dimension command, you go through several dimension-setting commands. In particular, you use Dimension Direction to draw differently oriented dimensions. Begin by drawing an object to dimension.

Using Linear Dimension and Dimension Direction

Prompt	Input	Description
Command	**SG**	Turns on Snap to Grid
Command	**OR**	Turns off ortho
Command	**ZO**	Zooms out
Pick center of zoom	Pick a point near midpoint of upper horizontal line	Centers zoom
Command	**LI**	Selects the Line command
Starting point dimension	Pick a point just above the center of the screen	Enters first point of line
Enter next point on line	Move cursor to right 6"	Enters second point of line
Enter next point on line	Move cursor down 6"	Enters third point of line
Enter next point on line	Move cursor to the left 10"	Enters fourth point of line
Enter next point on line	Connect last point with start point	Finishes four-sided polygon
Command	**A2**	Begins two-point arc
Enter center of arc	**SM**	Snaps to midpoint
Midpoint of	Pick right vertical line	Selects arc midpoint
Enter start of arc	Pick bottom of vertical line	Selects start of arc
Enter end of arc	Pick top of vertical line	Selects end of arc

The object you will dimension should look similar to the one in figure 13.2.

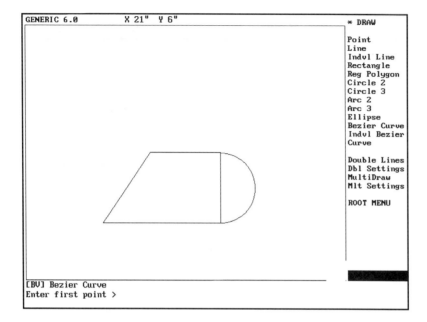

Figure 13.2:

Object to be dimensioned.

Proximity Fixed (PF)

The Proximity Fixed command is toggled from the DIMENSIONS menu or invoked by typing **PF**. When PF is on, extension lines automatically are drawn the specified length. For this exercise, toggle PF off. Don't be concerned if a few of the dimensioning commands you are instructed to try in this next exercise sequence have not been discussed yet. Just follow along for now; more details are introduced later.

Horizontal Dimensioning

Prompt	Input	Description
Command	**NF**	Selects Numeric Format
Angular (Degrees) **L**inear (Decimal) **D**ecimal value (3)	**D, 0**	Shows dimensions as whole numbers, so 2.000 becomes 2

continues

425

Prompt	Input	Description
`Command`	**PF**	Selects Proximity Fixed command to check its setting

`* [PF]`
`Proximity`
`Fixed ON`
	PF (omit if PF is already off)	Toggles PF from on to off

`Command`	**XS**	Selects Extension Stretch command to check its setting
`Offset (0.5")` `length`	If stretch is off, pick the word "Stretch" with your cursor in the prompt line	Turns XS from off to on
`Command`	**UD**	Selects Dimension Direction command
`Aligned` `(Horizontal)...`	**H**	Selects horizontal dimensioning
`Command`	**LX** or choose `Linear` from side menu	Starts a linear dimension
`Enter first` `point`	**SC**	Snaps to closest point
`Closest point` `to`	Pick left side of bottom horizontal line	Selects left side
`Enter next` `point`	**SM**	Snaps to midpoint of arc
`Midpoint of`	Pick midpoint of arc	Selects midpoint
`# = 13"`	Press Enter	Accepts dimension size without additional text
`Enter location` `of`	Pick a location on screen above object	Locates dimension line

Your first dimension should look like the one in figure 13.3.

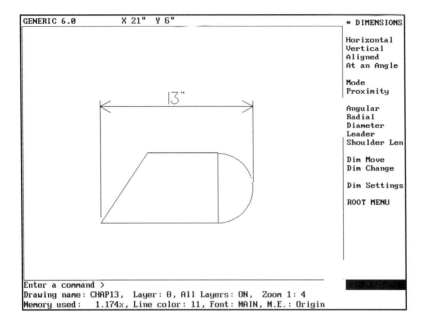

Figure 13.3:
Horizontal linear dimension.

Vertical Dimensioning

Prompt	Input	Description
Command	**UD**	Starts Dimension Direction command
Aligned... Vertical...	**V**	Selects vertical dimensioning
Command	**LX** or pick Linear from side menu	Starts a linear dimension
Enter first point	**SC**	Snaps to closest point
Closest point to	Pick left side of bottom horizontal line	
Enter next point	**SC**	Snaps to closest point
Closest point to	Pick top of angled line	

continues

Prompt	Input	Description
# = 6"	Press Enter	Accepts dimension size without additional text
Enter location of dimension	Pick a location on screen, left of object	Locates dimension line (see fig. 13.4)

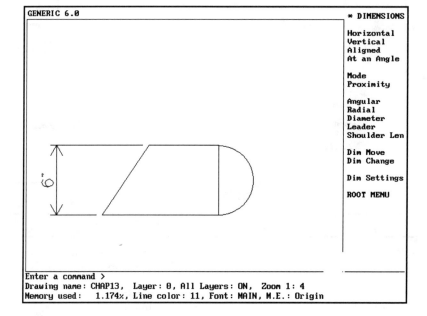

Figure 13.4:

Vertical linear dimension.

Aligned Dimensioning

Prompt	Input	Description
Command	OO	Undoes last action
Command	UD	Starts Dimension Direction command
...(Horizontal) Aligned...	A	You will be placing an aligned dimension

Prompt	Input	Description
Command	**LX** or pick Linear from side menu	Starts a linear dimension
Enter first point	**SC**	Snaps to closest point
Closest point to	Pick left side of bottom horizontal line	Selects left side
Enter next point	**SC**	Snaps to closest point
Closest point to	Pick top of angled line	Selects top of line
# = 7"	Press Enter	
> #	Press Backspace to erase the #; type **8"**	Erases the #
Enter location of dimension	Pick a location on the screen to left of object	Locates dimension line

This time, the dimension is at an angle. The aligned dimension should look like that shown in figure 13.5.

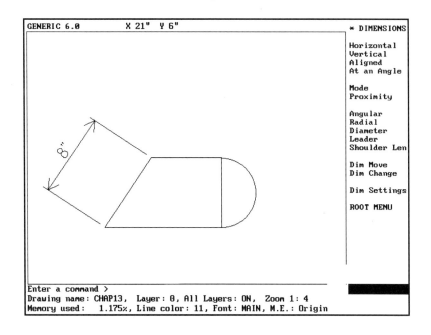

Figure 13.5:

Aligned linear dimension.

The last dimension was angled but aligned with a specific line. The next exercise shows you how to specify a dimension's angle.

Dimensioning at an Angle

Prompt	Input	Description
Command	**OO**	Undoes last action
Command	**UD**	Starts Dimension Direction command
...Vertical, at an anglE...	**E**	Starts dimensioning at an angle
Change Angle (30) Limits: -360 to 360	10	Gives dimension line a 10-degree angle
Command	**LX** or pick Linear from side menu	Starts a linear dimension
Enter first point	**SC**	Snaps to closest point
Closest point to	Pick left side of bottom horizontal line	Selects left side
Enter next point	**SM**	Snaps to midpoint of arc
Midpoint of	Pick midpoint of arc	Selects midpoint
# = 13" > #	Press Enter	Accepts dimension size without additional text
Enter location of dimension	Pick a location on the screen above the object	Locates dimension line

This time, the angled dimension should look like the one in figure 13.6.

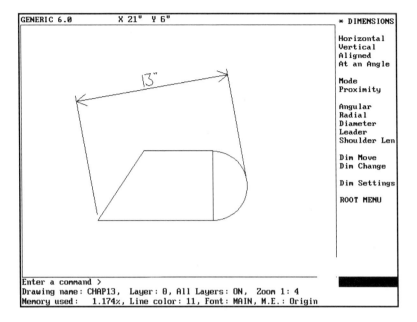

Figure 13.6:

Angled linear dimension.

Proximity Fixed is a toggle that works with most types of dimensions. You are most likely to use it with the linear dimension commands. In the preceding exercises, you placed the dimension line at various distances from the dimensioned object. This works well during practice but may look sloppy in a real set of plans. Fixed distances between the dimensioned object and the dimension line, and between one dimension line and the dimension line above it look much more professional. Turn Proximity Fixed on again for the next exercise.

Dimension Extensions

The Dimension Extensions command controls the following six options: offset distance, length of the extension line above the dimension line, length below the dimension line, whether the extension lines stretch from the offset to the dimension line, and a choice for the display of each extension line. You used this command earlier to turn Stretch on for the extension lines in the first exercise. Refer to figure 13.1 to refresh your memory of these terms. In figure 13.2, the left extension line stretches down to the first point, which would not happen if Stretch were turned off.

There are two ways to reach the Dimension Extensions command. In the first, the two-letter command XS takes you directly to the settings that control the extensions. The second method is by means of the Dimensions Settings command, listed in the menu as Dim Settings and available from the keyboard by typing **US**, then **E** for Extensions. (Before the release of version 6.0, only the XS command was available. A reorganization of the command structure in version 6.0 added the US command and eliminated a separate menu for dimension settings.)

After Dimension Extensions has been selected, the six options are displayed with the default values shown: **O**ffset (0.5") length, **A**bove (0.5") length; **B**elow (0.5") length; **S**tretch (off); display **1** (on); display **2** (on). To select these options, either type the upper-case letter or choose it from the screen, using the cursor.

Using Proximity Fixed and Dimension Extension

Prompt	Input	Description
Command	**OO**	Undoes last action
Command	**UD**	Starts Dimension Direction command
Aligned (Horizontal)...	**H**	Starts horizontal dimensioning
Command	**PF**	Selects Proximity Fixed command to check its setting
* [PF] Proximity Fixed is ON	If PF is on, skip next step	Retains PF setting
* [PF] Proximity	**PF**	Turns Proximity on
Command	From the side menu, choose Dim Set, then Extensions	Selects Dim Set

Prompt	Input	Description

`Offset (0.5")`
`length, Above`
`(0.5") length,`
`Below (0.5")`
`length,`
`Stretch (ON)`
	A, 1
	B, 4
	S
		Sets above length to 1", below length to 4", and turns Stretch off (offset is not changed)

`Command`	**LX** or pick `Linear` from side menu	Starts a linear dimension
`Enter first` `point`	**SC**	Snaps to closest point
`Closest point to`	Pick left side of bottom horizontal line	Selects left side
`Enter next point`	**SM**	Snaps to midpoint of arc
`Midpoint of`	Pick midpoint of arc	
`# = 13"` `> #`	Press Enter	Accepts dimension size without additional text
`Enter location` `of dimension`	Pick a location on screen above object	Locates dimension line

Your latest dimension should look like figure 13.7.

Dimension Tolerance

Dimension Tolerance, another facet of the Linear Dimension command, is used occasionally with radial and diameter dimensioning also. Just as tolerance implies that a certain amount of variance is acceptable, Dimension Tolerance allows the length of an object to vary by a certain value (usually within so many thousandths of an inch) and still be within acceptable limits.

433

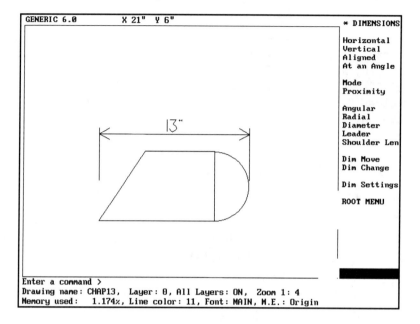

Figure 13.7:

Horizontal linear dimension with PF on and changed extension options.

As with the other commands that control dimensioning, two routes are available. You can type **UT** from the keyboard and find the Tolerance options listed in the prompt line, or you can reach the same options by typing **US** for Dimension Settings, then **T** for Text, and **T** again for Tolerance.

Tolerance is expressed in three ways—Fixed variance, Max/min variance, and Stacked variance—each of which is explored in the exercise that follows. There also is a No tolerance option if you do not use tolerancing (for nonengineering applications).

The last option available in Tolerance is the Multiplier, used for detailing applications. The default value for this option (also known as the *scale multiplier*) is 1. Whenever a dimension is placed in the drawing, the measurement about to be listed in the dimension line is multiplied by the value in the Multiplier. If a project requires that the dimensions reflect a specific scale, then make the number appropriate to the scale of the new value for the Multiplier. If an object is 1" long and the Multiplier has a value of 2, the dimension for the object will list the length as 2". Unless you have a specific use for representing scale values in your dimensions, leave the value in the Multiplier at 1.

Each option has different prompts. Fixed variance requires a single tolerance value, with precision limits for tolerance ranging from 0 to 6 decimal places. With Max/min and Stacked variances, you must provide lower and upper tolerances.

The following exercise demonstrates how each type of tolerance changes the look of the dimension string.

Using Dimension Tolerance

Prompt	Input	Description
Command	**OO**	Undoes last action
Command	**PF**	Selects Proximity Fixed command to check its setting
* [PF] Proximity Fixed is ON	If PF is on, skip next step	Retains PF setting
* [PF] Proximity	**PF**	Turns on Proximity
Command	**UT** or pick Tolerance from side menu	Selects Dimension Tolerance command
(None)...Fixed variance	**F**	Selects Fixed variance option
Change tolerance value	**.003**	Sets variance of plus or minus .003"
Change decimal Limits: 0 to 6	**3**	Sets a tolerance precision of three decimal places
Command	**LX** or pick Linear from side menu	Starts a linear dimension
Enter first point	**SC**	Snaps to closest point
Closest point to	Pick left side of bottom horizontal line	Selects left side

continues

435

Prompt	Input	Description
Enter next point	**SM**	Snaps to midpoint of arc
Midpoint of	Pick midpoint of arc	Selects midpoint
# = 13" > #	Press Enter	Accepts dimension size without additional text
Enter location of dimension	Pick a location on screen above object	Locates dimension line showing tolerance figure (see fig. 13.8)

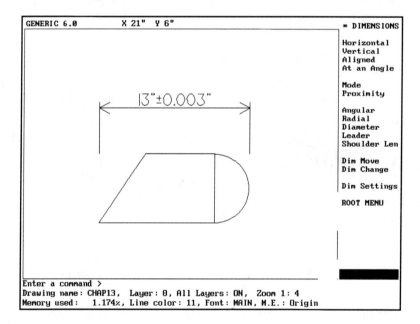

Figure 13.8:

Linear Dimension with a Fixed variance tolerance.

Using the Max/Min Variance

Prompt	Input	Description
`Command`	**OO**	Undoes last action
`Command`	**UT** or pick `Tolerance` from side menu	Selects Dimension Tolerance command
`(None)` `Max/min...`	**M**	Selects Max/min variance
`Change lower` `tolerance`	**.003**	Sets variance of minus .003"
`Change upper` `tolerance`	**.001**	Sets variance of plus .001"
`Change decimal` `Limits: 0 to 6`	**3**	Sets a tolerance precision of three decimal places
`Command`	**LX** or pick `Linear` from side menu	Starts a linear dimension
`Enter first` `point`	**SC**	Snaps to closest point
`Closest point` `to`	Pick left side of bottom horizontal line	Selects left side
`Enter next` `point`	**SM**	Snaps to midpoint of arc
`Midpoint of`	Pick midpoint of arc	Selects midpoint
`# = 13"` `> #`	Press Enter	Accepts dimension size without additional text
`Enter location` `of dimension`	Pick a location on the screen above the object	Locates dimension line

This dimension should look like the one in figure 13.9.

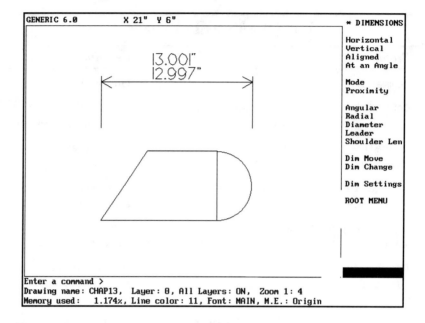

Figure 13.9:

Horizontal linear dimension with a Max/min variance.

Using the Stacked Variance

Prompt	Input	Description
Command	**OO**	Undoes last action
Command	**UT** or pick Tolerance from side menu	Selects Dimension Tolerance command
(None)... **S**tacked variance	**S**	Selects Stacked variance option
Change lower tolerance	**.003**	Sets variance of minus .003"
Change upper tolerance	**.001**	Sets variance of plus .001"
Change decimal Limits: 0 to 6	**3**	Sets a tolerance precision of three decimal places
Command	**LX** or pick Linear from side menu	Starts a linear dimension

Prompt	Input	Description
Enter first point	**SC**	Snaps to closest point
Closest point to	Pick left side of bottom horizontal line	Selects left side
Enter next point	**SM**	Snaps to midpoint of arc
Midpoint of	Pick midpoint of arc	Selects midpoint
# = 13" > #	Press Enter	Accepts dimension size without additional text
Enter location of dimension	Pick a location on the screen above the object	Locates dimension line

Your Stacked variance dimension should look like the one in figure 13.10.

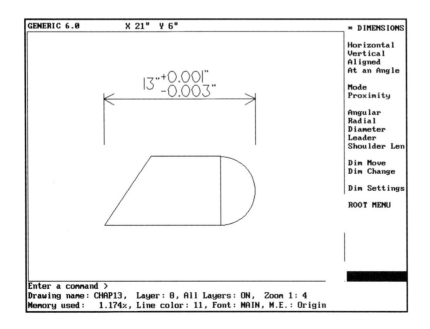

Figure 13.10:

Horizontal linear dimension with a Stacked variance.

Dimension Mode (UM)

Dimension Mode is another of the dimensioning commands that work with Linear Dimension. Dimension Mode determines whether the dimensions are Single, Partitioned, or Cumulative.

In the preceding exercises, you have been dimensioning in Single mode (the default setting). As the name implies, the command ends after a single dimension is completed. You placed one dimension; to place another, you had to type **LX** or press the spacebar to repeat the last command. There are two other approaches.

In Partitioned mode, you are prompted for the next point after the first dimension is completed. In fact, you are prompted for points until you press Enter to end the command. Partitioned mode creates a continuous horizontal line made up of the different dimension lines.

Cumulative mode combines the Single and Partitioned mode prompts. You pick a first point, a next point, and a dimension-line location. Then you pick a next point and a dimension-line location, continuing in this way until you press Enter to end the command. The result looks like inverted stair steps. Each dimension is a dimension from a base point rather than from point to point.

Because you have already completed several Single-mode dimensions, this exercise demonstrates Partitioned and Cumulative modes.

Using Partitioned Mode

Prompt	Input	Description
Command	**OO**	Undoes last action
Command	**UT** or pick Tolerance from side menu	Selects Dimension Tolerance command
(None) Max/min...	**N**	Selects No tolerance

Prompt	Input	Description
Command	**UM** or pick **Mode** from side menu	Starts Dimension Mode command
(**S**ingle) **P**artitioned...	**P**	Selects Partitioned mode
Command	**LX** or pick **Linear** from side menu	Starts a linear dimension
Enter first point	**SC**	Snaps to closest point
Closest point to	Pick top of angled line	Selects top of line
# = 4" > #	Press Enter	Accepts dimension size without additional text
Enter location of dimension	Pick a location on screen above object	Locates dimension line
Enter next point	**SC**	Snaps to closest point
Closest point to	Pick right side of top horizontal line	Continues dimension string
# = 6" > #	Press Enter	Accepts dimension size without additional text
Enter next point	**SM**	Snaps to midpoint of arc
Midpoint of	Pick midpoint of arc	Selects midpoint
# = 3" > #	Press Enter	Accepts dimension size without additional text

Your partitioned dimension should look like the one in figure 13.11.

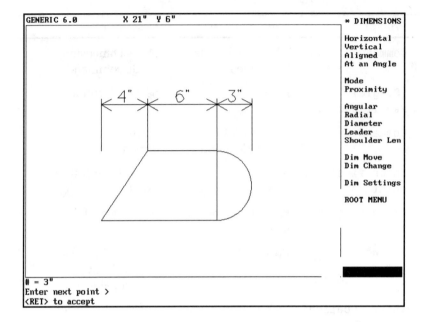

Figure 13.11:

Partitioned horizontal linear dimension.

Using Cumulative Mode

Prompt	Input	Description
Command	**UT** or pick Tolerance from side menu	Selects Dimension Tolerance command
Command	**OO**	Undoes last action
Command	**UM** or pick Mode from side menu	Starts Dimension Mode command
...Partitioned Cumulative	**C**	Selects Cumulative mode
Command	**LX** or pick Linear from side menu	Starts a linear dimension
Enter first point	**SC**	Snaps to closest point
Closest point to	Pick top of angled line	Selects top of line
# = 4" > #	Press Enter	Accepts dimension size without additional text

Prompt	Input	Description
`Enter location of dimension`	Pick a location on screen above object	Locates dimension line
`Enter next point`	**SC**	Snaps to closest point
`Closest point to`	Pick right side of top horizontal line	Continues dimension string
`# = 6"` `> #`	Press Enter	Accepts dimension size without additional text
`Enter next point`	**SM**	Snaps to midpoint of arc
`Midpoint of`	Pick midpoint of arc	Selects midpoint
`# = 3"` `> #`	Press Enter	Accepts dimension size without additional text

Your cumulative dimension should look like figure 13.12. Although the process of placing a cumulative dimension is like partitioned dimensioning in some ways, the end result is quite different.

Angular Dimension (AX)

The Angular Dimension command dimensions the angle of two lines. The text is displayed in degrees or in degrees:minutes: seconds. This command can be limited to any of the Dimension Mode (UD) options, and can show single, partitioned, or cumulative sets of dimensions.

After you select Angular Dimension, the first prompt asks for the center point. Additional prompts enable you to pick the two angled lines and show the dimension location. Depending on how the cursor is placed, Generic CADD gives you the option to show either the small or large angle. When the correct dimension is displayed, you can accept, modify, or add to the number placed in the dimension.

443

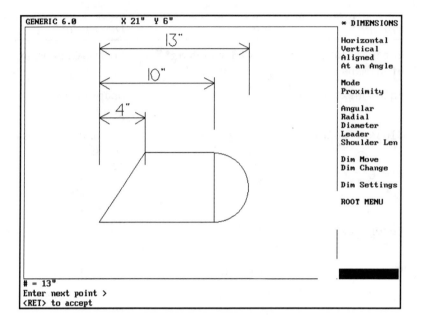

Figure 13.12:

Cumulative horizontal linear dimension.

In the next exercise, you will use the Angular Dimension (AX) command to display the small-angle dimension. Before you finally place the dimension line, you are asked to move the cursor so that you can see how the CADD program can display the large-angle dimension line as well.

Using the Angular Dimension Command

Prompt	Input	Description
Command	**OO**	Undoes last action
Command	**UM** or pick Mode from side menu	Starts Dimension Mode command
(**Single**) Partitioned...	**S**	Selects single mode
Command	**AX** or pick Angular from side menu	Starts an angular dimension
Enter center point	**SC**	Snaps to closest point

Prompt	Input	Description
`Closest point to`	Pick left side of bottom horizontal line	Locates center point
`Enter point on first line`	Pick bottom horizontal line	First radius line
`Enter point on next line`	Pick top of angled line	Second radius line
`Radius # = 56.310`	Press Enter	Accepts calculated radius
`Place dimension`	Move cursor from a point inside the two lines to a point to the left; pick a point inside the two lines	Shows both radius dimension lines

Your angular dimension should be similar to the one in figure 13.13.

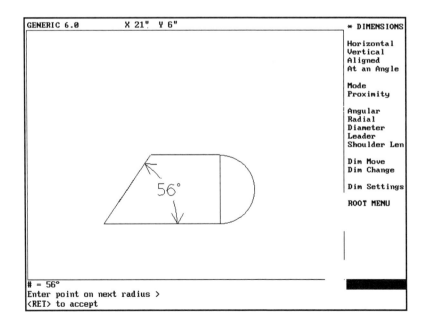

Figure 13.13:

An angular dimension.

Radial Dimension (RX)

The Radial Dimension command dimensions the radius of an arc or circle. Dimension Tolerance can be used with this command.

Select Radial from the DIMENSIONS menu or type **RX**. To use the command, you must select an arc or circle, then show the placement of the text. Radial Dimension displays the text inside or outside the arc (or circle), depending on the location you pick on-screen.

The following exercise takes you through this straightforward dimension command.

Using the Radial Dimension Command

Prompt	Input	Description
Command	**OO**	Undoes last action
Command	**RD**	Redraws screen
Command	**RX** or pick Radial from side menu	Starts Radial Dimension command
Select arc or circle	Pick the arc	Chooses the object
# = 3" > #	Press spacebar once, and then type **R**	Adds an R (for radius) to the dimension string
Place dimension	Move cursor to the left and right of arc; then pick a spot to the left of the arc	View the text placement options, and then place text

Your radial dimension should be similar to the one shown in figure 13.14.

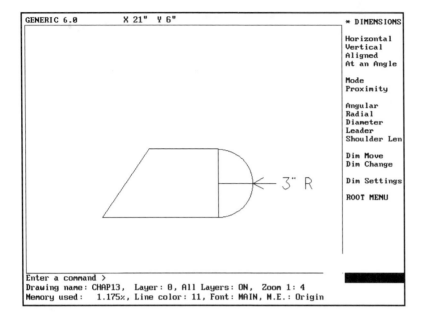

Figure 13.14:

A radial dimension.

Diameter Dimension (IX)

The Diameter Dimension command dimensions the diameter of an arc or circle. It will display a tolerance value or range, if required, by selecting the correct option in the Dimension Tolerance (UT) command.

To start Diameter Dimension, select Diameter from the DIMEN-SIONS menu or type **IX**. After you select an arc or circle, a default dimension is shown, which you can either accept or modify. The dimension text can be placed inside the arc or circle or it can be placed on the outside of the curve.

The Diameter and Radial Dimension commands follow parallel sequences. The next exercise is almost identical to the preceding exercise, except that it produces a diameter dimension.

Using the Diameter Dimension Command

Prompt	Input	Description
Command	**OO**	Undoes last action
Command	**IX** or pick Diameter from side menu	Starts Diameter Dimension command
Select arc or circle	Pick the arc	Chooses the object
# = 6" > #	Press spacebar once, and then type **Dia**	Adds Dia (for diameter) to the dimension string
Place dimension	Move cursor to the left and right of arc; then pick a spot to the left of the arc	View the text-placement options, and then place text

Your diameter dimension should be similar to the one in figure 13.15.

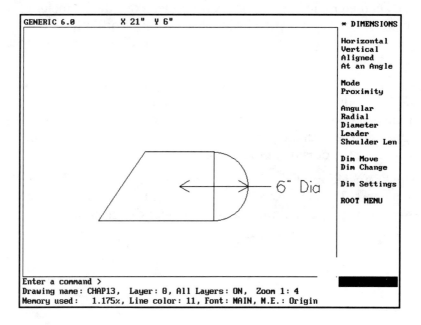

Figure 13.15:

A diameter dimension.

Dimension Leader (LE)

The Dimension Leader command enables you not only to add a note to a drawing but also to point to the object to which the note refers. The dimension leader entity is composed of an arrowhead, an angled line (also called the leader), a horizontal line known as the shoulder, and the text itself.

The Dimension Leader command is on the DIMENSIONS menu and also can be started by typing **LE**. At the beginning of the command, you are prompted to enter the desired text. To draw the leader, you must pick a starting point, a terminal point, and indicate the shoulder direction.

Shoulder Length (LL)

The Shoulder Length command, a modifier of the Dimension Leader command, adjusts the length of the leader shoulder. It follows the Leader command in the DIMENSIONS menu, or can be accessed by typing **LL** and then typing the size of the leader shoulder.

Using the Dimension Leader and Shoulder Length Commands

Prompt	Input	Description
Command	**OO**	Undoes action
Command	**LL** or pick Shoulder Length from side menu	Starts Shoulder Length command
Change leader shoulder size (1")	**3** shoulder to 3"	Changes length of
Enter string	**TOP**	Enters text label
Enter leader starting point	Pick top horizontal line	Starts leader line

continues

Prompt	Input	Description
Enter leader terminal point	Pick point above and to left of object	Ends leader line
Enter a point indicating shoulder direction	Pick to the left	Enables text string to be to the left or right

Your dimension leader should be similar to the one in figure 13.16.

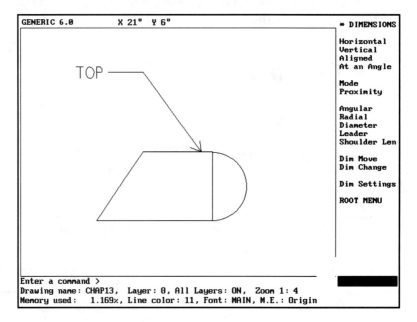

Figure 13.16:

The dimension leader.

Dimension Move (UV)

Dimension Move is a unique and powerful command. With it, both the dimension line and the text can be moved. Moving the entire dimension enables you to adjust the dimensioning positions for easier reading.

Using the Dimension Move Command

Prompt	Input	Description
Command	**OO**	Undoes last action
Command	**LX** or pick Linear from side menu	Starts a linear dimension
Enter first point	**SC**	Snaps to closest point
Closest point to	Pick left side of bottom horizontal line	Selects left side
Enter next point	**SM**	Snaps to midpoint of arc
Midpoint of	Pick midpoint of arc	Selects midpoint
# = 13" > #	Press Enter	Accepts dimension size without additional text
Enter location of dimension	Pick a location on screen above object	Locates dimension line
Command	**UV** or pick Dim Move from side menu	Starts Dimension Move command
Point to portion of dimension to move	Pick text	Selects text to be moved
Enter new dimension point	Pick a point to the left	Moves text to left
Point to portion of dimension to move	Pick the dimension line	Selects dimension line to be moved
Enter new dimension point	Pick a point above	Moves dimension line up

The moved dimension should look like the one in figure 13.17.

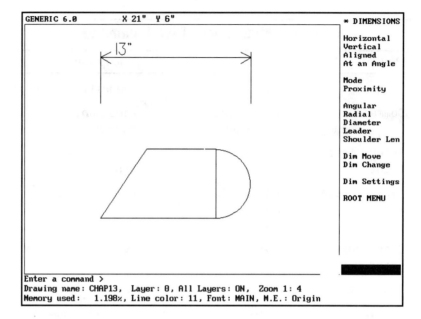

Figure 13.17:

Dimension Move command.

Dimensioning Setup

You have considerable control over the appearance of the dimension string. Arrow size and type, text height, font, placement, dimension layer, and color can all be altered to suit your needs. You can even hide different elements of the dimension string.

In earlier versions of Generic CADD, the commands to control Dimension Settings were listed in a separate menu (called DIM SETTINGS) off the DIMENSIONING menu. In version 6, this separate menu has been eliminated; it is replaced by a new command called, naturally, Dimension Settings. The two-letter shortcuts for many of these settings are the same as in previous versions and also are listed here.

Dimension Display

The Dimension Display command controls a series of toggles related to the display of different parts of a dimensioning line.

You can use the command to hide the left or right arrow, the dimension line, the left or right extension line, or the dimension text.

Dimension Display can be selected from the Dim Settings entry in the DIMENSIONING menu, by using the two-letter command **US**, or by using the shortcut **DD**. After this is done, the different toggles show at the bottom of the screen. You can change a toggle by typing the appropriate uppercase letter (or number) or by selecting the word with the cursor.

Every dimension placed after you change the Dimension Display settings reflects any changes you made. Dimensions placed before the changes are not affected.

Arrows

The Arrows command enables you to select the type, angle, length, and location (pointing inside or outside) of arrowheads. As with Dimension Display, any changes to the settings affect only dimensions and leaders placed after the changes are made.

To change any arrows-related setting, select the Arrows option from the Dimension Settings command, or type the shortcut **AR**. You can select the **T**ype, **A**ngle, **L**ength, l**O**cation, or the display of each arrow (**1** for left arrow, **2** for right arrow) by typing the appropriate uppercase letter (or by selecting it with the cursor). When you change the type, you choose between normal-**C**losed, normal-**O**pen, normal-**F**illed, **N**otched, circle-**U**nfilled, circle-f**I**lled, or **S**lash. The angle of the lines that form the arrowhead mat be set to any angle between –360 and 360 degrees. The length option gives you the chance to change the length of the arrowheads. Location is a toggle for inside or outside arrows.

Dimension Text Settings

All the settings and options for dimensioning text are available under two sections of the Dimension Settings (US) command. For all the settings except font selection, the older two-letter command

DT (for Dimension Text) is available also. After you type **UST** or **DT**, the choices are the same in either command.

Font

At the Dimension Settings prompt line, type **F** to select a font for dimensioning text. Every font you have installed on the hard drive is available. In reality, only a few of them should even be considered. The best fonts for dimensioning are Main, Text, Romans, Engineer, and Architek.

In earlier versions of Generic CADD, the Font Selection command was used to select the font for all three types of text that can appear in a drawing (drawing text, attribute text, dimension text). In version 6, each type of text has its own selection command grouped within the appropriate category.

Placement

Placement refers to the location of dimensioning text in relation to the dimension line. Press **T** for the Text settings list, then **P** for Placement. This is a toggle command. The options are above the line or in-line.

Direction

Direction controls whether text is parallel to the dimension line or always remains horizontal. Press **T** for the Text settings list, then **D** for Direction. The toggle switches between aligned and horizontal.

Centered

Centered determines whether text is centered along the dimension line. The command toggles on and off. Press **T** for the Text settings list, then **C** for Centered.

Size

Text in a dimension may be set at any size. If you do not have a standard to follow, a good setting for text size is to make it the same as the length of the arrowheads, and to have both set at 75 percent of the size of regular drawing text (as used for labels, bill of material lists, and title blocks). Press **T** for the Text settings list, then **Z** for siZe.

Offsets

There are two kinds of offsets to be adjusted. The In-line offset is the gap between the text and the dimension line caused when the text sits in the middle of the dimension line. Adjusting this command sets the size of the gap. A good rule of thumb is to set this offset to the same size as your dimensioning text. The Above-line offset is the space between the text and the dimension line when the text sits above the dimension line. A good rule of thumb is to set this distance at one-half the size of your dimension text.

Tolerance

Tolerance was covered earlier in this chapter; refer to that discussion.

Dimension Layer

The Dimension Layer command enables you to choose the layer on which dimensions will be placed. Press **L** for Layer at the Dimension Settings prompt line, then type the layer number or select it from the menu if the long list is visible. Putting dimensions on their own layer is important. You can choose not to print or plot the dimensions by temporarily hiding their layer. Set All Layers Edit (AL) to Off to avoid accidentally snapping to parts of a dimension when you edit the drawing, or accidentally including the dimension when you select the object to be edited.

Dimension Color (CS)

When selected, Dimension Color enables you to set the colors for lines, text, dimensions, attributes, hatches, and fills.

Summary

Dimensioning has many options because of the two major types of drafting styles—architectural and mechanical. All other styles fit somewhere between these two extremes. Generic CADD does an excellent job of catering to the varying needs of drafters and drafting techniques.

Dimensioning does, in fact, add dimension to your drawings. With dimension commands, components that make up the drawing are labeled explicitly. The power of dimension-related commands is that they provide concrete data: the length of a line, the location of a circle's center, or the number of degrees in an angle.

The basic dimensioning command is Linear Dimension (LX), which dimensions the distance between two points. As part of this labeling process, dimension lines, arrowheads, extension lines, and text are all used to indicate size.

Linear Dimension is affected by the dimension variables, particularly Dimension Direction and Dim Mode. These options allow you to dimension in different directions and to dimension more than one object at a time. Because CADD provides so much flexibility in the placement and appearance of dimensions, this chapter covers many commands and options designed to provide the exact look you need.

After you are comfortable with dimensioning commands and concepts, think about combining that knowledge with the power of menus and macros (covered in Chapters 18 and 19). These advanced approaches streamline the drafting process and your personal drafting style. Macros can turn toggle commands, such as Proximity Fixed, off and on and set the extension size to different lengths. So much to do, so little time—but at least with CADD, you can do more in less time.

Attributes

L ike their counterparts created at the drafting table, Generic CADD drawings often are used for recording and storing information. Because every line and object can be drawn with precision, the final drawing can be used as a visual database. Questions like "How many 2x8 floor joists are there?" and "How many feet of 12-gauge wiring are needed for this project?" can be answered by consulting the CADD drawing. Thus, the visual representation of objects in Generic CADD becomes a database of physical information and quantities.

Jobs such as the design of objects and the creation of working drawings are only a few of many tasks facing the average Generic CADD user. Some common tasks include creating job estimates, compiling a bill of materials, and maintaining inventory levels. Much of the information required for these jobs relates back to the objects depicted in the CADD drawings. But such facts as item number, price, brand names, hours of labor to produce, weight, and markup percentage do not lend themselves to being drawn the way size and quantity do. These pieces of information are nongraphic by nature, yet they also relate to items depicted in CADD drawings. Without a way to attach these kinds of information to the objects, a CADD drawing is an incomplete source of information.

Fortunately, Generic CADD includes a way to unite the graphic and nongraphic data generated by a drawing project. By using features called *attributes*, nongraphic data can be attached to objects in the drawing and made available for a variety of purposes.

Understanding the Way Attributes Work

Generic CADD attributes enable you to attach data to components in a drawing. The information can be prepared in advance and attached at will to components in the drawing. Attributes also may be created "on the fly" at any time and attached immediately to a component.

This book has implied that Generic CADD is a database-management program—which is not exactly correct. Attributes, in particular, are similar to the records generated by a database-management program, but the comparison does not hold if it is stretched too far. To help you better understand the uses and limitations of attributes, the following example compares the use of a database-management program and Generic CADD for recording information about a farmer.

Just last week the county tax collector drove by, looking at farms in the area. When he passed the land belonging to our farmer, the tax collector muttered to no one in particular, "There he is, standing in a field; he is of value to us. We have a record of that man. We keep it in our file." Although this tax collector is a bit eccentric, his muttering happens to be a good description of the database-management program the tax collector uses.

When the tax collector said, "There he is, standing in a field; he is of value to us," he was referring to the relationship between the farmer's name and its place in the tax-collection database. The farmer's name is a piece of information. A single piece of information, called a *value*, is stored in a *field* in a database program. Other individual pieces of information (individual *values*) about the farmer—date of birth, address, telephone number, and so forth—are kept in separate *fields*. For every farmer in the county, the tax collector uses the same *fields*; the *values* change for each farmer.

Next, the tax collector said, "We have a record of that man." All of the fields that describe the farmer, with the values filled in, are stored as one *record*. If the information in the computer were printed, it would fit on one sheet of paper and would serve as a *record* of what the county knows about the farmer.

Finally, Mr. Taxman said of the record, "We keep it in our file." All of the records of all the farmers are kept in one computer *file*. Fields filled with values, records, and files—these are the essential elements of a computerized database.

Compare this to Generic CADD, specifically to attributes. A *field* in Generic CADD would be an *entity*, such as a line, a circle, or a component. As you draw, you provide *values* to these fields. If the tax collector were to use Generic CADD to keep a record of the farmer, he would start by drawing a silhouette of the farmer (probably to real scale). The silhouette of the man can be considered a *field*; the height assigned to the outline, the *value*. If the tax collector labeled the outline with the farmer's name, the line of text could be considered another *field*, with the name typed in that line considered the *value*.

All the different fields reside together in one particular Generic CADD drawing. When saved on disk, it is referred to as a *file*. As for the level of record—perhaps each layer in the drawing is a record, or perhaps each object. As you can see, the comparison is not perfect. But then, we are dealing with only the visual representation of data at this point. The following section discusses the use of attributes with nonvisual data.

If the tax collector were forced to use Generic CADD as his only database, it would be very limiting. Adding more text would be unwieldy, creating a huge file. By creating an attribute to attach to the outline of the farmer, however, the tax collector can store much more data with the drawing and have it available for retrieval. The attribute, like the database, is made up of fields. *NAME:* would be one field; *TELEPHONE:* would be another. For each farmer, the tax collector can attach an attribute to the outline, filling in the values on each farmer as the attribute is placed. Figure 14.1 shows two silhouettes, representing two farmers. An attribute is attached to each.

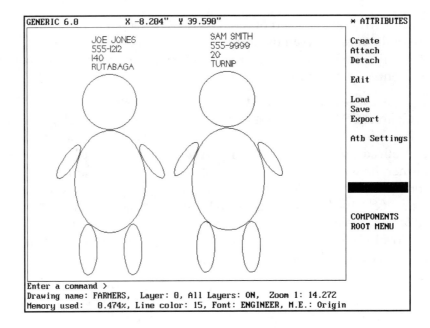

```
        JOE JONES           SAM SMITH              Create
        555-1212            555-9999               Attach
        140                 20                     Detach
        RUTABAGA            TURNIP
                                                   Edit

                                                   Load
                                                   Save
                                                   Export

                                                   Atb Settings




                                                   COMPONENTS
                                                   ROOT MENU
```

```
Enter a command >
Drawing name: FARMERS,  Layer: 0, All Layers: ON,  Zoom 1: 14.272
Memory used:    0.474%, Line color: 15, Font: ENGINEER, M.E.: Origin
```

Figure 14.1:

Each outline is a component with an attribute attached.

In this example, the fields are the following:

> NAME: ACREAGE:
>
> TELEPHONE: MAIN CROP:

The data assigned to each field are the values. In Generic CADD, the set of fields is called an *attribute*, not a record. The same attribute (the same set of fields) is used for each farmer, like a template. The attribute "template" was attached to the component when it was created. Generic CADD prompts the user to fill in the values each time the component is placed in a drawing.

Attributes have fields that hold values, and one attribute is the equivalent of one record in a database-management program. Generic CADD attributes also can be assembled into a collection of attributes, equivalent to a collection of records in a database file. Using a command called Attribute Export (XA), you can select some of the attributes on the screen or all the attributes in a drawing, and save the data to a file. The file can be created in either of two formats: the first format can be read by Lotus 1-2-3 and compatible spreadsheets (WK1); the second format is designed for use by programs that read comma-separated ASCII files (ASC).

This particular version of ASCII text also is known as Comma-Separated-Values, or CSV. Most database programs read the CSV format, as do some programs in other application categories. You occasionally may need to change the extension of your exported attribute files from ASC to CSV so that the program importing the files recognizes them. Virtually all word processors can read comma-separated ASCII files, and experienced programmers can easily write their own programs to take advantage of this data.

Creating and Placing Attributes

This section offers a step-by-step exercise for creating and using attributes. To follow the exercise, you need to use some of the components distributed with each copy of Generic CADD. If you removed the components from your hard drive, you can either restore them by reinstalling Generic CADD or take a few minutes to create some simple components.

All attribute commands are in the ATTRIBUTES menu, which branches off the COMPONENTS menu (you will not find AT-TRIBUTES listed in the ROOT menu). Most of the two-letter commands for attributes start with the letter *A*, but there are exceptions.

Before you can create and place attributes, you must first know what kinds of data you are working with, and then you must design an attribute to match. This exercise creates an attribute template, which is placed on four bathroom fixtures. To keep it simple, only four fields—ITEM:, COLOR:, STOCK #:, and COST$:—are recorded. Three of the fixtures are components supplied with Generic CADD; you draw the fourth fixture. By drawing a new component, you can use the option to preattach an attribute to a component at the time the component is created.

To do the exercises in this chapter, you can either place three components shipped with Generic CADD 6.0, or draw three components to represent the three shown in the illustrations accompanying the exercises. If you installed all the components that come with Generic CADD 6.0, use the ones available in the C:\CADD6\CMP\ARCHITEC\PLUMBING or

C:\CADD6\CMP\ARCHITEC\BATHROOM directories.
Figure 14.2 shows the list of components available in
C:\CADD6\CMP\ARCHITEC\PLUMBING.

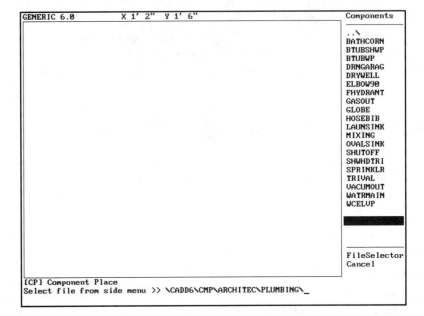

Figure 14.2:

List of components available on disk.

The components available to you will vary in detail from the ones
shown here, which have been kept simple for the sake of clarity
(see fig. 14.3). The components you draw or place from disk do
not have to look exactly like these. Just remember which of your
components represents each one in the illustrations.

> **NOTE** If you did not choose to have Generic CADD
> copy the architectural components to disk when
> you installed CADD, you may do so now. Run
> the INSTALL program on disk #1 of your Generic CADD
> 6.0 disks. Answer all the questions about the directories to
> match your existing directory structure. When you reach the
> screen that enables you to choose which parts of the pro-
> gram are to be installed, put a NO by every choice except
> architectural symbols. Use the arrow keys to move among
> the choices, and use the spacebar to switch between YES
> and NO for each of the choices.

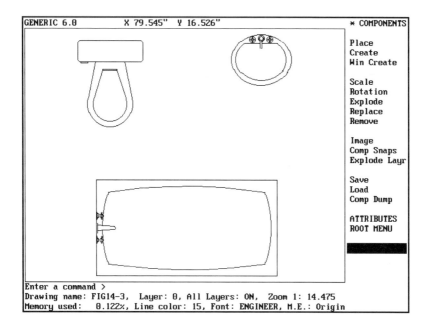

Figure 14.3:

Sample components for attributes exercise.

Allow room on the screen for a fourth component, which you will draw by following the next set of instructions. First, however, you must create the attribute that will be preattached to this new component.

Attribute Create (AC)

Use the Attribute Create command to define an attribute that will be attached to one or more components. The attribute name must follow the rules of DOS file names (maximum of eight characters; certain characters not allowed) because it is saved on disk as a separate file, like a component or a drawing file.

An attribute can have as many as 128 fields. The field names and their default values (or the values later assigned to the fields) also can contain as many as 128 characters. For each field in an attribute, Generic CADD asks for a default value. You may enter a value or leave the value blank by pressing Enter.

When an attribute is attached to a component, it can be set so that the attribute is visible or not visible. Because the field names and their default values are displayed if the attribute is visible, you may want to keep the field names brief.

Follow these steps to create a new attribute:

Creating a New Attribute

Prompt	Input	Description
Command	Move menu bar to ATTRIBUTES and press second mouse button or Home	Switches to ATTRIBUTES menu
Command	Move menu bar to Create and press second mouse button or Home	Selects Attribute Create command
Enter attribute name	**BATHROOM**	Names the new attribute BATHROOM
Enter first label	**ITEM**	Names the first field ITEM (see fig. 14.4)
Enter default ITEM	Press Enter	Leaves value blank
Enter next label	**COLOR**	Names the second field COLOR
Enter default COLOR	**WHITE**	Gives default value of WHITE for this field; value can be changed each time the attribute is attached to a component
Enter next label	**STOCK #**	Names the third field STOCK #

Prompt	Input	Description
Enter default STOCK #	**XXXX-000**	Gives the default value for STOCK #, a place-holder that reflects future stock codes of four letters and three numbers
Enter next label	**COST$**	Names the fourth field COST$
Enter default COST$	**100.00**	Puts in a value to show the correct format for future entries
Enter next label	Press **F10**	Finishes attribute definition; CADD prompt line reads Attribute has been defined

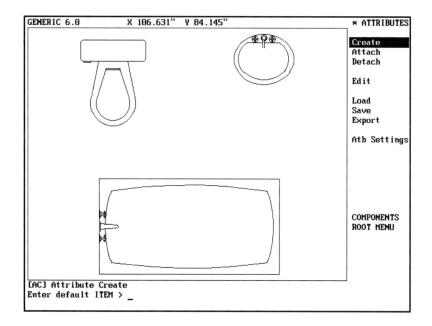

Figure 14.4:

Generic CADD asks for a default value for each field.

For the next exercise, draw one more object, a circle with three
ellipses, to represent a drain cover. Save it as a component; later,
you will preattach an attribute to it.

Drawing a Circle with Three Ellipses

Prompt	Input	Description
Command	Move cursor to center of screen	Selects center of screen as location for cover
Command	C2	Selects Two-point Circle command
Enter center of circle	Press Enter	Places center of circle
Enter a point on the circle	Nudge cursor in any direction, and type 6"	Uses direct distance to set radius of circle
Command	ZW	Selects Zoom Window command (see fig. 14.5)
Place window	Draw window around circle	Gives close up of circle
Command	EP	Selects Ellipse command
Enter start of major axis	Move cursor to upper left quarter of circle and click	Starts ellipse in upper left portion of circle
Enter end of major axis	Drag cursor down and left, then press Enter to set end of major axis	Sets length of ellipse (see fig. 14.6)
Enter an endpoint of the minor axis	Move crosshairs slightly away from center of major axis and press Enter	Sets width of ellipse
True or Constructed ellipse?	T	Makes true ellipse (not one made from arcs)

Prompt	Input	Description
Command	**RC**	Selects Radial Copy command
...Object...	**O**	Selects Object option
Pick object	Move cursor onto ellipse and click	Selects ellipse to copy
Window, Object...	Press Enter	Ends selection
Enter an axis point	**SN**	Snap to Arc Center (see fig. 14.7)
Center of	Move cursor onto any part of circle and click	Snaps to center of circle
Enter total degrees to span	**360**	Copies objects in a full circular pattern
Enter total number of items in span	**3**	Creates three ellipses, including original (see fig. 14.8)

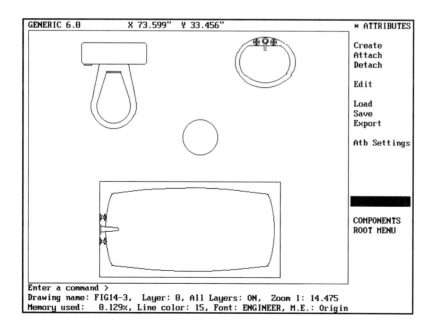

Figure 14.5:

Circle drawn in the center of the screen.

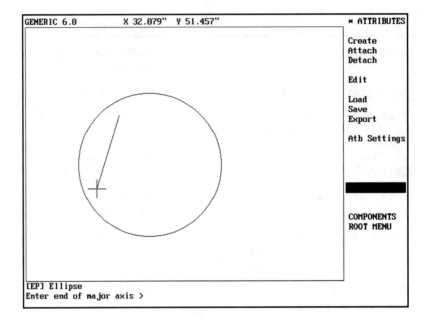

Figure 14.6:

End of the major axis set.

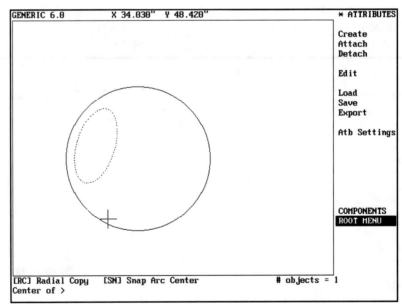

Figure 14.7:

Snap to Arc Center locates the center of the circle.

468

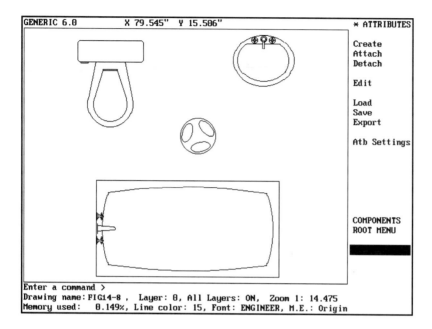

```
GENERIC 6.0        X 79.545"  Y 15.506"            * ATTRIBUTES

                                                   Create
                                                   Attach
                                                   Detach

                                                   Edit

                                                   Load
                                                   Save
                                                   Export

                                                   Atb Settings




                                                   COMPONENTS
                                                   ROOT MENU



Enter a command >
Drawing name:FIG14-8 ,  Layer: 0, All Layers: ON,  Zoom 1: 14.475
Memory used:   0.149%, Line color: 15, Font: ENGINEER, M.E.: Origin
```

Figure 14.8:

*Radial Copy adds
two more ellipses.*

Now make the drain cover a component and attach the attribute
defined earlier. After the attribute is attached, Generic CADD
gives you the option of displaying the attribute on-screen. Con-
clude the exercise by displaying the attribute next to the component, being careful not to obstruct the drain.

Displaying the Attribute On-Screen

Prompt	Input	Description
Command	**ZA**	Selects Zoom All command
Command	**CC**	Selects Component Create command
Window...	**W**	Selects Window option
Place window	Draw selection window around circle with ellipses	Selects object just drawn to save as a component

continues

Prompt	Input	Description
`Window...`	Press Enter	End selection process; `# objects = 4`
`Enter component name`	**DRAIN**	Names new component DRAIN (see fig. 14.9)
`Enter component reference point`	**SN**	Snaps to center of arc
`Center of`	Move cursor to any part of circle and click	Selects center point of circle as new component's reference point
`...Attach attribute...`	**A**	Attaches attribute to new component (see fig. 14.10)
`Select Attributes from side menu`	Move menu bar to BATHROOM and press second mouse button or Home	Selects an attribute defined earlier
`Display Attribute On oFf`	**O**	Attribute is displayed with component (see fig. 14.11)
`Display default attribute label On oFf`	**F**	Attribute's label will not show on-screen
`Enter default placement location`	Move cursor and attached box to position just below drain, and click	Sets location of the attribute
`Replace original`	**R**	Replaces current drawing of drain with component made from it

Prompt	Input	Description
Enter ITEM	**DRAIN**	Selects DRAIN as value for ITEM field
Enter COLOR	**BLACK**	Selects BLACK as value for COLOR field
Enter STOCK #	**BATP-013**	Selects BATP-013 as value for STOCK # field
Enter COST$	**4.95**	Selects 4.95 as value for COST$ field
Enter placement location	Press Enter	Accepts previously defined default location attribute placement
Command	(No action required)	Attribute appears on-screen just below new component

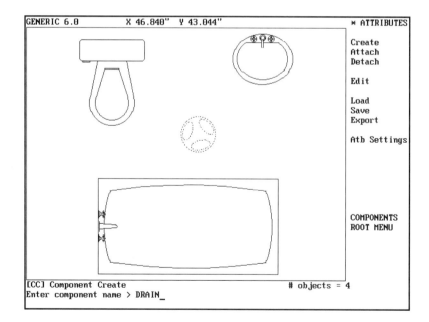

Figure 14.9:
Naming the object.

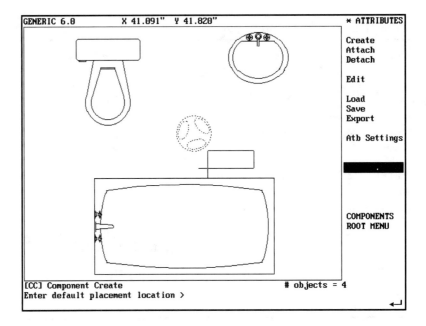

Figure 14.10:

Attribute placed so that it is readable and nonobstructive.

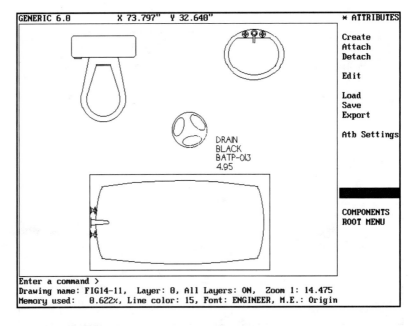

Figure 14.11:

New component with the attribute next to it.

Attribute Attach (AT)

After an attribute is defined, a copy of the attribute can be attached to a component at any time. In the preceding exercise, you attached a copy of the BATHROOM attribute to the floor drain cover; now use the Attribute Attach command to link data with the other components on the screen.

In regular practice, you probably would check and adjust the settings for items such as the color and size of the attribute text. These commands are explained in the next section. If your copy of the attribute attached to the floor drain cover doesn't look like the one illustrated here, refer to the discussion of attribute settings, and then return here to continue attaching attributes.

Using Attribute Attach To Link Data

Prompt	Input	Description
Command	Move menu bar to Attach and press second mouse button or Home	Selects Attribute Attach command
Select a component to attach attribute to	Move cursor to sink (top right) and click	Attaches attribute to sink
Select Attribute from side menu	Move menu bar to BATHROOM and press second mouse button or Home	Attaches copy of BATHROOM attribute
Enter ITEM	**ECONOMY OSINK**	Selects ECONOMY OSINK as value for the ITEM field (see fig. 14.12)
Enter COLOR	Press Enter	Accepts default value WHITE as value for COLOR field

continues

Prompt	Input	Description
Enter STOCK #	**BATS-057**	Selects BATS-057 as value for STOCK # field, replacing previous value
Enter COST$	**19.95**	Selects 19.95 as value for COST$ field, replacing previous value
Display Attribute **O**n oFf	**O**	Attribute is displayed along with component
Display Attribute On o**F**f	**F**	Label will not appear
Enter placement location	Move cursor just beneath sink and click	Places attribute directly below sink (see fig. 14.13)
Command	**AT**	Selects Attribute Attach command
Select a component to attach	Move cursor onto toilet and click	Selects toilet as next component for Attribute Attach command
Select Attributes from side menu	BATHROOM attribute should appear in prompt line; if so, press Enter. If not, select BATHROOM through the menu bar or type in at the prompt line	Selects BATHROOM attribute
Enter ITEM	**ECONOMY WATER SAVER**	Selects ECONOMY WATER SAVER as value for ITEM field
Enter COLOR	Press Enter	Accepts default value WHITE as value for COLOR field

Prompt	Input	Description
Enter STOCK #	**BATT-001**	Selects BATT-001 as value for STOCK # field
Enter COST$	**49.95**	Selects 49.95 as value for COST$ field
Display Attribute On oFf	**O**	Attribute is displayed along with component
Display Attribute On oFf	**F**	Label will not appear
Enter placement location	Move cursor just beneath bowl of toilet and click	Places attribute directly below toilet
Command	Press spacebar	Repeats last command, Attribute Attach
Select a component to attach	Move cursor to bathtub and click	Selects bathtub as next component for Attribute Attach command
Select Attributes from side menu	BATHROOM should appear in prompt line; if so, press Enter. If not, select BATHROOM through the menu bar or type in at the prompt line	Selects BATHROOM attribute again
Enter ITEM	**BUDGET TUB**	Selects BUDGET TUB as value for ITEM field
Enter COLOR	**PINK**	Selects PINK as value for COLOR field, replacing previous value
Enter STOCK #	**BATB-127**	Selects BATB-127 as value for STOCK # field, replacing previous value

continues

475

Prompt	Input	Description
Enter COST$	**199.95**	Selects 199.95 as value for COST$ field, replacing previous value
Display Attribute **O**n o**F**f	**O**	Displays attribute along with component
Display Attribute **O**n o**F**f	**F**	Label will not appear
Enter placement location	Move cursor toward center of tub and click	Places attribute inside tub; figure 14.14 shows all components with attributes attached

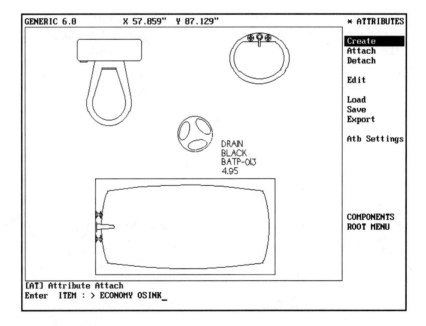

Figure 14.12:

Values entered for each field.

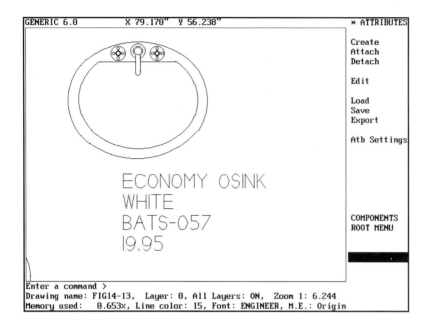

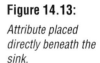

Figure 14.13:

Attribute placed directly beneath the sink.

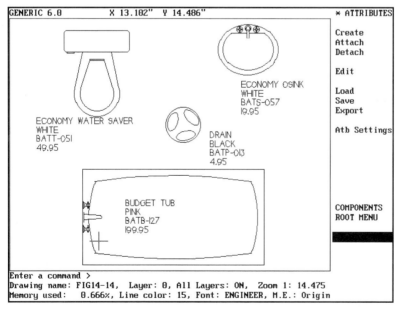

Figure 14.14:

All four components with attributes attached.

Attribute Save (SA)

As you may recall from the discussion of components, merely creating a component does not mean that it is safely stored on disk—saving is a separate process. The same is true for attributes. Although the BATHROOM attribute is placed in this drawing four times, it is not yet stored on disk as an attribute. To make it available for use in other drawings, it must be saved. Generic CADD automatically adds the file extension ATB when it saves attributes. Unless you specify otherwise, Generic CADD saves attributes to the default directory used to store components. (For most users, this is the C:\CADD6\CMP directory.)

In the next exercise, you save the attribute.

Saving an Attribute

Prompt	Input	Description
Command	**SA**	Starts the Save command
(Save options appear)	**T**	Selects Save Attribute options
Select Attributes from side menu	Move menu bar to BATHROOM and press second mouse button or Home	Selects attribute BATHROOM
Save file as	Prompt line should show default directory for components with attribute BATHROOM listed.	Saves attribute to drive and directory as indicated

Press Enter to save BATHROOM to default directory. To save to a different drive and directory, type the new path, type the file name, and then press Enter.

Attribute Load (LO)

As you build your collection of attributes, you probably will want to use them again in other drawings. Use the Load command, with the Attribute option, to load one or more attributes into active memory.

If you need to load more than one attribute for use with a particular drawing, use the File Selection option, which enables you to mark more than one file for selection. Loading several attributes at once enables you to select attributes from the side menu as you need them, instead of waiting until the first occurrence of the attribute to load it into memory.

Attribute Detach (DE)

Attributes add to the size and complexity of a drawing. When you no longer want attributes attached to one or more of the components in a drawing, use the Attribute Detach command. It works like a single-choice editing command. When you type **DE** at the prompt or select Detach from the ATTRIBUTES menu, you are prompted for the attribute to detach. Move the cursor onto the attribute to delete and press Enter or click. The attribute disappears.

Detaching an attribute from a component does not erase the attribute from active memory or from the disk, nor does it alter the existing values of other placements of the same attribute. It simply gets rid of the one attribute you select.

Attribute Edit (AE)

As some wag once said, "Just about the time you get two ends to meet, somebody moves the middle." In other words, things are always changing. If the data associated with a component changes after you attach an attribute to it, you can edit the attribute to maintain its accuracy. It also is possible to edit the template version of an attribute, changing the default values so that all future placements of this particular attribute will be up-to-date.

When you type **AE** for Attribute Edit or select Edit from the ATTRIBUTE menu, the prompt asks you to select whether you will edit a definition (the "template" version of the attribute, with default values), or edit a placement (an attribute already attached to a component). Type **D** for Definition or **P** for Placement, as appropriate.

If you choose to edit the definition, you are asked to select the attribute to be edited; select it from the menu or type the name at the prompt line. Generic CADD prompts you to accept or edit each field name and value. To accept an entry, press Enter; to make a change, type the corrections and press Enter. Use the up- and down-arrow keys to move quickly through the fields and values. You need not go through every field and every default value. After you have made all the necessary changes, press **F10** to complete the editing session. If you realize that you prefer not to make any changes, press Esc to exit the Attribute Edit command.

If you choose to edit a particular placement of an attribute, Generic CADD asks you to pick the appropriate component. Next, you are asked whether you want to edit the fields in this attribute or change the display status. If you type **F** for edit Fields, you are prompted to accept or change fields and values, as if you were editing the definition. Press Enter to accept current fields and values; type in changes and then press Enter to edit the fields and values. Press **F10** to finish; press Esc to abort the session. If you decide to make no changes, press Enter.

The Attribute Edit command's Display default option is a toggle; selecting this option switches the existing value (from off to on, from on to off).

Using Attribute Settings (AS)

Like text, components, and dimensions, attributes appear in a specified size, font, color, and rotation. Each option of the Attribute Settings command controls how attributes look.

The Attribute Settings (AS) command is used to set the appearance and function of attributes. If you used Attributes with version 5.0 of Generic CADD, you may notice that this command has changed. Functions that formerly were given separate commands are now included as options in the Attributes Settings command.

When you type **AS** or select Settings from the ATTRIBUTES menu, the options appear at the bottom of the screen (see fig. 14.15).

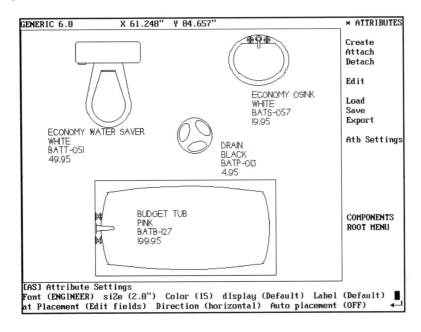

Figure 14.15:

The prompt line when Attribute Settings is in use.

Here are descriptions of all the options. If you need to use any of them, follow the steps listed for each option. Many of the options are toggles. Once you select the toggle, its setting flips to the opposite choice.

F**ont**: In version 5.0, a single font was used for both attributes and dimensions. To give attributes their own font, use this option. Press **F** and select the font.

siZe: This option controls the size of text when attributes are visible in the drawing. For the sake of clarity, the attributes depicted in this chapter are larger than you might normally want them to be in a drawing. Press **Z** to set the size you require. The default size is 1". Don't forget that you can use

481

the Like command (=) to set the size of attribute text, if you want it to match the size of an object already in the drawing. If the size of attribute text is changed after some attributes have been placed in the drawing, only newly placed attributes display the new text size; the size of existing attribute text does not change.

Color: This option sets the color of attribute text in the drawing. Press **C** and select a color.

dIsplay: When attributes are first defined, you are asked to choose whether they should appear in the drawing when attached to a component. If you use a variety of attributes, some may have a default setting On (visible), others a default setting oFf (not visible). The dIsplay option can override the default status of every attribute in a drawing. You can turn all attributes on, off, or simply let them be displayed according to their default status.

Label: Label works the same way as the dIsplay option, except that it controls only the attribute's label (name). You can set all labels on, off, or let them be displayed according to their default status.

at Placement: This option enables you to choose whether the default values in an attribute are accepted automatically as the values for the new placement, or whether Generic CADD prompts you for new values each time an attribute is attached to a component.

Direction: This option enables you to choose whether attributes that are made visible are horizontal or set in the drawing at the same angle of rotation as the component. Type **D** to switch between the two choices.

Auto placement: This option controls the placement of attributes that were preattached when the component was created. When Auto placement is on, the attribute location given when the component was created is accepted automatically. When Auto placement is off, you are prompted to select a location for the attribute, even though you designated one when you created the component and attached the attribute. Type **A** to switch between the two choices.

Figure 14.15 shows the prompt line when Attribute Settings is in use. To change any of these values, move the prompt-line cursor over the choice and click or type the highlighted letter to toggle the option.

Extracting Information from Attributes

It is not uncommon for Generic CADD to enter a professional's life through the back door. A contractor or consulting engineer may buy a computer to take care of the books and then discover the value of computer-aided design and drafting. If this has happened to you, you probably are using programs that can manipulate the same data as attributes. Using the Attribute Export (XA) command, you can pass the information from the attributes in a drawing to other programs. The new Bill of Material (BOM) program included with Generic CADD 6.0 also can make use of the data stored in attributes. BOM is covered in Chapter 15.

Attribute Export (XA)

The Attribute Export command uses the same selection process as multiple-object editing commands. When you type **XA** at the prompt or select Export from the ATTRIBUTES menu, the list of selection options appears in the prompt line, enabling you to select the exact attributes you need for a special report. Perhaps you have a large floor plan filled with components and attributes and you need to prepare a bid estimate for only one room. By using Attribute Export, you can select the components in that room and have the attribute data saved to a file.

The file created by the Attribute Export command can take either of the two file formats mentioned earlier: the WK1 file specification, for spreadsheets compatible with Lotus 1-2-3, and an ASCII-text format that database-management programs can read. As displayed in the prompt line, there are two choices for .WK1 files: rows or columns.

Follow these steps to save all the attributes in your drawing to the comma-separated ASCII format:

Saving Attributes to an ASCII File

Prompt	Input	Description
Command	Type **XA** or select Export from the ATTRIBUTES menu	Selects Attribute Export command
(Selection options appear)	**D**	Selects Drawing option; all components and their attached attributes are selected and highlighted
(Selection options appear)	Press Enter	Ends selection of attributes
Export format: ASCII ...	**A**	Selects ASCII as file format for attributes file about to be created (see fig. 14.16)
Save file as	**BATHROOM.ASC**	Saves attributes in file named BATH-ROOM.ASC
Command	(Do nothing)	File is created; components (and their attached attributes) are no longer highlighted

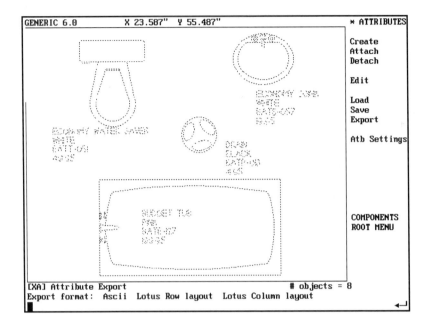

Figure 14.16:

Choose an export format.

The resulting file created by the Attribute Export command looks like the following:

```
/100,"DRAIN",    36.532291,    53.446995,    1.000000,    1.000000
/200,"BATHROOM"
/300,"ITEM","COLOR","STOCK#","COST$"
/400,"DRAIN","BLACK","BATP-013","4.95"
/100,"OSINK",    57.858589,    87.128868,    1.000000,    1.000000
/200,"BATHROOM"
/300,"ITEM","COLOR","STOCK#","COST$"
/400,"ECONOMY OSINK","WHITE","BATS-057","19.95"
/100,"TOILET",    7.821259,    85.122841,    1.000000,    1.000000
/200,"BATHROOM"
/300,"ITEM","COLOR","STOCK#","COST$"
/400,"ECONOMY WATER SAVER","WHITE","BATT-051","49.95"
/100,"STUB",    3.160999,    6.506025,    1.000000,    1.000000
/200,"BATHROOM"
/300,"ITEM","COLOR","STOCK#","COST$"
/400,"BUDGET TUB","PINK","BATB-127","199.95"
```

Each /100 item is the name of the component, followed by the coordinate location (two numbers), and the scale of the component (two numbers, for X-scale and Y-scale). Each /200 item is the name of the attribute. Each /300 item lists the names of the fields in the attribute, and each /400 item provides the values for each field. For more information on how this information is used, consult the reference manual of the database-management program you plan to use.

Summary

The addition of attributes to Generic CADD makes it possible to deal not only with the design and drafting of objects but also with the storage of data associated with these objects. CADD drawings identify real-world objects. Such drawings can depict size and quantity. Certain items of information (such as cost, stock number, weight, and terms of warranty) are nonvisual, however, and cannot easily be depicted. Attributes can be used to attach such nonvisual information to objects in a CADD drawing. The only restriction on the placement of attributes is that they must be attached to components rather than to individual lines.

The format of an attribute in Generic CADD is similar to that used by database-management programs. Individual pieces of data, known as values, are grouped together to form one attribute, which can be created before anything is drawn on the screen. You can then reuse the attribute, like a template, making changes to reflect new data accurately.

Attributes can be created "on the fly" as they are needed. They can be displayed on-screen, remain invisible, or be saved on a disk for repeated use. Like other forms of text available in Generic CADD, attributes can be edited to correct errors. The data can be extracted from a CADD drawing and used in other software. Both the WK1 format used by Lotus 1-2-3 and compatible spreadsheets, and the Comma-Separated-Values format (CSV) used by many database-management programs are supported by Generic CADD.

Using the Bill of Material Utility

Most people use Generic CADD to draw things they or someone else will build. After a drawing is completed, it becomes a guide for construction or manufacturing. On a basic level, certain things must happen as soon as the drawing is complete. A list of parts and supplies must be made, and the items on the list need to be purchased. Then construction can begin.

Until the release of version 6.0, Generic CADD helped you draw what you wanted to build, but then left you on your own for the other steps. Now, thanks to the new Bill of Material (BOM) utility program included with version 6.0, you have help. You can use Bill of Material to count objects in a CADD drawing and prepare a shopping list of those objects. The program can identify components and attributes in a CADD drawing and prepare lists based on them. And it can combine information from database and spreadsheet files utilizing the information gleaned from a CADD drawing.

Bill of Material is designed to create two types of lists. The first is the Bill of Material—a summary of items in a CADD drawing. A Bill of Material can show calculated totals and accepts simple formulas to calculate prices, total quantities, and so on. The second list is the Component Data Book (CDB)—a simplified version of the Bill of Material report. A Component Data Book can be created in the Bill of Material program or imported from a spreadsheet or database file. Think of it as a catalog or price book.

Bill of Material can be put to work in virtually every occupation in which CADD is used. Landscape designers can count how many plants and ornaments of each type are being used in a project, for instance. Home builders can quickly identify the cost of a project by running a Bill of Materials report on a home plan. By using components and attributes, tool designers can identify the materials and equipment they need. Engineers can make their CADD drawings more useful by developing BOMs and Component Data Books from their designs. For everyone who uses Generic CADD, the new Bill of Material utility makes the job of preparing written reports based on the information in a drawing much easier.

The Bill of Material program is a useful addition to Generic CADD, but do not expect too much. This limited utility program is designed for a specific purpose—to count items in a CADD drawing and list them, with totals. Do not expect to write fancy formulas as you would for a spreadsheet and do not look for elaborate sort routines for the data in a BOM or CDB. Although the Bill of Material has limited capabilities for each of these functions, the BOM utility is not as powerful as spreadsheets and database-management programs.

The prime benefit of the Bill of Material utility is that it enables you to import data from a drawing or another file. From then on, manipulation of the data is up to you. Most of the commands in the Bill of Material program should be considered as housekeeping functions, not as data processing. Moving columns, adding new columns, and extracting selected items for a report must be done manually. It is not possible to sift automatically through the data, using Boolean logic to find specific items. As you use the Bill of Material program, do not confuse data processing with housekeeping.

The Bill of Material utility should not be considered a substitute for a formal estimating program, such as those produced by a number of software developers. Many sole proprietors may find that the Bill of Material utility fits their needs; others may find the program limiting. If bidding on construction projects is a regular part of your business, a Bill of Material report is only part of what you need. Overhead expenses, labor costs, time factors, and conflicting projects also occupy your attention, and the Bill of Material program is not designed to address these issues.

Creating Drawings with BOM in Mind

The best way to take advantage of the Bill of Material program is to plan ahead. If you heed the lessons of Chapters 11 and 14 (Components and Attributes), you can create BOMs and CDBs with the Bill of Material utility. Make sure that you draw an item only once, saving it as a component to be used again and again. Take time to consider what bits of information are important about each component, and design one or more attributes to match. Consistently use your components and consistently attach attributes to them, even if you are not sure you will be creating a Bill of Material or a Component Data Book later.

The next hands-on example uses the design of a computer Local Area Network (LAN) to illustrate the use of Bill of Material. The drawing is included with every copy of Generic CADD 6.0 as LAN.CGD (see fig. 15.1). Load up the drawing and follow along at your computer to gain first-hand experience using the Bill of Material utility program.

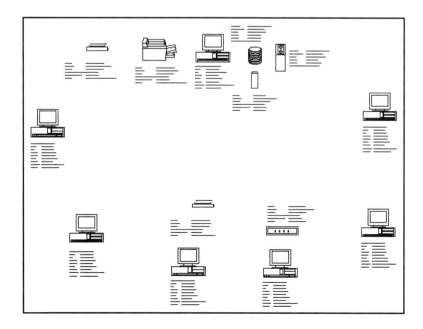

Figure 15.1:

LAN.CGD included with Generic CADD 6.0.

If the Generic CADD installation program copied all drawings and components onto your hard drive, you can simply load the drawing from the C:\CADD6\CGD directory (or other directory, if you changed the directory path for CADD). The components related to this drawing are in C:\CADD6\CMP\BUSINESS \LANS if the installation program copied them to your hard drive. If you did not install all drawings and components, you can run the installation program again and choose to have only drawings and components copied to your hard drive. You cannot simply copy LAN.GCD (and the components to be used) from your master disks. All the files on the distribution disks are in archived (compressed) form and must be removed from the archive format by the installation program.

After loading LAN.GCD into CADD, take a look at what is already in the drawing. Figure 15.2 shows a close-up of two of the devices in the drawing with their attached attributes.

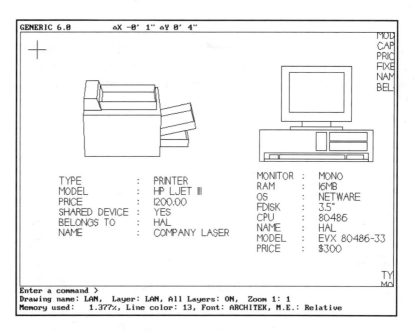

Figure 15.2:

Two devices with attributes attached and visible.

To create drawings that can take advantage of the Bill of Material, you need to have components and attributes loaded in CADD, ready for use. In this example you use one of the LAN components shipped with Generic CADD and modify one of the attributes already used in the drawing.

Placing a Component in LAN.GCD

Prompt	Input	Description
Command	**CP**	Starts the Component Place command; a directory list appears in the menu
(Select...	Click on Look on disk in menu	Places a component directly from disk
(Place...	Click on /BUSINESS, and then on /LANS	Moves down the directory path toward the LAN components
(Place...	Click on EPLOT-3	Selects EPLOT-3.CMP (see fig. 15.3)

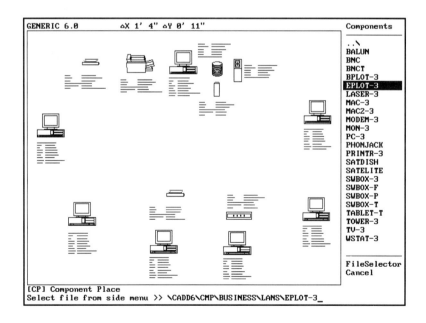

Figure 15.3:

Selecting a new component.

The scale of the devices already in the drawing is different from the scale of the LAN components on disk. The next step uses Component Scale (CZ) to change the size of the incoming component before it is placed in the drawing.

Changing the Scale of EPLOT-3.CMP

Prompt	Input	Description
Enter placement location	**CZ**	Starts the Component Scale command
Enter new X scale	**.1** and press Enter	Changes X scale to .1 of current size
Enter new Y scale	Press Enter	Changes Y scale to .1 of current size
Enter placement location	Move cursor to center of drawing, click to place component	Places in the drawing a component of an E-size pen plotter (see fig. 15.4)

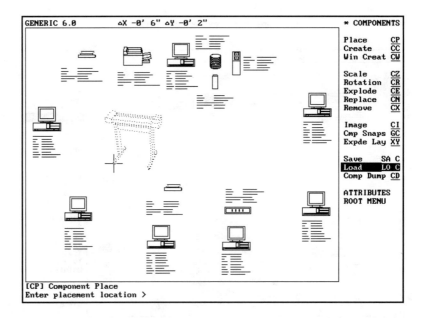

Figure 15.4:

EPLOT-3 is now in the drawing.

The Bill of Material utility can identify and tabulate components that do not have attributes attached, but why not take complete advantage of the resource? To modify the fields of an existing attribute—to be attached to EPLOT-3—follow the steps in this exercise.

Attaching an Attribute to EPLOT-3

Prompt	Input	Description
Command	**AT**	Starts the Attribute Attach command
Select...	Click on plotter	Selects the plotter as the component to attach to
Select...	Click on PERIPH in the menu	Selects the existing attribute PERIPH to be attached to the plotter (see fig. 15.5)
Enter TYPE	**Plotter**	Fills the TYPE field
Enter MODEL	**HP 7550**	Fills the MODEL field
Enter PRICE	**$3500.00**	Fills the PRICE field
Enter SHARED DEVICE	Press Enter	Accepts YES as the field value
Enter BELONGS TO	**HAL**	Fills the BELONGS TO field
Enter NAME	**HALSPLOT**	Fills the NAME field
Display...	Press Enter	Accepts the default (display attribute fields)
Display...	Press Enter	Accepts the default (display attribute labels)
Enter placement location	Click below plotter	Attaches the attribute under the plotter (see fig. 15.6)

After all required objects have been placed in the drawing, the next step is to organize the drawing to take maximum advantage of the information in the drawing using Bill of Material. The goal of this project is to create two reports: one on the printers and plotters being used, and the other on the computers and other devices. One way to make generating separate reports easier is to organize the drawing by using layers. By placing the printers and the plotters on a layer separate from the other devices, you can easily select that layer and save it as a separate drawing.

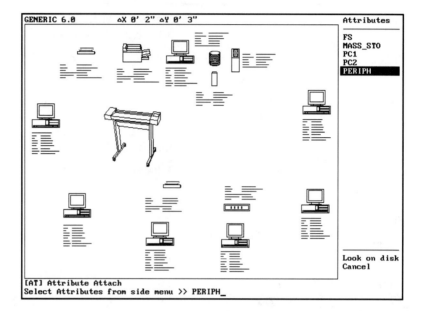

Figure 15.5:

Attach an attribute to the plotter.

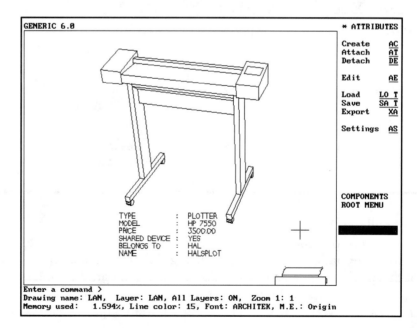

Figure 15.6:

Plotter with attribute attached.

Because only a few objects are involved in this example, using Selection Save is just as fast as moving objects to separate layers. Using Selection Save, you choose the printing devices to be saved as a separate file, without first putting them on another layer. In the long run, however, the best approach is to incorporate layers into your drafting plans so that your work is simple when you need to create BOM reports. Selecting a layer is faster than identifying individual objects. For this project, putting the objects on another layer would be an extra step; you use Selection Save instead.

Whichever method you use to segregate the objects, all the current data must be stored on disk before you use the Bill of Material utility. BOM gathers information from drawings on disk only, not from RAM where the current information also resides if you use the Shell to BOM menu command in CADD. The Bill of Material (BI) command, explained later, reads the version of the drawing in RAM, but BI is used only to create a Bill of Material list included in the drawing.

Before you start the Bill of Material utility, save the drawing to disk so that the saved version is current, and save the printers and plotters (identified in fig. 15.7) in a separate drawing.

Saving Printers as a Separate File

Prompt	Input	Description
Command	DS	Starts the shortcut for the Drawing Save command
Save file as...	Press Enter	Saves LAN.GCD to the current directory
File exists...	R	Creates a backup file while saving the current version
Command	SV	Starts the Selection Save command

continues

495

Prompt	Input	Description
Window...	Type **W** and draw a window around one printer and its attributes. Repeat for the other printer and the plotter (refer to fig. 15.7).	Selects items to be saved in a separate drawing
Save as	**HARDCOPY** and press Enter	Saves selected objects to HARDCOPY.GCD
Command	**ER**	Erases objects moved to the new drawing
Window...	**L** (for Last Selection)	Selects previously selected objects
Window...	Press Enter	Ends selection of objects and erases all selected items

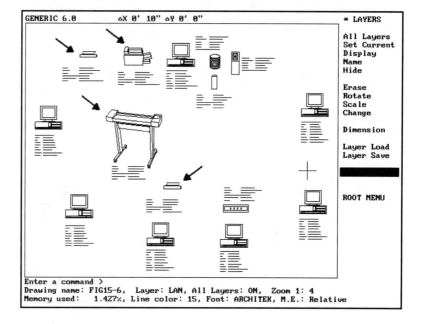

Figure 15.7:

Components to be selected.

Importing Data

The Bill of Material utility is, primarily, a data collection device. The data it gathers is no better, of course, than the data you provide as you create drawings with Generic CADD. The Bill of Material utility can gather data from three sources: Generic CADD and Generic 3D drawings, comma-delimited ASCII files, and Lotus 1-2-3 (and compatible) .WK1 files. Information on each is provided in the following sections.

From Drawing Files

The Bill of Material utility can read files created by Generic CADD 5.0, Generic CADD 6.0, and Generic 3D (components only; Generic 3D does not provide attributes). When creating a Component Data Book (CDB), the utility reads directly from the drawing file stored on disk. When creating a Bill of Material (BOM) report, the utility can read from one or more drawing files and from a previously created CDB.

Be aware that the Bill of Material utility reads drawing files from the disk. If you run the utility by shelling out from CADD, you can not create a BOM or CDB report on the version of the drawing currently in use in CADD. The utility extracts data from the last-saved version of that drawing, which resides on disk.

Both BOMs and CDBs are arranged by columns. Each column in a BOM represents a single attribute field, or a field that you define while using the Bill of Material utility. Figure 15.8 shows a typical BOM. When created by reading a drawing, a CDB lists only component names and quantities; it does not provide totals and does not list attribute fields. Figure 15.9 shows a typical CDB.

Lotus-Format Files

Files created by Lotus 1-2-3 in the .WK1 format can be imported by the Bill of Material utility to create BOMs and CDBs. Avoid using .WK1 files with graphs created by Lotus 1-2-3 version 1a.

A variety of spreadsheet programs can create files compatible with this format. Version 1a of Lotus 1-2-3 sets the standard for the .WK1 format, although the newer versions of Lotus 1-2-3 also write to this format. Other popular programs that can save files in this format include Excel, Works, and Multiplan (all from Microsoft), Quattro Pro (from Borland International), and many others.

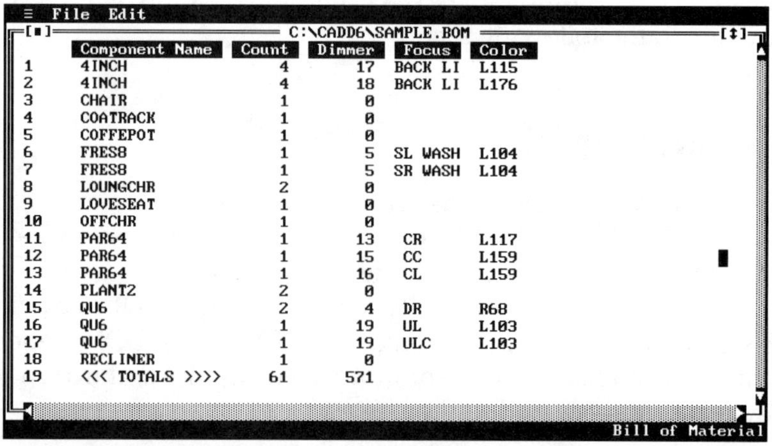

	Component Name	Count	Dimmer	Focus	Color
1	4INCH	4	17	BACK LI	L115
2	4INCH	4	18	BACK LI	L176
3	CHAIR	1	0		
4	COATRACK	1	0		
5	COFFEPOT	1	0		
6	FRES8	1	5	SL WASH	L104
7	FRES8	1	5	SR WASH	L104
8	LOUNGCHR	2	0		
9	LOVESEAT	1	0		
10	OFFCHR	1	0		
11	PAR64	1	13	CR	L117
12	PAR64	1	15	CC	L159
13	PAR64	1	16	CL	L159
14	PLANT2	2	0		
15	QU6	2	4	DR	R68
16	QU6	1	19	UL	L103
17	QU6	1	19	ULC	L103
18	RECLINER	1	0		
19	<<< TOTALS >>>>	61	571		

Figure 15.8:

A sample Bill of Material (BOM) report.

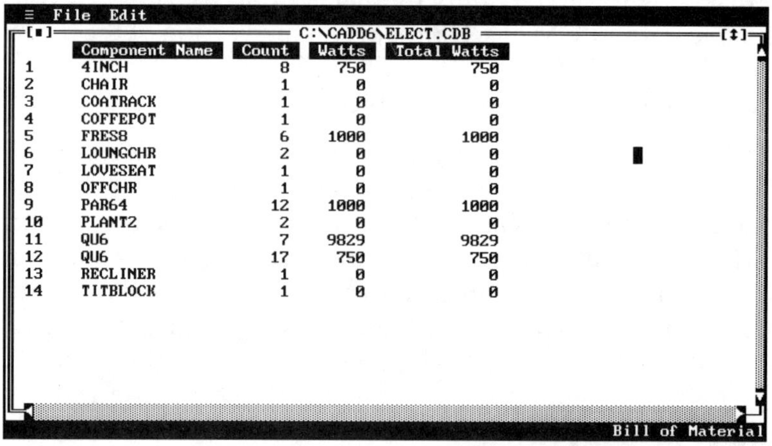

	Component Name	Count	Watts	Total Watts
1	4INCH	8	750	750
2	CHAIR	1	0	0
3	COATRACK	1	0	0
4	COFFEPOT	1	0	0
5	FRES8	6	1000	1000
6	LOUNGCHR	2	0	0
7	LOVESEAT	1	0	0
8	OFFCHR	1	0	0
9	PAR64	12	1000	1000
10	PLANT2	2	0	0
11	QU6	7	9829	9829
12	QU6	17	750	750
13	RECLINER	1	0	0
14	TITBLOCK	1	0	0

Figure 15.9:

A sample Component Data Book (CDB) report.

Comma-Separated ASCII-Format Files

The Bill of Material utility can import files created by a variety of database programs. These files must adhere to a standard format known either as *Comma-Separated Values* ASCII files (CSV) or *delimited* ASCII files. Programs that can create files in this format include dBASE IV, from the Ashton-Tate division of Borland International; Paradox, from Borland International; Alpha Four, from Alphasoft; PC-File, from Buttonware; and many others. Although the process is tedious, any word processor that can save files in ASCII format also can be used to create comma-separated ASCII-format files. If you know BASIC or another programming language, you also can write programs that output data in ASCII format for use in Bill of Material. A typical CSV file is shown in fig. 15.10.

```
                        BOMPRACT.ASC
/100,"4GRAY",   113.975029,    40.673645,     1.000000,     1.000000¶
/200,"ZINGER"¶
/300,"ad#","weight","price","vendor"¶
/400,"45","123",".25","Valuco"¶
/100,"3BLUGRE",   85.867157,    38.819283,     1.000000,     1.000000¶
/200,"ZINGER"¶
/300,"ad#","weight","price","vendor"¶
/400,"15","45",".19","Zucon"¶
/100,"2VIOLET",   55.972416,    38.819283,     1.000000,     1.000000¶
/200,"ZINGER"¶
/300,"ad#","weight","price","vendor"¶
/400,"100","225",".19","Zucon"¶
/100,"4GRAY",   113.975029,    10.442305,     1.000000,     1.000000¶
/200,"ZINGER"¶
/300,"ad#","weight","price","vendor"¶
/400,"45","123",".25","Valuco"¶
/100,"3BLUGRE",   85.867157,     8.587942,     1.000000,     1.000000¶
/200,"ZINGER"¶
/300,"ad#","weight","price","vendor"¶
/400,"15","45",".19","Zucon"¶
```

Figure 15.10:

A file in Comma-Separated ASCII format.

The advantage of importing data from spreadsheets or database-management programs is that you can create one Bill of Material or Component Data Book report by combining data created with Generic CADD with other sources of information about the objects. If you have a great deal of information to include in your BOM or CDB, you may prefer to store related information in another file type instead of burdening your CADD drawings with large attribute files. Then you could use the BOM and CDB reports to bring together your separate sources of data. Uniting separate sources of data in a BOM or CDB is especially helpful if you used your computer for other aspects of your business before turning to CADD.

Assembling a Report

When the drawing is complete and any other sources of data are ready, you can assemble a report. The drawing files LAN.GCD (shipped with Generic CADD 6.0) and HARDCOPY.GCD (created earlier in this chapter) are the sources of data for the next exercise, in which you create both a Bill of Material (BOM) report and a Component Data Book (CDB) report.

The Bill of Material (BOM) Report

The Bill of Material utility is a separate program from Generic CADD. It can be run from the DOS command prompt, or it can be run from inside Generic CADD by using the Shell to Executable command. But Generic CADD also has a Bill of Material (BI) command, which is used to create a simple Bill of Material list for placement in a drawing. For a complete explanation of this command, see the "Exporting Data to a Generic CADD Drawing" section later in the chapter.

A macro for shelling out of CADD CADD and opening the Bill of Material program is in the UTILITIES menu and is used in the exercise below. If you want to start the Bill of Material utility from DOS, type **BOM** at the DOS prompt in the \CADD6 directory.

Starting the Bill of Material Utility Program

Prompt	Input	Description
Command	From the ROOT menu, move the menu bar to UTILITIES and press Home or mouse button 2	Selects the Utilities menu

Prompt	Input	Description
Command	Move the menu bar and press Home or mouse button 2	Execute a macro command to shell CADD and run the Bill of Material program

Two pull-down menus (File and Edit) provide access to all features of the Bill of Material program. You can run the program with either a mouse or from the keyboard. The exercises in the rest of the book provide the keyboard instructions. If you prefer to use a mouse, be sure to use the first mouse button at all times. One click highlights a selection, making it available for use. Two clicks (in rapid succession) execute the command. If you select an item that requires a response (naming a column, for example), make sure you click only once, provide the information, and then click once again (or press Enter).

Designing the Layout

The first step in using Bill of Material to create a new report (either a BOM or CDB) is to design a layout. You do so by naming and formatting each column in the report. The layout designed in the following exercise has seven columns, corresponding to information to be gleaned from the two drawings. This layout can be considered a template. All the information gleaned from the CADD drawings fits into the format identified in the layout.

A completed layout can be used to generate both a BOM and a CDB. To modify a report, edit the layout and run a new BOM or CDB using the new layout. Layouts have the extension .LYT and are stored on disk as separate files from the BOMs or CBDs you create. To begin the design of a new layout, follow the steps in the next exercise.

Opening the New Layout Screen

Prompt	Input	Description
Opening screen	Press Alt-F	Accesses the File menu
	Type **N**	Starts New layout (see fig. 15.11)
New File screen	Press Tab until Create New Layout is highlighted	Requests a screen for the design of a new layout (see fig. 15.12)

Figure 15.11:

The File menu.

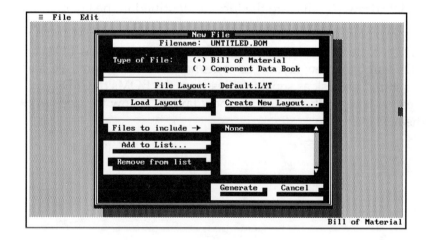

Figure 15.12:

Selecting Create New Layout from the New File menu.

From the Create Layout screen, shown in figure 15.13, design each column and save your design as a new layout. Column: identifies each column by number (from left to right, as they are created). To the right of Column: are three choices— New, Insert, and Delete. New is used to request another column; Insert places a new column between two existing ones, and Delete erases an existing column.

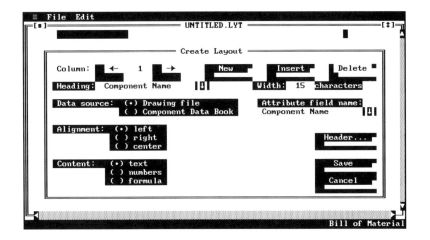

Figure 15.13:
The Create Layout screen.

In the Heading space, name each column; to the right is Width, where you set how many characters wide the column is to be. Note that if the name you type in Heading has more characters than the width you set, the program truncates the name.

Under Data Source, you identify the source of the data for each column as it is created. As mentioned earlier, the data for your reports can come from two sources: either a Generic CADD drawing file or an existing Component Data Book. A column may have only one data source, but you are free to set the source for each column. To the right of Data Source is Attribute Field Name. If the column is drawing data from a drawing, it may need to look to an attribute, which you would name here. When you give each column a Heading name, that also appears in the Attribute Field Name section. Generally, you should name columns to match the attribute field names you created earlier, but if you choose to give the column a different name, you can edit the Attribute Field name here.

Alignment refers to the way the characters in the column are arranged. For text (labels, names, and so on), use left or centered alignment; for numbers, use right alignment. Below Alignment is Content, where you identify the characters in the column as Text, Numbers, or Formula. If you select Numbers, a new set of formatting options appears in what is now an empty part of the screen (see fig. 15.18). The Numbers and Formula options are explained a little later in the chapter.

Header, in the lower right corner of the screen, enables you to place a title or explanation at the top of the BOM or CDB. Below Header are options to save the layout or to cancel your work.

Use the Tab key to move from option to option, top to bottom (or, if you are using a mouse, click on the option you need). To move backward using the keyboard, press Shift-Tab.

The seven columns of the layout are defined, one by one, in the steps that follow. The first column identifies components.

Designing the First Column of the Layout

Prompt	Input	Description
Create Layout screen	Press Tab until Heading is highlighted; type **Component Name**	Names the first column
Create Layout screen	Press Tab to highlight Width, and then type **15**	Sets first column to a width of 15 characters
Create Layout screen	Press Tab to highlight New; press Enter	All other settings are OK; continue to the next column

Figure 15.13 shows the Create Layout screen at the completion of the first column. It was not necessary to enter data at the Attribute Field Name option because in this case it matches the Heading name. This match between the Heading and Attribute Field Name

options holds true for most of the columns in this example. The Data Source, Alignment, and Content options need no adjustment because the default for these three matches the type of information being placed in this column.

The second column identifies the name of the item shown in the component. This name matches a category in the attributes used in the drawings, as do most of the columns designed in this exercise.

Designing the Second and Third Columns of the Layout

Prompt	Input	Description
Create Layout screen	Press Tab to highlight the Heading option; type **Name** and press Enter	Names the second column "Name"
Create Layout screen	The Width column is highlighted; type **10** and press Enter	Sets the width of column 2 to 10
Create Layout screen	Press Tab repeatedly until New is highlighted; press Enter	All other options are OK (see fig. 15.14)
Create Layout screen	Press Tab to highlight Heading; type **Model** and press Enter	Model becomes the heading of column 3
Create Layout screen	Width is highlighted; type 7 and press Enter	Sets width of column 3 to 7
Create Layout screen	Press Tab repeatedly until New is highlighted; press Enter	All other options are OK (see fig. 15.15)

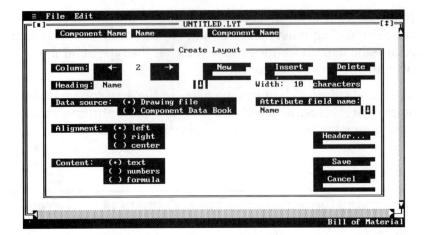

Figure 15.14:

Design options for the second column.

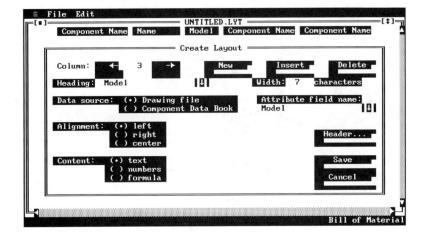

Figure 15.15:

Design options for the third column.

NOTE If you have been using the mouse instead of the keyboard to navigate the Create Layout screen, you may have discovered differences in the way you enter the data. When you use the Tab key to select an option, the existing data is replaced by whatever you type. If you select an option with the mouse, the information you type is appended to the existing data; you must erase the existing information before you can type in new data.

Follow the next set of instructions to format the remaining columns.

Adding Columns to the Layout File

Prompt	Input	Description
Create Layout screen	Press Tab to high-light Heading; type **CPU** and press Enter	Makes CPU the heading of column 4
Create Layout screen	Type **5** and press Enter	Makes this column five characters wide
Create Layout screen	Press Tab until New is highlighted; press Enter	All other options are OK (see fig. 15.16)
Create Layout screen	Press Tab to high-light Heading; type **Component** and press Enter	Makes Component the heading of column 5
Create Layout screen	Type **10** and press Enter	This column will be 10 characters wide
Create Layout screen	Press Tab until New is highlighted; press Enter	All other options are OK (see fig. 15.17)
Create Layout screen	Press Tab to high-light Heading; type **Price** and press Enter	Makes Price the heading of column 6
Create Layout screen	Type **6** and press Enter	This column will be 6 characters wide
Create Layout screen	Press Tab until Alignment is highlighted; press down-arrow key to select Right, and press Enter	Sets the column to right alignment

continues

Prompt	Input	Description
Create Layout screen	Press down-arrow key to select numbers	Numbers will be displayed in this column
Create Layout screen	Press Shift-Tab to select Format; Press down-arrow key until $##.## is highlighted; press Enter	Numbers in this column will be displayed as dollars and cents
Create Layout screen	Press Tab until New is highlighted; press Enter	All other options are OK (see fig. 15.18)

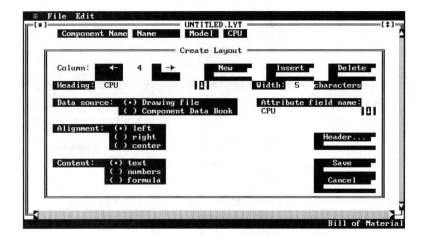

Figure 15.16:

Design options for the fourth column.

As you created the sixth column, you pressed Shift-Tab to change the default status of the Number display. After Number is selected in the Content option, the cursor moves on to the Formula column when you press Enter. Because the default option at this point is to accept the current format for numbers and move on, you have to back up a step to change the Number display.

One more column to go. Follow the next set of steps to finish designing the layout:

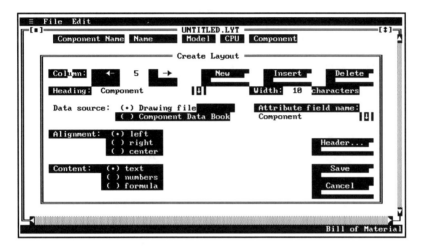

Figure 15.17:

Design options for the fifth column.

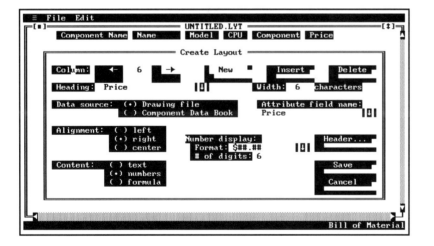

Figure 15.18:

Design options for the sixth column.

Finishing the Design of Columns for the Layout File

Prompt	Input	Description
Create Layout screen	Press Tab to highlight Heading; type **Quantity** and press Enter	Makes Quantity the heading of column 7
Create Layout screen	Type **8** and press Enter	Makes this column 8 characters wide, so that the name is not truncated
Create Layout screen	Press Tab to highlight Attribute Field Name; type **Component Count** and press Enter	Lists the number of matching components
Create Layout screen	Press down-arrow key until Right is highlighted; press Enter	Right alignment is required for number display
Create Layout screen	Press down-arrow key until Numbers is highlighted; press Enter	Sets accepted content of column to numbers
Create Layout screen	Press Shift-Tab to highlight Format; press down-arrow key to highlight Whole Number; press Enter	Whole numbers (no decimals and no dollar amounts) will be displayed (see fig. 15.19)
Create Layout screen	Press Tab until Save is highlighted; press Enter	The last column has been designed. Save the layout. The Save File As screen appears (see fig. 15.20)
Save File screen	Type **BOMPRACT.LYT** and press Enter; press Esc	Saves the seven-column layout just created as BOMPRACT.LYT

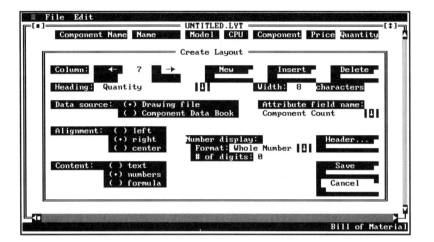

Figure 15.19:

Design options for the seventh column.

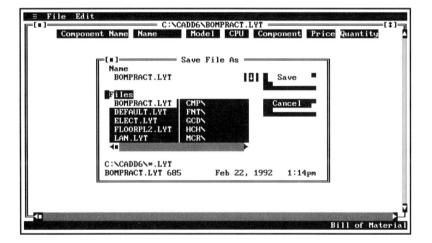

Figure 15.20:

The Save File As screen.

In the Number Display section, you may have noticed the # of digits option (which refers to the number of digits to the right of the decimal). Because the two columns of numbers in this example are either dollar amounts or whole numbers, it is not necessary to change this option.

Generating the Report

After creating a layout, the next step is to generate a report. As stated earlier, the majority of your work is completed when the layout is done. When the Bill of Material utility creates a report (whether BOM or CDB), it filters through the layout file the information from the drawing files you select. If the report is wrong, the layout file—not the report file—must be edited. The next example illustrates a situation in which a report needs to be fixed.

To generate a BOM report from a layout file, select New File from the program's File menu and identify both the layout file and the drawing files to be used to create the report. The hands-on exercise that follows walks you through the process of creating a BOM report based on the layout file you just created.

Creating a BOM Report

Prompt	Input	Description
Main BOM screen	Press Alt-F	Opens the File menu
File menu	Press **N**	New File screen appears (see fig. 15.21)
New File screen	Tab until Load Layout is high-lighted; press Enter	Select Layout File screen appears (see fig. 15.22)
Select Layout File screen	Tab until BOMPRACT.LYT is highlighted; press Enter	The file name BOMPRACT.LYT appears as the selected Name
Select Layout File screen	Tab until OK is highlighted; press Enter	BOMPRACT.LYT is selected; New File screen reappears
New File screen	Tab until Add To List is high-lighted; press Enter	Select a Drawing or CDB file screen appears (see fig. 15.23)

Prompt	Input	Description
Add To List screen	Tab to Files menu and use the down-arrow and Enter keys to select the directory that holds HARDCOPY.GCD and LAN.GCD; high-light HARDCOPY.GCD and press Enter	HARDCOPY.GCD is selected and the New File screen reappears
New File screen	Tab until Add To List is high-lighted; press Enter	Returns to Add To List screen
Add To List screen	Tab until Files is highlighted, then use down-arrow key to high-light LAN.GCD; press Enter	LAN.GCD is selected and the New File screen reappears
New File screen	Tab until Generate is highlighted; press Enter	All files have been selected; the BOM may be created

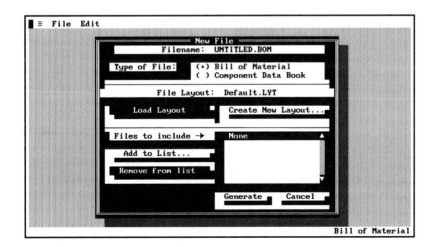

Figure 15.21:
The New File screen.

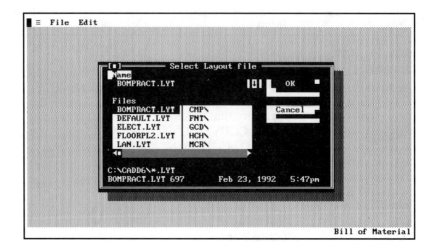

Figure 15.22:

The Select Layout File screen.

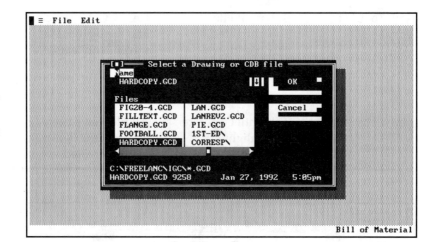

Figure 15.23:

The Select a Drawing or CDB File screen

After you highlight Generate and press Enter, the program goes to work. It scans each of the drawing files you selected, looking through the components and attributes for information that matches the list you supplied in the layout file. The key piece of information is the Attribute Field Name item. If the program finds a match between an Attribute Field Name in the layout file and an attribute name in the drawing, all the information from that attribute is captured and placed into the report file, matching each of the attribute names with the appropriate column.

Figure 15.24 shows the BOM report created by following the preceding steps. Notice that column 5 (Component) is blank. Why? For the answer, look at sample attributes from the drawing files used to generate the report. Figure 15.25 shows the two types of attribute files used in the two drawings. Note that Component is not an attribute field name. The column is blank because there was no match between Component in column 5 and any of the field names. When column 5 was specified in the hands-on exercise, Component was listed as the Heading for the column, and the Attribute Field Name item was not changed. Because the default for Attribute Field Name is the item listed as the Heading, column 5 searched for items that were not to be found. The name that appears in Attribute Field Name must exactly match an attribute in the drawing; otherwise, no data is extracted.

```
 ≡  File  Edit
┌─[■]────────────────────── UNTITLED.BOM ───────────────────────[↕]─┐
│    ┌Component Name│ Name     ┌ Model │ CPU │ Component │ Price│Quantity┐│
│  1 │ DM PTR       │ DM PTR   │ EPSON F         │                  │$18.00│    1  │
│  2 │ DM PTR       │ DM PTR   │ OKIDATA         │                  │$18.00│    1  │
│  3 │ EPLOT-3.CMP  │ EPLOT-3.CM│ HP 7550        │                  │$18.00│    1  │
│  4 │ LASER PTR    │ LASER PTR │ HP LJET        │                  │$18.00│    1  │
│  5 │ COMPUTER     │ COMPUTER  │ EVX 286  80286 │                  │$18.00│    2  │
│  6 │ COMPUTER     │ COMPUTER  │ EVX 386  80386 │                  │$18.00│    4  │
│  7 │ COMPUTER     │ COMPUTER  │ EVX 004  80486 │                  │$18.00│    1  │
│  8 │ DISK SUBSYS  │ DISK SUBSY│ LAN600E        │                  │$18.00│    1  │
│  9 │ MODEM        │ MODEM     │ HAYES 2        │                  │$18.00│    1  │
│ 10 │ TAPE BACKUP  │ TAPE BACKU│ CYBER 6        │                  │$18.00│    1  │
│ 11 │ UPS          │ UPS       │ APC 520        │                  │$18.00│    1  │
│ 12 │ <<< TOTALS >>>│ <<<< TOTAL│               │                  │$198.0│   15  │
│                                                                   │
│                                                Bill of Material   │
└───────────────────────────────────────────────────────────────────┘
```

Figure 15.24:

The Bill of Material report.

To correct the problem in column 5, you need to edit the layout file and regenerate the report. You will learn how to edit layout files soon, in the "Adding or Deleting Columns" section. First, however, read about the Component Data Book (CDB), the other kind of report available in the Bill of Materials utility.

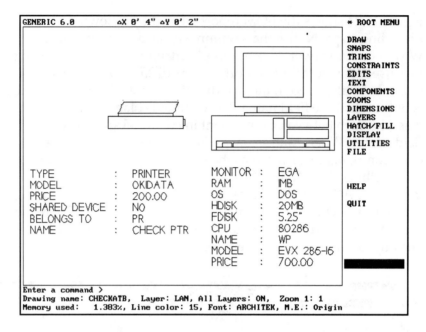

Figure 15.25:

Sample attributes used to generate the BOM report.

The Component Data Book (CDB) Report

A Component Data Book (CDB) is best used as an addition to a BOM, not as a replacement for one. Because a Bill of Material is generated from the attributes in a drawing, it can reflect the variety of data about the components that is being stored in the drawing. A Component Data Book generated from a CADD drawing just lists each component by name, as well as the quantity of each component. A CDB does not scan attributes in a CADD drawing when looking for data, and it does not list totals for any of the columns.

The advantage of the Component Data Book format is that you can use it to list data from spreadsheets or database programs to create a price book (or catalog) of the components in one or more drawings. BOM reports can use Component Data Books as a source of information. By generating well-informed CDBs, you provide yourself an opportunity to create comprehensive BOMs.

Organizing and Generating a CDB

The steps used earlier to organize a layout for a BOM work also for organizing a layout to create a CDB, with one difference—in the New File screen, you must set Type of File to Component Data Book rather than Bill of Material. When you create a layout for a CDB, the Attribute Field Name option changes to Column Name. This reflects the fact that CDBs do not import data from attributes in drawings but can be used to organize data from spreadsheets and database programs.

Using the Data Book To Expand a Bill of Material

Both Bill of Material and Component Data Book reports have strengths and limitations. BOMs gather data from CADD attributes and CDBs and can provide totals, but they cannot read information from other file types. CDBs can gather data from non-CADD sources but cannot read CADD attributes. By capitalizing on the strengths of each file type, you can build custom reports that provide exactly the kinds of data you need.

The key to the successful merging of BOMs and CDBs depends on wise management of layout files. As mentioned earlier, after a layout file is completed, your work is essentially completed. Generating a report from a layout is just a matter of reading and organizing the kinds of data you request in the layout file.

If you keep information related to your design work in a spreadsheet, you can combine that information with data stored in your CADD attributes. As an example, consider the example of a patio contractor named Max Gravel. For every job, Max designs the patio in Generic CADD and uses Quattro Pro to calculate the amounts of cement and gravel needed for the job. Max also has a database file in PC-File, listing the patio furniture available from the manufacturers with whom he has accounts.

When a customer comes to Max for a bid on a patio job, Max draws up two or three possible designs for the patio. He also prepares two Bill of Material reports: one for the client and one for himself. The client BOM lists the retail cost of various pieces of patio furniture; Max's BOM lists the same information but also shows his cost and markup. Because not every customer has the same taste or budget when buying patio furniture, Max keeps several CDB files on hand, each one listing furniture in different price and style options.

The layout files are the key to success. Max has designed several layout files, each one referencing various CDB files. Each CDB file, in turn, was created from various spreadsheet and database files. When Max knows what the customer has in mind, he either prints a previous BOM report that matches the current need or runs a new BOM using one of his custom layout files. By having on hand several CDB reports summarizing the information held in his spreadsheet and database files, Max can create BOMs that use the information from other software programs.

Editing Reports

After you have created a few BOMs and CDBs, there undoubtedly will be times when you want to make changes to existing reports. If you make changes in a CADD drawing, for example, the BOM report created from it is no longer accurate. Other changes you may want to make will not be related to changes in the original data but rather in the kinds of information you want in your reports. Adding formulas to reports, adding or deleting columns, renaming fields, and entering new data are covered in the sections that follow.

Adding Formulas

One of the options in the Create Layout screen's Content field is Formula. Like a spreadsheet, a BOM or a CDB report may show the results of a simple calculation. The formula is placed in the column during Create Layout and calculated for each row as the BOM or CDB is generated.

Formulas in the Bill of Material utility can calculate from inform-ation in other columns, from numbers you supply, or from a combination of both. For example, the LAN BOM report created earlier in the chapter can be modified to calculate a total price for the different kinds of equipment. As illustrated in figure 15.24, column 6 shows price, and column 7 shows quantity. A new column can be added to the report to multiply the price times the quantity. To define the column, you place the formula C6*C7 in the Content field (C6 and C7 refer to Column 6 and Column 7, respectively).

There are three ways to write a formula in the Bill of Material utility:

1. Use column numbers, as in the preceding example.

2. Use the Column Heading Name. In the preceding example, the formula would be PRICE*QUANTITY instead of C6*C7.

3. Mix the two styles. PRICE*C7 is a valid formula.

If you are creating a BOM that shows retail markup, you can write a formula that multiplies wholesale cost in a column by a set percentage to arrive at the retail price. If the wholesale COST is in column 2, and the markup is always 15 percent, a valid formula would be COST + (C2*.15).

Standard math rules are in effect when the Bill of Material utility reads and calculates formulas. Multiplication and division are performed before addition and subtraction, equations are calculated from left to right, and calculations are performed first on functions inside parentheses, from innermost out.

If you add a formula to a layout that already has been used to generate one or more BOM or CDB reports, use the Regenerate option in the File menu (Alt-F-R) to create a new BOM or CDB.

Adding or Deleting Columns

Adding new columns to or deleting columns from a layout is a simple task. In the top row of the Create Layout screen are three buttons: New, Insert, and Delete (see fig. 15.19). The New option (used extensively in the preceding hands-on example) creates a new column. To use one of the other choices, press the Tab key until the column number is highlighted, and then type in a column number. If you are deleting, type the number of the column to be removed, press Tab until Delete is highlighted, and press Enter. If you are adding a new column, type the number of the column that will precede the new column. Press Tab until Insert is highlighted, and press Enter. A new column is inserted immediately to the right of the column you used as a reference. Proceed to define this new column as required.

Renaming Fields and Columns

The Heading and Attribute Field Name options can be used to rename any column. In the Create Layout screen, identify the column to be renamed by typing its number in the Column field. Press Tab to highlight either the Heading or Attribute Field Name option, type in a new name, and press Enter. Remember that if you change the Attribute Field Name, the new name must exactly match the name of an existing attribute field name; otherwise, no data is imported into the column. (If you are creating a CDB instead of a BOM, Attribute Field Name becomes Column Name, and whether the names match exactly or not is no longer an issue.)

Entering New Data

To enter new data into a BOM or CDB, you either add a new column or edit an existing column in a layout, following the guidelines given earlier. After the layout has been edited, use the Regenerate command to replace the existing BOM or CDB with a new one. Then save the regenerated file, using the file name of the existing report.

Exporting Data

The focus of this chapter to this point has been on getting data into BOM and CDB reports, but exporting data from these reports also is possible. Specifically, files can be exported for use in spreadsheets, database programs, and word processors. Placing a Bill of Material list into a CADD drawing as a component also is possible.

Exporting Data to a Generic CADD Drawing

Placing a Bill of Material as part of the final set of drawings, right alongside the drawings, is quite common. Generic CADD and the Bill of Material utility offer two ways to place a BOM into a drawing. Use the first method when running Generic CADD; the second, when running the Bill of Material utility.

There is a command in the UTILITIES menu called Bill of Material (BI). When you select the command, the current drawing is scanned. A list of all components in use, with the quantity of each, is determined, and the result is assembled into a component ready for placement. Figure 15.26 shows the result of using the Bill of Material (BI) command on LAN.CGD.

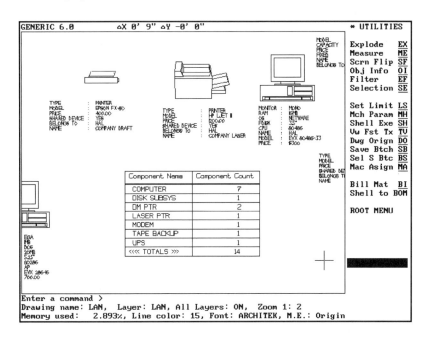

Figure 15.26:

A Bill of Material placed using the BI command.

The second way to place a Bill of Material list in a CADD drawing is to export a BOM or CDB as a Generic CADD component. To do this, the file you want to export must be open in the Bill of Material utility (press Alt-F-O to open a file). Press Alt-F-E for Export and then press Tab to highlight Component (.CMP). Now press

Enter to save the contents of the open BOM or CDB as a Generic CADD component. When you go into Generic CADD, the component can be placed like any other component.

Placement Options

When placing a BOM or CDB into a Generic CADD drawing as a component, two problems may arise. If using the BI command from within Generic CADD, the size of the component may not match the scale of the drawing, and the contents of the BOM may not match your requirements. Each situation is discussed in the following sections.

Changing Scale

When you are placing as a component a BOM generated by the BI command or created while using the Bill of Material utility, the component may be at a scale that does not fit the rest of the drawing. The size of the text used by the BI command is not controlled by the Text Settings (TS) command; the size is always 1 (1", 1', and so on, depending on which units of measurement is in effect).

To fit the BOM component to the drawing, type **CZ** (for Component Scale) when you are prompted to select a placement location for the component. Make an educated guess as to the correct scale you need and type the number for both the X and Y scale, pressing Enter each time. (See Chapter 13 for a review of the Component Scale command.) If the drag image of the BOM component dwarfs all other objects in the drawing, a scale of .1 or .2 may be necessary. If the drag image of the BOM component appears as little more than a dot, a new scale of 2 or more may be necessary.

Changing Rotation

If Component Rotation is set to zero degrees, the BOM component is placed horizontally, as shown in figure 15.28. If you need to rotate it, type **CR** and specify a new rotation when asked to identify the placement location on-screen.

Changing Default Layout

When you use the BI command from Generic CADD to place a BOM in a drawing as a component, the layout file DEFAULT.LYT is used to create the BOM. DEFAULT.LYT lists only two columns, Component Name and Component Count. If you want to use the BI command, and you want more than just these two types of information to appear in the BOM, edit DEFAULT.LYT before using the BI command. DEFAULT.LYT can be modified in the same way as any other layout file. Before you edit the file, be sure to save a copy of the original version of DEFAULT.LYT under another name.

Exporting a BOM or CDB to Other Software

As mentioned earlier, any BOM or CDB may be exported for use in other software. To export a report, open the report file you want to export and select the Export option from the File menu (press Alt-F for File menu, E for Export). Press the Tab key to select the option you need: Lotus (.WK1), ASCII Delimited (.TXT), or ASCII (.DOC). Press Tab again to highlight Export, and then press Enter.

Summary

The more you learn about Generic CADD, the more new ways you have to increase productivity. By planning carefully, you can amplify the use of components and attributes in Generic CADD to create Bill of Material and Component Data Book reports using the Bill of Material utility program.

Although the Bill of Material features are relatively simple, Generic CADD users should not underestimate their usefulness. The Bill of Material (BI) command automates the placement of a Bill of Material in a drawing whereas the Bill of Material utility program offers ways to combine data from CADD drawings and other software files to create a variety of reports.

When integrated into the regular work routine, the Bill of Material utility becomes a link between designing products and the business tasks that accompany any design work.

Transferring Files between Generic CADD and AutoCAD

One of the new features in Generic CADD 6.0 that has generated considerable interest is Generic CADD's capability of directly importing drawing files created by AutoCAD. The direct import of AutoCAD drawing files opens new doors of opportunity to Generic CADD users. AutoCAD, the first successful CAD program to run on a microcomputer, has become the top-selling CAD program of all time on any computing environment.

After Autodesk acquired Generic Software in 1989, a high priority was given to forging closer links between AutoCAD and Generic CADD. Autodesk understood the desire in the marketplace for both programs; Generic CADD's new features are a direct result of the company's goal of serving a wide range of CAD users.

Generic CADD 6.0 does more than just directly import AutoCAD drawing files. Previous versions of Generic CADD offered the capability to exchange drawings with AutoCAD through use of the AutoConvert utility, sold separately. An improved version of AutoConvert is included in the Generic CADD 6.0 program. All translation of files between the AutoCAD and Generic CADD environments can now be accomplished from inside Generic CADD and can be done much faster than with previous versions.

The tighter link between Generic CADD and AutoCAD, forged by the new import and translation features, creates many new opportunities for Generic CADD users. Because AutoCAD is the top-selling CAD software for personal computers (Generic CADD is second), many construction and engineering firms have made AutoCAD their standard. Now Generic CADD users subcontracting for such firms can accept drawings from the contracting firm without asking for a DXF version of the file. (*DXF* stands for *Drawing Interchange File*; Autodesk developed the file format for the translation of files between AutoCAD and other CAD environments.)

To encourage designers to specify their products, many companies that supply the construction and manufacturing industries make drawings of their products available as components (also known as *symbols*) in AutoCAD format (where they are called *blocks*). Now Generic CADD users have equal access to the symbol libraries originally designed for AutoCAD users.

Having selected AutoCAD, an organization often provides only a few key drafters with the product because of AutoCAD's cost (of more than $3,000 per copy). By adding Generic CADD (at under $500) to the work environment, the organization can afford to issue CAD software to every person in the firm who may benefit from it. Having a CAD program on every computer in an organization is especially helpful to managers who need to review AutoCAD drawings but do not need to create them. Now managers can use Generic CADD to review and red-line drawings.

This chapter focuses on how to import AutoCAD files into Generic CADD 6.0 and export files from Generic CADD to AutoCAD.

Using File Formats Currently Available

When software publishers create a program, they must decide how to save to disk (and retrieve from disk) information created by the program. Historically, if a program becomes extremely popular, the file format developed by the publisher of that program is used throughout the industry. Perhaps the most famous example of this fact is the file format used by Lotus 1-2-3. Lotus 1-2-3's dominant market share has forced virtually every competing spreadsheet to include the capability to read and write files in Lotus format. Many other kinds of software (including Generic CADD, as explained in the chapters on Attributes and Bill of Material) also import and export files in Lotus format.

If you are deliberating whether or not to share files between AutoCAD and Generic CADD, several file formats must be considered. Each is discussed in the following sections.

Drawing Interchange File (DXF) Format

In the realm of computer-aided design, AutoCAD has achieved status equal to that of Lotus 1-2-3 among spreadsheets. As the product developed, Autodesk recognized the need to make it easier for publishers of other software products to prepare files for use with AutoCAD. At the same time, however, Autodesk did not want to reveal the inner workings of the AutoCAD DWG file format. The company knew that the DWG format would change with each new update, and they also knew that keeping the format proprietary gave them a competitive edge in the marketplace.

Instead of publishing the DWG file format, Autodesk developed the Drawing Interchange file format (DXF). All implementations of AutoCAD accept this format and are able to convert it to and from their internal drawing file representation. The specifications for creating files in DXF format are available to any software developer, directly from Autodesk. The publication of the DXF format encouraged developers to include support for it in their products. Software for a wide variety of endeavors, from surveying and metal lathe work, to sign making and technical illustration, has chosen to support the DXF format.

Early in the development of Generic CADD, long before Autodesk acquired Generic Software, the company decided to use the DXF

527

format as the primary means of communicating with other programs. A program called AutoConvert was developed and sold separately. AutoConvert, which could read DXF files and convert them to the Generic CADD drawing format, also could read Generic CADD drawing files and convert them to DXF format for use with AutoCAD and other products. With each release of either Generic CADD or AutoCAD, AutoConvert was updated to match the new features of both products. As part of the growth of Generic CADD, Autodesk Retail Products decided to incorporate the features of AutoConvert directly into the latest release of Generic CADD. Although no longer a separate program, this utility is still referred to as AutoConvert in the Generic CADD documentation.

The release of Generic CADD 6.0 created one small problem for the developers: Both AutoCAD and Generic CADD used DWG as the extension on drawing files. Adding the capability to read AutoCAD drawing files increased the possibility that users would have two very different file types (both with the extension DWG) coexisting on disk. Because both CADD and users might find this confusing, the decision was made to rename the Generic CADD file extension. It is now GCD (*Generic CADD Drawing*).

Generic CADD still uses the DXF format to export drawings to AutoCAD. The capability to both read and write in DXF format remains a part of Generic CADD; it is now incorporated into CADD, not kept as a separately purchased program.

DXF files are standard ASCII text files. AutoCAD also can produce or read a binary form of DXF. Binary DXF files are primarily for use by Numeric Control (NC) and other Computer-Aided Manufacturing (CAM) programs. AutoConvert does not read the binary form of DXF. If you are given a binary DXF file for use in Generic CADD, the file must be reloaded into AutoCAD (using the AutoCAD DXFIN command) and a version of it saved as either a drawing file or an ASCII DXF file.

In addition to the drawing files created by both Generic CADD and AutoCAD, and the DXF files both can create, other file formats must be considered when transferring files between these two programs.

Font File Formats

AutoCAD fonts are stored in a file format with the extension SHX. AutoCAD users (like Generic CADD users) can create additional fonts. Many fonts for AutoCAD are available from third-party developers or as public-domain software. A utility program (DWG2GCD.EXE) shipped with Generic CADD can be used to convert AutoCAD SHX files to Generic CADD's FNT format. For instructions, see the "Translate AutoCAD Drawing Files" section, later in this chapter.

When an AutoCAD drawing is loaded directly into Generic CADD, the program looks for font names that match those in the AutoCAD drawing. To make the file translation easier, Generic CADD version 6.0 includes 19 fonts that match fonts found in AutoCAD Release 11.

Although a DXF file created from a drawing that includes text contains a list of the fonts used, the descriptions of the strokes that form each character are not part of the DXF file. When translating the DXF file to another format, the translating device must map the fonts in the DXF file to fonts in the receiving program. AutoConvert automatically maps AutoCAD fonts with the matching Generic CADD fonts, or the user may specify the fonts to be used in the translation.

Component File Formats

Components—known as *blocks* in AutoCAD—are more generally known in software terminology as *symbols*. As mentioned earlier, more and more manufacturers are publishing symbols of their products for use by designers. Most provide the symbols in DXF format; many provide them in both DXF and AutoCAD DWG format. AutoConvert can translate symbols (blocks) from DXF to Generic CADD's component (CMP) format without having to place the components in a drawing. When Generic CADD imports an AutoCAD drawing, blocks from the AutoCAD drawing are saved as components with the drawing. To save the blocks permanently to disk for use with other drawings, you would have to save them using either the Component Save (SA) or Component Dump (CD) commands.

AutoCAD, a full 2D/3D CAD program, can be used for drawing three-dimensional designs. Although Generic CADD is 2D only, the companion program Generic 3D is available for three-dimensional drafting. AutoConvert can translate three-dimensional AutoCAD blocks into the CM3 format Generic 3D uses for components. (For more information on Generic 3D, see Appendix C of this book.)

Understanding Specifics of AutoCAD File Translation

In addition to the various file types mentioned earlier, many specific objects and settings must be cared for when you translate DWG or DXF files from AutoCAD to Generic CADD. Most of the objects in AutoCAD have equivalents in Generic CADD although there are differences due to fundamental differences in the design of the two programs. A few objects and settings from AutoCAD have no comparable object or setting in Generic CADD, and substitute object types are specified by either the DWG2GCD program (for importing AutoCAD DWG files directly into Generic CADD) or AutoConvert (for importing DXF files).

AutoCAD objects and settings are listed by category in tables 16.1 through 16.4. The tables show the specific entities for each category and how each item is translated into Generic CADD.

Table 16.1
Simple Objects

AutoCAD Entity	Converts to Generic CADD as
Point	A standard point
Line	A line
Arc	An arc
Circle	A circle

Table 16.2
Complex Objects

AutoCAD Entity	Converts to Generic CADD as
Shape (similar to block)	Individual lines, arcs, and so on
Trace	Two lines with solid color fill between them (actually four lines; close to double lines)
Solid	Triangular or quadrilateral areas with boundaries
Text line	Text line
Dimension	A dimension
Block	A component
Attribute	An attribute
Polyline	Individual lines
Block Ellipse	Arcs
Polyarc	Arcs
Polyline Spline	Lines or curves (user's choice); lines conform better to the original shape but take up more memory
Hatch	A component

Table 16.3
3-D Entities

AutoCAD Entity	Converts to Generic CADD as
Mesh	Lines, with DWG2GCD. DFX converts the boundary definitions to lines
3-D Face	Four lines
3-D Line	A line
Extruded Point	A line
Extruded Line	A line
View-rotated objects	Lines

Table 16.4
Settings

AutoCAD Entity	Converts to Generic CADD as
Line Type	User must set conversion in advance
Line Width	Not offered in AutoCAD
Chamfer A and Chamfer B	Chamfer Distance
Filletrad	Fillet Radius
Colors	Converted based on settings in AutoConvert
Attmode	Attribute display toggle
Blipmode	Standard Points
Clayer	Current Layer
Fill mode	Display Fill
Dragmode	Object Drag
Lupred	Decimals display
Orthomode	Ortho Mode
Qtextmode	Fast Text
Textstyle	Current font
Gridmode	Grid On/Off toggle
Gridunit	Grid Size
Snapbase	Grid Origin
Snapmode	Grid Snap

Importing AutoCAD Drawings into Generic CADD

There are two ways to make an AutoCAD drawing usable in Generic CADD without using DXF as an intermediate translation.

The first way is to simply load the drawing while you are using Generic CADD. The second is to create a GCD version of an AutoCAD DWG file at the DOS prompt. The advantages to each method are explained in the following sections.

Load AutoCAD Drawing (LO)

To load an AutoCAD drawing directly into Generic CADD, use the Load (LO) command. When the list of options appears at the bottom of the screen, type **A** for AutoCAD drawing. A list of drawings in the default directory (files with a DWG extension) appears in the side menu. If you need to change directories, select ../ from the menu or use File Selector to select a drawing from a different subdirectory.

All files with the DWG extension are displayed in the video menu or File Selector when you want to load an AutoCAD drawing. If older Generic CADD drawings with the DWG extension (created by all versions of Generic CADD prior to 6.0) are in the directory, they also appear in the list. If you select one of these files to be loaded into Generic CADD, the program begins the load process, but then stops. Generic CADD notifies you that the file can not be loaded because it is not an AutoCAD drawing.

If you have Generic CADD drawing files created by older versions of the program, you should rename them all, replacing the DWG extension with GCD. (The Install program has an option to re-name any DWGs found on the target drive or directory.)

You can use the DOS RENAME command to rename one file or— if all you are doing is changing the extension—many files. From the DOS prompt, type

RENAME *.DWG *.GCD

to rename all files in the directory with an extension of DWG (changing the extension to GCD).

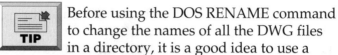 Before using the DOS RENAME command to change the names of all the DWG files in a directory, it is a good idea to use a defragmentation program (such as the one included with PC Tools or Norton Utilities) on your hard drive. If the existing data on the hard drive is significantly fragmented, an extremely small possibility exists that using RENAME to globally rename a group of files could cause one or two of the files to lose data. Consult a book on hard drive maintenance for more information about hard disk fragmentation and how to fix it. This problem is not caused by the CADD drawing files; it can affect any type of file renamed globally on a fragmented hard drive.

When the file is selected, Generic CADD uses the current settings in AutoConvert to guide the translation of all relevant AutoCAD features as it creates a GCD version of the drawing. The drawing that appears on-screen is a Generic CADD drawing file, which can be saved the same way you save any other drawing. The original AutoCAD DWG drawing remains on disk. The process of translating an AutoCAD drawing for use in Generic CADD creates a copy; it does not change the original.

Translate AutoCAD Files (DWG2GCD.EXE)

When an AutoCAD drawing is loaded into Generic CADD, CADD invisibly uses the utility program DWG2GCD.EXE, which is placed in the /CADD6 directory when you install CADD. When you select the Load command's AutoCAD drawing option, Generic CADD runs a macro that activates this program.

DWG2GCD.EXE also can be used from Generic CADD's Convert menu or from the DOS prompt. Using DWG2GCD.EXE from the DOS prompt enables you to convert AutoCAD drawings or fonts to Generic CADD format without loading them into CADD first. Using standard DOS wild cards, DWG2GCD can convert several AutoCAD drawings or fonts simultaneously. To convert all drawings in a directory, type

DWG2GCD *.DWG *.GCD

To convert all AutoCAD fonts in a directory, type

DWG2GCD *.SHX *.FNT

To use DWG2GCD from inside Generic CADD, you must use the on-screen menu; no two-letter command is available. Select the File menu from the ROOT menu. Then, from the File menu, select the Convert menu. Click on DWGIN. From here on, the steps are the same as if you had used the AutoCAD option of the Load command.

Importing and Exporting DXF Files

If you need to import a drawing saved in DXF format, or if you need to share with an AutoCAD user a drawing you created in Generic CADD, you must use AutoConvert, the DXF translation utility included with Generic CADD 6.0.

As tables 16.1 through 16.4 illustrate, there are many differences in how Generic CADD and AutoCAD identify objects and settings. AutoConvert can be adjusted as necessary to account for the differences between the two file types.

AutoConvert can be used without change, but for best results, you should take the time to configure this utility to match your requirements.

From inside Generic CADD, you use the Exchange Setup (XG) command to summon the AutoConvert Main Menu (see fig. 16.1). Select Xchg Setup from the Convert menu (a submenu of the File menu) or type **XG** at the CADD prompt.

In earlier versions of AutoConvert—before its integration into Generic CADD—the main menu not only listed the different options available for settings but also was the screen from which you actually converted files to and from DXF format. Now, if you want to convert a Generic CADD drawing to DXF or want to import a DXF file into Generic CADD, you do it from the Convert menu. Click on DXFIN to import a DXF file into Generic CADD; click on DXFOUT to save the currently loaded Generic CADD drawing as a DXF file. To create a DXF file from a CADD drawing, use the Save (SA) command's X option. To import a DXF file into Generic CADD use the Load (LO) command's X option.

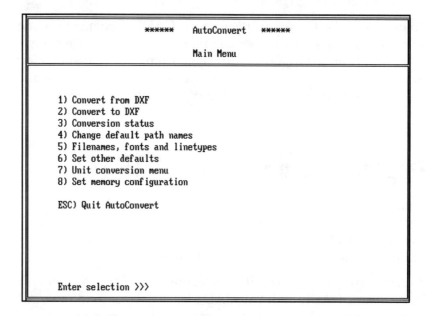

```
******    AutoConvert   ******

              Main Menu


    1) Convert from DXF
    2) Convert to DXF
    3) Conversion status
    4) Change default path names
    5) Filenames, fonts and linetypes
    6) Set other defaults
    7) Unit conversion menu
    8) Set memory configuration

    ESC) Quit AutoConvert




    Enter selection >>>
```

Figure 16.1:

The AutoConvert Main Menu.

From the main menu, type the number corresponding to the option you need, or use the mouse or the arrow keys to move the character-sized cursor to the option you want. Then press Enter. These steps select any item on any AutoConvert menu. An item followed by characters that look like an arrow (——>) is a toggle command. Selecting that command switches the setting from one available choice to the other.

Because there are so many choices, and the need for them varies so much from one user to another, this chapter does not address each specific item that can be adjusted in AutoConvert. Loading and saving DXF files and AutoCAD drawing files is mentioned under the references for Load and Save in the *Generic CADD 6.0 Reference Manual,* but the best source for information on the specifics of DXF-file translation is Appendix A in the *Generic CADD User's Guide.* Unless you have very specific needs, however, following the menus in AutoConvert may be all the help you need.

Generally, you import DXF files as Generic CADD drawings and export Generic CADD drawings as DXF files. Figure 16.2 shows the Convert From DXF menu; Figure 16.3, the Convert To DXF menu. Do not let the "To" and "From" designations confuse you. Item 1 on the main menu says Convert From DXF. When you select this item, the new menu reads Convert to:. This is not a misprint. You are converting from DXF to whichever choice you make (most likely Generic CADD drawing file). The same logic is used in option 2 on the main menu, Convert To. In this case, because you are converting a DXF file to another format, the Convert To menu lists the choices available to convert from.

```
                ******    AutoConvert    ******



    Convert to:

    1) Generic CADD drawing file (.GCD)
    2) Generic CADD components (.CMP)
    3) Generic 3DD (.3DD)
    4) Generic 3DD components (.CM3)

    ESC) Return to Main Menu








    Enter selection >>>
```

Figure 16.2:
The AutoConvert Convert From menu.

Figure 16.4 illustrates the Default Path Menu, choice number 4 on the main menu. When you install Generic CADD, the file directories you select at that time are configured for use by AutoConvert. Unless you want to save drawings to different menus than the ones you already use in your CADD work, you probably do not need to change the existing settings in AutoConvert.

Figure 16.5 illustrates the Filenames, Fonts, and Linetypes Menu.

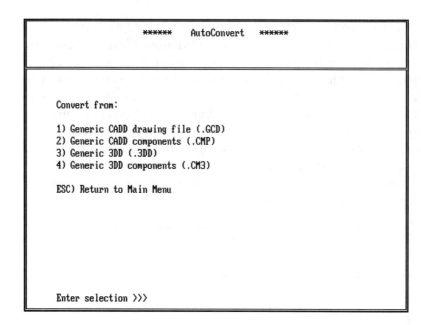

Figure 16.3:

*The AutoConvert
Convert To menu.*

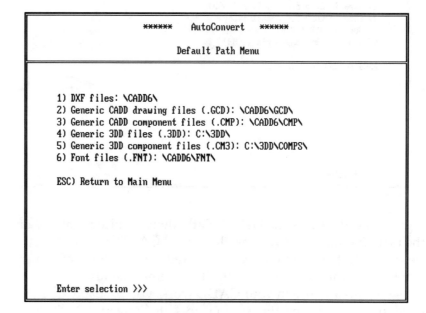

Figure 16.4:

*The AutoConvert
Default Path Menu.*

CADD 6.0, with its 19 new fonts that match AutoCAD fonts, makes setting up for translation of fonts between AutoCAD files and Generic CADD files much easier. The Font Conversion Table, selection number 6 on the Filenames, Fonts, and Linetypes Menu, is shown in figure 16.6. This choice is used to determine how fonts are translated between the two programs. Linetypes, which have names in AutoCAD but numbers in Generic CADD, continue to be a conversion challenge. The Linetype Conversion Table, selection number 7 from the Filenames, Fonts and Linetypes Menu, is shown in figure 16.7. The AutoConvert default selections for both fonts and linetypes should be adequate in most situations.

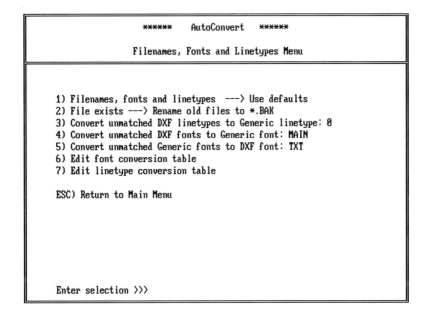

```
******    AutoConvert    ******

Filenames, Fonts and Linetypes Menu


1) Filenames, fonts and linetypes  ---> Use defaults
2) File exists ---> Rename old files to *.BAK
3) Convert unmatched DXF linetypes to Generic linetype: 0
4) Convert unmatched DXF fonts to Generic font: MAIN
5) Convert unmatched Generic fonts to DXF font: TXT
6) Edit font conversion table
7) Edit linetype conversion table

ESC) Return to Main Menu




Enter selection >>>
```

Figure 16.5:

The Filenames, Fonts, and Linetypes Menu.

Although the assorted settings in the Defaults Menu (see fig. 16.8) do not fit into a single category, such as font conversion or default paths, they guide AutoConvert in various aspects of the translation process.

After completing all the different settings, press Esc until you reach the main menu. Press Esc once more. Now AutoConvert asks whether or not you want to save the changes you have made. Type **Y** for yes, **N** for no. No matter which choice you make, the next prompt asks whether or not you want to quit AutoConvert. Press **Y** to exit AutoConvert and return to Generic CADD.

```
                    ******   AutoConvert   ******

                       Font Conversion Table

                      Generic        DXF
                   1) SYMATH         SYMATH
                   2) SYMAP          SYMAP
                   3) SYASTRO        SYASTRO
                   4) TEXT           TEXT
                   5) ITALIC         ITALIC
                   6) SCRIPTS        SCRIPTS
                   7) SCRIPTC        SCRIPTC
                   8) ROMANT         ROMANT
                   9) ROMANS         ROMANS
                  10) ROMAND         ROMAND

   1) Edit a pair
   2) Add a pair
   3) Delete a pair

   ESC) Return to previous menu              PG DN) More fonts

   Enter selection >>>
```

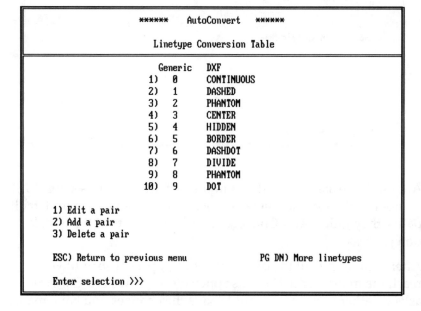

Figure 16.6:

The Font Conversion Table.

```
                    ******   AutoConvert   ******

                     Linetype Conversion Table

                     Generic   DXF
                   1)   0      CONTINUOUS
                   2)   1      DASHED
                   3)   2      PHANTOM
                   4)   3      CENTER
                   5)   4      HIDDEN
                   6)   5      BORDER
                   7)   6      DASHDOT
                   8)   7      DIVIDE
                   9)   8      PHANTOM
                  10)   9      DOT

   1) Edit a pair
   2) Add a pair
   3) Delete a pair

   ESC) Return to previous menu              PG DN) More linetypes

   Enter selection >>>
```

Figure 16.7:

The Linetype Conversion Table.

```
******    AutoConvert    ******

              Defaults Menu


    1) Generic CADD save  ---> Version 6.0 format
    2) AutoCAD Save  ---> Release 11
    3) Component files ---> Add component placement at 0,0
    4) Save Ellipses to DXF as  ---> Polyarc
    5) Number of line segments to break bezier curves into: 10
    6) Number of facets for circles and arcs: 16
    7) Colors ---> Preserve screen colors
    8) Traces and Solids ---> Create fills
    9) Convert AutoCAD Polyline Splines ---> Line Segments

    ESC) Return to Main Menu




    Enter selection >>>
```

Figure 16.8:

The Defaults Menu.

If you ever need to run AutoConvert from the DOS prompt without going into Generic CADD first, type **ACON** from the DOS prompt of the CADD6 directory.

Summary

Loading and using AutoCAD drawings in Generic CADD is a simple process. Unless you have special needs, all you need to do is use the Load command with the AutoCAD option. The hard disk spins, and after a few seconds an AutoCAD drawing appears, ready to be edited in Generic CADD.

To send drawings from Generic CADD to AutoCAD, you must create a copy of the file, using the DXF format. The AutoConvert program is used to create DXF files from CADD drawings and can be used also to import DXF files into Generic CADD. Not only is DFX used to send drawings from one CAD program to another; manufacturers of a variety of architectural and engineering products often use DFX as a neutral format for the distribution of symbol libraries.

Automating Repetitive Tasks with Macros

T he real power in using a computer for drafting comes not so much from its speed and accuracy, but from its capability to automate repetitive tasks. Most CADD packages, including Generic CADD, enable users to automate tasks by grouping commands into strings. Commands grouped together in such a manner are called *macros*.

Using Generic CADD for fun or profit becomes more fun and certainly more profitable if you use macros. You almost can't avoid using them, in fact. A macro can be used for nearly every command, providing endless opportunities to save keystrokes. Macros, batch files, and custom menus make an already fast CADD program even faster.

Macros also improve accuracy. They reduce input errors because—properly written—they do not make mistakes. Unlike people, macros never change a value, misspell a word, or get distracted by the telephone.

Macros can do just about anything that can be done manually—they can place text, place components, edit, even do some automatic drawing. If a task can be done with the keyboard, digitizer, or mouse, it can be done with a macro.

The information you learn in this chapter forms the foundation for an understanding of the material in the next three chapters. This chapter introduces you to macros in Generic CADD and gives you some sample macros to try.

Defining Macros

A macro can be as simple as stringing together one command and its single-letter option, such as TS,F (Text Setting, Font). This simple macro, for example, prepares the program to load a new font. A macro can include 250 characters, sometimes more, and about 80 commands—enough to perform just about any environmental update a user might want.

A macro's maximum length is determined by its use. Macros used in a menu are limited to 80 characters, minus the number of characters in the menu item name or line number. Macros assigned to a function key or pointer button are limited to 250 characters. Macros in the form of batch files are limited only by the computer's memory.

Macros can be made up of anything that can be typed on the keyboard. They may contain any legal Generic CADD command, any user response to a previous command, and even variables. Macros can perform most of the mundane drafting tasks that take up productive time; they can, in fact, be the most important tool in Generic CADD's toolbox.

Understanding How Macros Work

Basically, a Generic CADD macro works by temporarily using previously stored commands as input. The macro may be invoked by pressing a function key or pointer button, or by clicking on a menu selection. The CADD program acts on each command in sequence until it reaches the end, signified by a semicolon.

The following macro sets a chamfer distance and then issues a command to chamfer:

```
CA,.25",.25",CH;
```

Why combine the two commands? Because setting the chamfer distance every time a chamfer is required is redundant and uses CPU time. Using a macro saves at least one keystroke or click of the mouse, and the user always gets the correct chamfer size.

Writing and Saving Macros

Macros may be stored and used through four input methods: function keys, pointer buttons, menus, and batch files. Function keys and pointer buttons are discussed here; menus and batch files are explained in the next three chapters. All macros are written in the same command language, however.

Understanding the Ground Rules for Writing Macros

Only a few rules are required for writing macros, but those rules must be followed to the letter. Leave out a single character, even just a comma, and the macro will not work. The following special characters are used in macros:

- The comma (,) separates legal commands, data, and other special characters. It must be used to separate every command and response in a macro.

- The tilde (~) is used whenever the macro requires the user to type in any single value or a name (X and Y values count as one value each, that is (,~,~,)).

- The at sign (@) prompts the user to enter a point from the pointer or keyboard.

- The pound or number sign (#) acts as an Escape key and is used to end text placement in a macro.

- The semicolon (;) denotes the end of a macro. Anything after it is ignored; explanatory notes can be stored after the semicolon.

- The exclamation point (!) acts as an Enter key.

- The slash (/) deactivates a special character when placing text with a macro, so that a special macro character is read as text and not as part of a command. The slash is used prior to a special character. For example, put a slash before a comma, a number sign, or a slash that you want to appear as text (/,), (/#), or (//).

- The double plus (++) or double minus (--) signs set toggles on or off, in or out, and this or that. These symbols are used only after a toggle and have no effect when used anywhere else. Be prepared for a little trial and error when setting some toggles in macros.

Do not assume anything when you are writing macros. The only thing you should assume is that the settings your macro needs to run correctly may not be set properly. Use the double plus (++) or double minus (--) signs to set any toggles that are required in the macro.

Always identify units when you set a value in a macro. Setting the units ensures that the macro returns a value of one inch instead of one millimeter, for example. It is not necessary to use units for values of zero or when you set scale values.

Examining Macros

Many options are available when you write a macro. A detailed examination of two macros—one that places a component and one that draws a balloon—shows how they work.

Introducing the Component-Placing Macro

```
CR,A,@,@,GC,++,CZ,~,~,CI,++,CP,~,~,@,IP,@,@,@;
```

The first few characters control component rotation. There are actually three ways this section could have been written:

```
CR,A,@,@
```

This method enables the user to match the rotation with another line or direction. In most cases, the user should first snap to the leftmost or bottommost point and then to the second point.

`CR,V,@,@,@`

This method requires the user to select three points, following the prompt located in the status area of the screen. The three points selected form the angle that sets the component rotation.

`CR,~`

This method looks the simplest, but it requires the user to type the rotation from the keyboard (hence the tilde symbol). Remember, the zero-degree angle is at the 3 o'clock position on the monitor.

The Component Snap command in the macro enables you to use other points within the component as construction or snap points rather than the defined reference point:

`GC,++`

Turns on the Component Snap command. This is very useful for insertion of screw heads, clamps and so on.

`GC,--`

Turns off the Component Snap command.

The Component Scale (CZ) command should be included in every macro that places components because you probably will not know the scale setting when the macro is typed in:

`CZ,~,~`

This macro segment enables you to select X and Y scales that are either different from each other or the same. Remember, circles and arcs in exploded components cannot have different scales. Actual values can replace ,~,~, if you want to lock in a certain scale.

The Component Image (CI) command is included to make sure that the command is turned on or off in the macro:

`CI,++`

Places components as images. Images should be used whenever you are sure that the component is to be edited or when the drawing is to be converted to a DXF file.

CI,--

Places components as components. Components can be exploded for editing.

Placing the component is very simple in a macro. The user has two choices: "component name specific" or "user defined during execution of the macro." Either choice has its use and value, depending on the situation:

CP,name

Name-specific placement commands are used primarily in menus. They also can be used where special components used as drawings or dimensional symbols are employed.

CP,~,~,@

This command invokes the side bar menu and displays any components already loaded into memory. You also are enabled to look at the disk for components. You can click on one of these displayed components or type one from the keyboard. Digitizer users do not have the side bar option unless a video menu is loaded first. (See Chapter 18 for more information on loading video menus.)

The Insertion Point (IP) command, the last item in this macro, is used to reset the point of insertion of a macro. It enables you to set down the component temporarily and pick it up again. Then the components can be inserted with a different reference point and with more precision:

IP,@,@,@;

The first @ symbol pauses the macro so that you can choose a temporary resting place. The second @ is for choosing another insertion point. The third @ is for picking the placement point.

Introducing the Balloon Macro

The individual commands of the balloon macro are discussed in the following section. Make sure that your program is set to Manual Entry Offset Relative (MR) before trying out this macro.

```
YC,~,LT,0,LC,3,C2,@,.281",0,L1,
-.562",0,.562",0,PO,-.281",.04",PO,0,-.205";
```

```
YC,~
```

Current layer is user-selectable. Even if the layer in use is the desired layer, the user must still enter a layer number because pressing Enter without selecting a layer makes Generic CADD return a value of –1. Having a layer called –1 may be possible, but is not a good practice.

```
LT,0
```

Selects Line Type Zero (solid).

```
LC,3
```

Selects Line Color 3.

```
C2,@,.281",0
```

Draws a circle .562 inches in diameter and places it at the point you designate.

```
L1,-.562",0,.562",0
```

Draws a horizontal line through the center of the circle.

```
PO,-.281",.04"
```

Places a standard point for text insertion in the upper half of the balloon.

```
PO,0,-.205";
```

Places a standard point for text insertion in the lower half of the balloon.

Using Macro Assign (MA)

The Macro Assign command enables you to create and save macros on the fly. It is accessed in CADD by typing **MA** or clicking on Macro Assign from the UTILITIES menu. The prompt area at the bottom of the screen displays the prompt Press a function key or a pointer button to be assigned a macro >>. The choices, although not displayed, are as follows:

Pointer buttons B3 through B16 (B1 and B2 are reserved by Generic CADD)

Function keys F1 through F12

Ctrl + Function keys F1 through F12

Shift + Function keys F1 through F12

Alt + Function keys F1 through F12

It is possible to program as many as 62 macros using the function keys and pointer buttons. How can you remember exactly which does what? A list of your macros can be viewed in at least two ways.

The least complicated way is to use the Screen Flip command (SF) and select the third item (Display assigned macros). The screen display lists the macros. A secondary menu appears under the list, offering these choices:

Shift Alt Ctrl Function_key - Pointer_button

Selecting any one of these secondary menu items displays an additional 12 function keys (except Pointer button, which displays 16 button selections).

The second way to examine your macros is slightly more complicated at first, but may prove easier to use in the long run. In this method, you must use a video driver that supports the use of the Image Save (SA,I) command. Use the Load ASCII (LA) command, introduced in Chapter 6, to load MACROCMD.FIL as a "drawing." When the drawing is complete, save a GX2 image of it. (Erase the drawing; you only wanted it so that you could create a GX2 image file.) Then place the following macro on a function key:

```
LO,I,\path\macro;
```

F1 is a logical choice; most programs use F1 to access help.

When you are using a mouse or the keyboard, the primary function keys should be programmed with snaps to increase the input speed. When you are using a 16-button puck or a digitizer, the snaps should be assigned to the buttons.

When selecting the secondary function buttons for assignment, you must press Ctrl, Shift, or Alt as well as the function keys because the menu displays only the current status of the function keys.

Using Screen Flip (SF)

The Screen Flip (SF) command assigns, edits, and saves macros. The command works in much the same way as the Macro Assign command. The primary difference is that Screen Flip displays a menu. Choosing #3 from the SF menu displays the choices as follows:

```
Shift  Alt  Ctrl  Function_key - Pointer_button
```

Editing is accomplished in the following example.

Using Screen Flip (SF) To Write and Save a Macro

Prompt	Input	Description
Command	**SF**	Starts the Screen Flip command
Enter Selection>	**3**	Accepts Display assigned macros
Press a function key or pointer button to be assigned a macro	Press a function key and then use Backspace until cleared	Clears any previously assigned macro and prepares line for new macro
Edit macro [Fno.]>>	**CA,.5",.5",CH;** and Press Enter	Establishes and saves new macro

When selecting the secondary function buttons for assignment, you must press Ctrl, Shift, or Alt along with the function keys, because the menu displays only the current status of the function keys.

Creating Some Sample Macros

The best way to learn how to write macros is to try writing and using some of the sample macros in this chapter. These sample macros use component placement, environment settings, and editing sequences. The following macros can preset dimensional displays, set dimension offsets, place text, construct drawing elements, and select line color and type.

Setting Up Dimensional Display Macros

One of the major obstacles when finishing a drawing is selecting dimensional displays. How the dimension is displayed is not particularly important until the plot is finished. That is when all the multiple lines in the same spot show up. Turning off different witness lines and arrows for each dimension can be a hassle.

The following macro sets options available in the Dimension Display (DD) and Arrows (AR) commands:

```
DD,L,++,R,++,D,++,E,--,X,--,T,++,!,AR,O,++,!;
```

The macro hides both extension lines and sets arrows outside pointing in (see fig. 17.1).

The next macro:

```
DD,L,++,R,++,D,++,E,--,X,++,T,++,!,AR,O,++,!;
```

hides the first (left) extension line and sets arrows outside pointing in (see fig 17.1).

When almost every dimension requires a different setting, the macro becomes even more important.

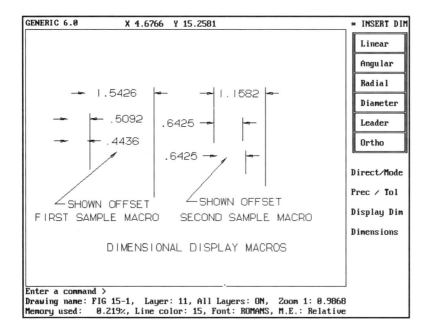

The unusual CADD menus shown in this chapter were created by using Extended ASCII characters to define borders. Writing custom menus is explained in the next chapter.

When returning to standard dimensioning from an ortho dimensional display, extension line offsets must be reset. The next macro:

```
XS,0,.06",A,.12",B,.44",!,DT,P,++,D,--,!;
```

sets the line gap, above and below line distance, dimension text placement, and direction (see fig 17.2).

Constructing a Split Assembly Balloon

Every drawing has certain elements that serve to clarify the drawing. The following macro constructs a split assembly balloon (commonly used in engineering drawings to label objects) and places text location points inside the balloon to center text. Remember to set your program to Manual Entry Offset Relative (MR) before trying this macro.

```
YC,~,LT,0,LC,3,C2,@,.281",0,L1,
-.562",0,.562",0,PO,
-.281",.04",PO,0,-.205";
```

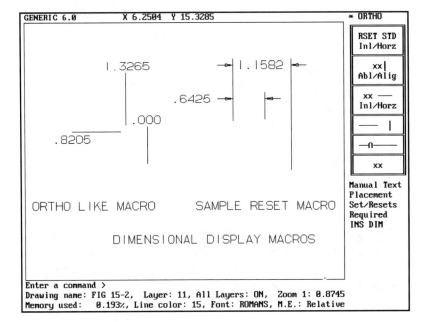

Figure 17.2:

Resetting offsets.

Figure 17.3 shows the text location points.

Standardizing Text Input

Standardized text placement with macros speeds input. The following example demonstrates just how effective macros can be.

```
TL,@,TEXT PLACE,!,#;
```

Figure 17.4 shows the insertion point.

Standardized text, whether accessed through pointer buttons, function keys, or menus, can speed text input by a factor of 15.

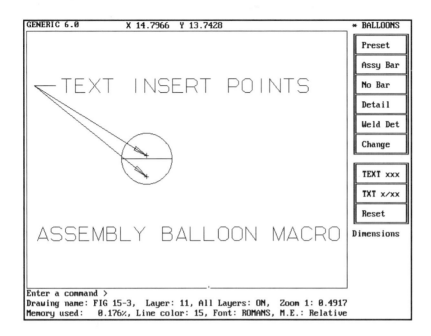

Figure 17.3:

Assembly balloon with text location points.

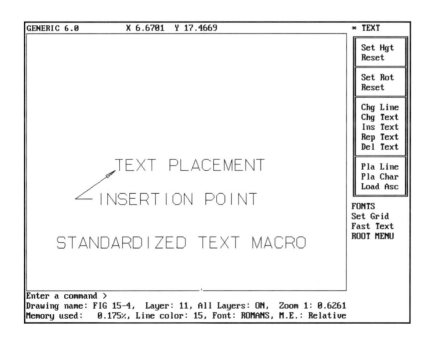

Figure 17.4:

Standardized text input.

Setting Line Type and Color

The following simple macro ties line type to line color. The layer, width, scale, and so on could be included also.

```
LT,0,LC,1;
```

Placing Components

Macros should be used to place every component. All conditions can be set with a macro and are not forgotten, including scale, rotation, layer, image on/off, component snap, insertion point, and the component itself. The following macro includes all of these components:

```
CR,A,@,@,GC,++,CZ,~,~,CI,++,CP,~,IP,@,@,@;
```

The user must decide whether to use A or V after CR; ++ or -- after GC and after CI; O,C, or P after XY; and whether IP is to be used at all.

The preceding macro enables you to set the rotation by pointing to the ends of an existing line, setting the X and Y scale, naming the component, and changing the insertion point.

Setting Up the Environment

Macros can be written to set or reset any or all default values. When you are starting a drawing that is going to be plotted at half size, clicking on a macro that sets all affected defaults to double scale makes quick work of a very time-consuming process.

Text height, dimensional offsets, arrowhead lengths, and shoulder lengths are just a few items that can be included in a macro.

```
TS,Z,~,!,XS,0,~,A,~,B,~,!,AR,L,~,!,LL,~;
```

If the macro contains actual values instead of the tilde for user input, the process is even faster. Several macros could be written for all the different scales used.

Using Common Editing Sequences

Because editing drawings takes more time than constructing them, reducing the number of keystrokes is essential. Just as components reduce input time for drawing, macros can reduce editing time. Macros that select, chamfer, fillet radii, and change dimensions reduce keystrokes. A few examples of editing macros follow:

    CA,.25",.25",CH;

Sizes and places the command for chamfer

    FR,.5",FI;

Sizes and places the command for fillet

    UG,@,O,!;

Changes the location of dimension arrows (see fig. 17.5)

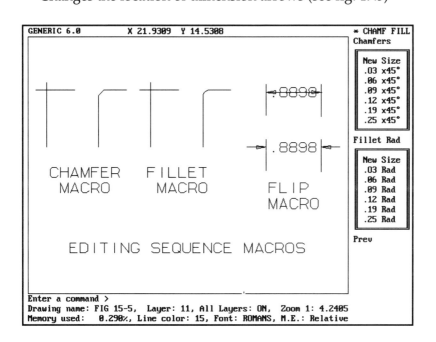

Figure 17.5:

Sample editing sequences.

Hundreds of editing macros are possible, but you can get along nicely with about 24.

Summary

In this chapter, you learned many things about macros. You know now from examples that macros are nothing more than command strings that automate repetitive tasks. You learned about the maximum lengths of macros and how to use the Generic CADD commands to achieve greater ease and speed in your use of Generic CADD.

Learning how macros work and the rules that govern them is a good foundation for writing your first macros. Several macros were examined to show the different options available to you. You have been guided through several sample macros, ranging from dimensional-display macros to common editing-sequence macros. These examples enabled you to expand your understanding of macros.

You learned through the Macro Assign (MA) and Screen Flip (SF) commands how macros can be written and saved. These two commands guide the user through the macro-writing process.

The next three chapters build on the material covered in this chapter. It will be assumed as you work through them that you have already reviewed the material presented here. If you think that writing macros to place on function keys adds a great deal of power to Generic CADD, wait until you see what can be done with menus!

Tailoring the Menu System

C hapter 17 introduced macros, which provide the capability of stringing together several commands to be executed with one keystroke (or one set of keystrokes). The next level of Generic CADD customization is tailoring the menu system. Menus are easy to edit, easy to use, and surprisingly powerful. Not only can a custom menu execute CADD commands, it also can provide custom access to directories on your disk without using File Selector. Many experienced Generic CADD users consider their custom menu system to be the backbone of their automated drafting work.

The standard menu structure provided with Generic CADD is stored in a special ASCII text file called CADD6.MNU. The program looks for and loads this menu because it is listed in the environmental file. The menu is not simply a list of command choices; it is a hierarchy that begins at the base menu, known as the ROOT menu, which lists the other menu choices. In this chapter, all other menus are referred to as submenus or pages. A *submenu* lists available commands, and on occasion, other submenus or pages.

After Generic CADD boots and the first screen has been displayed, the program loads the menu system, starting with the ROOT menu (see fig. 18.1). ROOT MENU, the first item at the top of the menu, is followed by a blank line, below which is a list of items that can be selected to view the various submenus. The ROOT menu in figure 18.1 is an edited version in which the standard menu selections precede the added options.

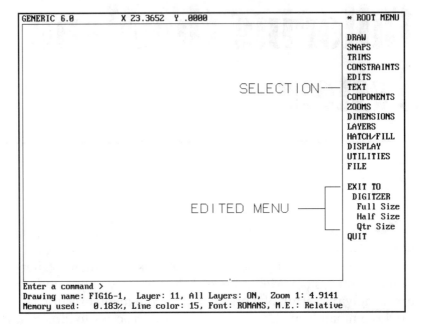

Figure 18.1:

ROOT menu.

After one of these submenus is selected, the appropriate submenu is displayed. The first item indicates its submenu or page name, followed by a blank line which separates the submenu name from the command choices available. As figure 18.2 shows, the last three choices may be menu selection options such as Previous, ROOT menu, or More. Choosing the Previous option returns the menu to the last-displayed page, whereas choosing the More option advances the menu to whatever you have named as the next page. Some first-time users mistakenly think that "More" means there are more menu choices of the same type, but the More option actually can take you to any specified location in the file, by naming a location to match the request accompanying the More statement.

Certain commands, such as Hide, Display, Current Layer, call up a unique feature known as the *sidebar*. This feature is Generic CADD's answer to pull-down menus. The sidebar not only lists the current contents of the database but also enables you to browse through the hard disk and pick items for insertion into the drawing file. When you select Cancel, the program returns to the submenu that was in use before you began browsing. Figure 18.3 shows a sidebar menu that lists all the drawing files in the directory.

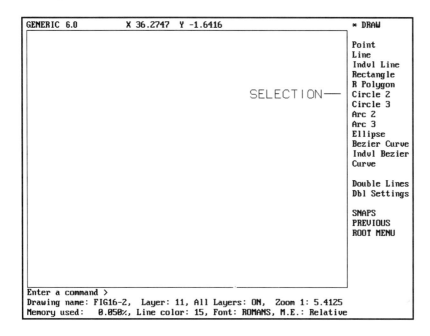

Figure 18.2:

Typical submenu.

The sidebar feature does much more than most menu systems. When you select Line Type, Line Width, or Line Color, the sidebar displays the actual line type, width, or color rather than the corresponding numerical equivalent. The sidebar lists any file that is assigned one of the default paths for drawings, components, images, fonts, batches, and hatches. The user can set the current layer, hide or display layers, or set the display to show only the layers that contain data.

Unlike most other CADD programs, Generic CADD offers a unique menu system with a command structure or user interface that enables you to do simple editing. You don't have to be a programmer to edit a Generic CADD menu, and the menu does not have to be compiled before it can be used. For instance, very few of the menu items in the Generic CADD video menu (CADD6.MNU) can be considered true macros. Even so, the capability exists to customize the existing menus or to replace them with new ones. Generic CADD menus can include macro commands that also could be assigned to a function key. CADD menus also may be used to load batch file macros (covered in Chapter 20).

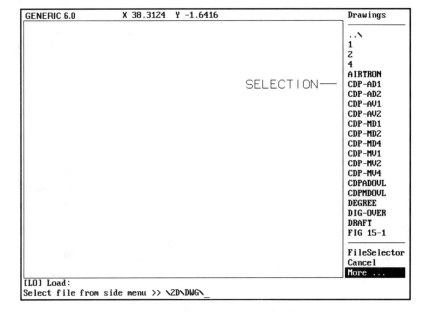

Figure 18.3:

Typical sidebar.

Introducing the Anatomy of Generic CADD's Menu System

One of the best automobile engines ever developed was the Ford flat-head V-8. It delivered plenty of power and respectable gasoline mileage, and any shade-tree mechanic could modify it. It was a people's engine. Generic CADD's menu system is one of the flat-head V-8s of this world.

Viewing the existing CADD menu is a good way to begin learning how to write a menu. Making a printout of the menu so that it is available at all times for reference also helps. If you look at the CADD6.MNU in your text editor, for example, you can see that the menu has two parts: the name and the action. The name section displays menu names and notes. Names must consist of at least one character; although more than 12 characters can be used for a name, only as many as 12 are displayed when the menu is in use. You can add additional text or instructional notes such as *Go to XYZ menu* or *Return to ABC menu*. All lines containing text in the menu name section must be followed by a comma; otherwise, the program will not display that line.

The action section follows the name section's last comma. The action section consists of any legal commands. Each command, symbol, or user-supplied name or value must be separated by a comma. This section ends with a semicolon. Instructions or programming notes may be included in the menu file after the semicolon, because the program ignores everything after the semicolon.

The total length of any one line (including name and action) must not exceed 80 characters, counting from the first character to and including the semicolon. Spaces count as characters.

Submenu names must begin with an asterisk (*), followed by a space, and then the name. To create a submenu named Draw, you would type *** DRAW**. A call to the Draw submenu from another part of the menu would be written as **DRAW,****. Returning to the ROOT menu would be **ROOT menu,****. Semicolons are not used to identify the end of a menu name.

Another way to call the DRAW submenu is to use the Page command (PG). Thus, **Draw,PG,DRAW;** displays the submenu DRAW. The Page command **Prev,PG,0;** recalls the previously displayed page. If the submenu contains more items than fit on a single page, *** DRAW2** adds a second page. The following list sums up the different ways to page submenus. The first column lists ways to summon another menu; the second column shows the submenu that appears when you pick the listing from the video menu.

Menu Line Listing	New menu
DRAW,**	* DRAW
Draw,PG,DRAW;	* DRAW
More,PG,DRAW2;	* DRAW2
Prev,PG,0;	* DRAW

Adding Items to a Menu

Adding a menu item is very simple in Generic CADD. As you develop a working knowledge of the CADD6.MNU, you undoubtedly will want to edit the menu. The Generic CADD menu is the logical place to make improvements; it is the platform on which to build the enhancements that are uniquely yours. You can write a completely new menu, if you wish—one uniquely tailored to your needs. The end result is a menu that improves your efficiency because it reflects *your* approach to automated drafting.

Editing an Existing Menu

Because CADD video menus are simply text files, you can edit them with a text editor or with a word processor that imports and exports ASCII text. Editing the existing menu is another good way to start learning to write a menu. Using the existing menu as a model, you can examine and imitate it. Be sure to make a backup copy of your CADD6.MNU file before you try editing it.

You cannot add more lines to a menu below the last effective line in a menu page. If you do, the new lines are not visible on-screen and do not appear when you scroll down to the next menu page. The number of lines in a menu page on your computer depends on the resolution of the video display you use. Count the number of available lines, and then be careful to stay within the limit for each menu page.

In the following example, the Constraints submenu is being edited by adding a 1/8" grid setup selection on line 106. In your text editor, scroll down to the Constraints menu and add a line, as marked in figure 18.4. (This is line 106 if your text editor displays line numbers.) To add the line, type the following:

```
.125 Grid,gs,.125,.125,!;
```

```
89: * CONSTRAINTS
90:
91: Ortho Mode,or;
92: Ortho Angle,oa;
93:
94: Tracking,tk;
95: Cursor Free,cf;
96:
97: Grid On/Off,gr;
98: Snap Grid,sg;
99: Grid Size,gs;
100: Grid Reorgin,go;
101: Curs Move,cm;
102:
103: 1.0  Grid,gs,1,!;
104:  .5  Grid,gs,0.5,!;
105: .25  Grid,gs,0.25,!;
106:*
107:
108:                          Insert new line
109: ROOT MENU,**
110: * EDITS
111:
112: Move Point,mp;
```

Figure 18.4:

Constraints submenu in a text editor.

A digitizer menu is edited the same way a video menu is edited. Because the menu name is not displayed in a digitizer menu, however, there is no need to make the name describe the submenu. Many digitizer users assign numbers to their menus. Numbering schemes range from simple to elaborate, from 1,2,3,...,512 to M01L01B26 (menu 1, line 1, and box 26). It is acceptable to use just one character followed by a comma.

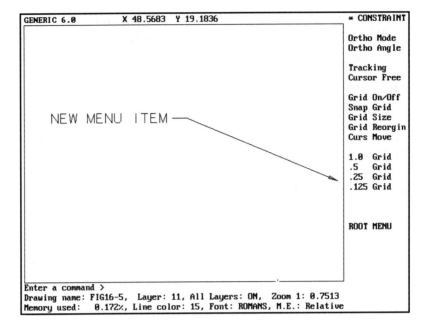

Figure 18.5:

Edited Constraints submenu screen.

Writing a New Menu

At some point, you may discover that the CADD6 menu does not completely meet all your requirements. The CADD6 menu was not designed to be an all-encompassing, do-everything menu. It does cover all the commands, in a logical order. You may need several menus: one for your applications, another to plot scales, and another to meet individual client needs. The next two sections cover developing video and digitizer menus. Don't try to reinvent the wheel; print a hard copy of CADD6.MNU to use as a guide.

Video Menus

To write one menu that meets all your requirements can lead to a megamenu. A full-blown menu loaded with macros can require 19-20K, five to six times the RAM used by the CADD6.MNU file. Unless the memory capacity of the computer is greater than 1M, you are better off having separate menus that accomplish different tasks.

You could create three submenus, such as Main, Draw, and Dimension. In figure 18.6, the Main submenu (shown as a sidebar) includes Display, Setup, Utilities, Input, Output, Menu, as well as options to Go to Draw, Go to Dimensions, and Quit. The Go to items toggle from the Main submenu to either the Draw or Dimension submenus. As part of your customized solution, you can choose as many different divisions as you need.

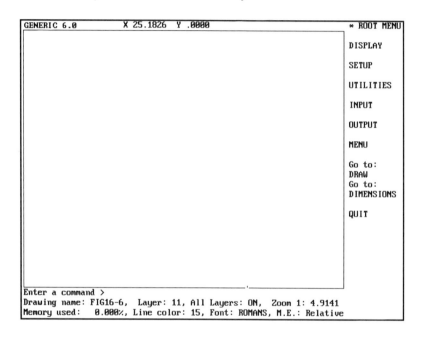

Figure 18.6:
ROOT menu of the Main menu.

Part of the Main submenu, the Display submenu, could contain Color, Points, Coordinates, Screen, and Misc. The Setup submenu could contain all items set to update the environment. Utilities could include Manual Entry, Measure, Drawing, and a Misc. category for other utilities. The Input submenu could contain all the load commands; Output could have the plot and save commands. The Menu submenu could contain other menu toggles, trace commands, and so on. The Draw selection toggles out to the Draw submenu.

As figure 18.7 shows, the Draw menu's ROOT-menu page could list the following: Draw (selects two or more submenu pages), Layers, Text, Fonts, Edits, Components, Attributes, Shortcuts,

Units, as well as the Go to Dimensions and Return to Main Menu toggles.

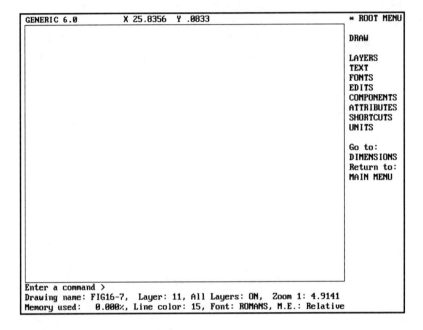

Figure 18.7:

ROOT menu page of the DRAW menu.

Selecting Draw brings up the first drawing menu page (see fig. 18.8), from which you can access lines, arcs, circles, redraws, erase, zooms, line type, and snaps menu pages.

> **TIP** The borders you see around various parts of the menus in this chapter were created by using Extended ASCII characters. Consult your DOS manual or the manual provided with your text editor for a guide to Extended ASCII characters. For best results, end each line of Extended ASCII characters with a **,pu;**.

Clicking on More displays the second Draw menu page (see fig. 18.9). In this example, the second page accesses (in addition to most of the Generic CADD entity commands), Standard Components (on-line), Grids, Redraw, Erase, Zooms, Chamfers, Fillets, Hatches, and Fills. Notice the repeats in the menu selections. By repeating selections in different locations, you reduce the need to switch pages. (Switching pages can be a time-consuming burden.) Selecting the Prev option returns you to the first drawing page, whereas choosing the Root menu returns you to the first menu page.

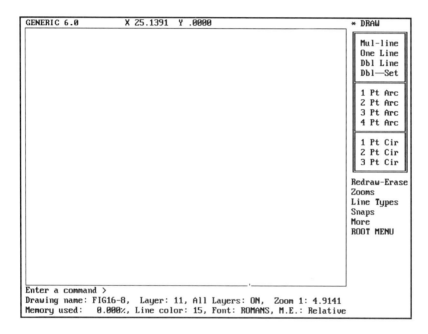

Figure 18.8:

First Draw menu page.

By returning to the Draw submenu's ROOT-menu page, you can select Go to Dimensions to toggle out to the Dimensions submenu (see fig. 18.10). The selection options include Dimensions, Layers, Text, Fonts, Zoom View, Redraw Era, Grid-Ortho, Go to Draw, and Return to Main Menu.

Selecting the Dimensions submenu calls up another page (see fig. 18.11). Each option in the list calls up other menu pages. The Shoulder selection is for setting the leader shoulder length, for example.

If you select Ins Dims, a page similar to that shown in figure 18.12 is displayed; you can select Generic CADD dimension commands from this page. Other selections call up pages that offer Dimensions, Direction, Mode, Precision, Tolerance, and Display command choices.

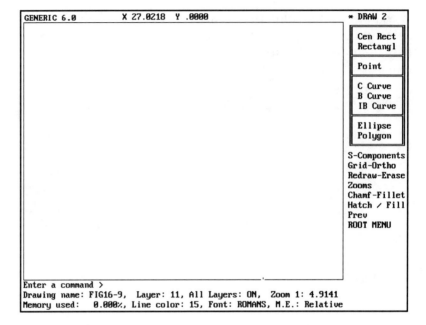

Figure 18.9:

Second menu page.

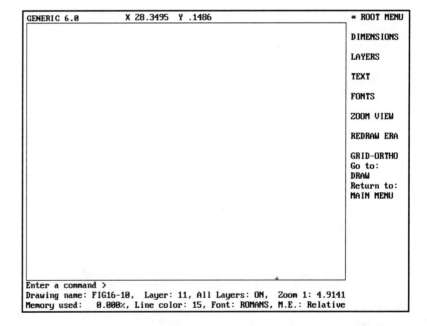

Figure 18.10:

Dimension Root menu.

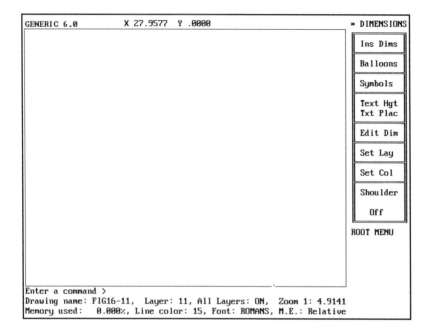

Figure 18.11:
Dimension submenu page.

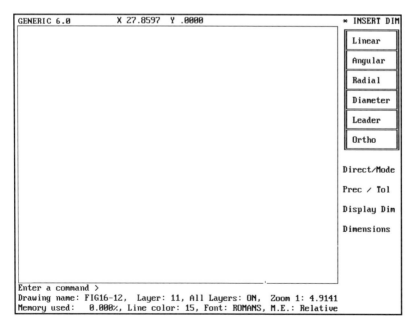

Figure 18.12:
Insert Dimension submenu.

Selecting Display Dim displays a page of Dimensional Display presets (see fig. 18.13). The symbols displayed in the menu represent various dimensional settings used in the drawing process. Selecting one of these symbols runs a macro that sets all Dimension Settings to match. With a little imagination, you can see the dimension Generic CADD displays. Other pages show more presets and other variations.

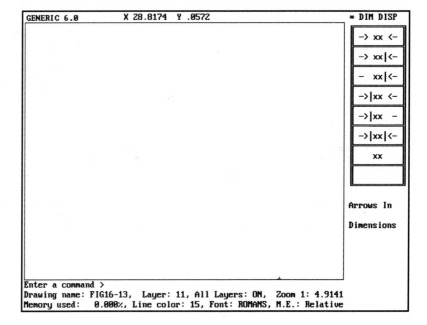

Figure 18.13:

Dimensional presets.

You are not limited by the CADD6.MNU file when writing your own menu. Let your imagination run freely. Your menu can be as plain and simple or as complex as you want it to be. The important thing is that it fulfills your requirements. As you gain experience in editing and writing menus, other ideas will occur to you. Editing is a continuing process in which you are always improving, always tailoring your CADD menus to match specific needs.

Digitizer Menus

Digitizer menus are like video menus but they do not have submenus and do not display menu names. They require an overlay drawing. Digitizer menus are much faster to use than video menus, and video menus can still be accessed. Digitizer menus require a bit more work to set up. The overlay drawing must be well thought out. Perfecting a working model may take several attempts.

Generic CADD can display as many as 10 digitizer menus at one time. These menus may be contained in a single file or in 10 separate files. You probably will only use 4 or 5, at most. The digitizer menu requires an active area in addition to the enabled menus.

As in video menus, the maximum memory available to store the menu is limited only by the amount of memory you are willing to allocate to digitizer menus. Each line in a digitizer menu can have 80 characters—including spaces.

Where do you start—with the menu file or the overlay drawing? Although both steps are done concurrently, you should start by developing your digitizer menu on a hard-copy layout of the proposed overlay. How many squares are enough? The largest practical number for a 12×12 tablet is 26×26 = 676 squares.

The menu file does not have submenus, but the overlay does. When you design the overlay, you need to consider not only the number but also the shape of the squares. The example in figure 18.14 demonstrates this treatment for text.

When you design the overlay, delete commands that have little or no relevancy to your application. Devote your planning time to the commands that actually are going to be used and consider carefully which of these remaining commands should or should not be combined into macros. In general, the use of macros (as opposed to using only single two-letter commands for each menu item) makes the best use of any menu. Macros reduce the number of keystrokes necessary to carry out an editing sequence.

As you write the menu file, take care to group similar commands in the spot that matches the overlay. Digitizer menus are numbered from left to right and from top to bottom. To avoid confusion, number the overlay hard copy with the correct number and the command you want. Refer to this reference for each line of the menu file, to ensure that the commands and overlay match.

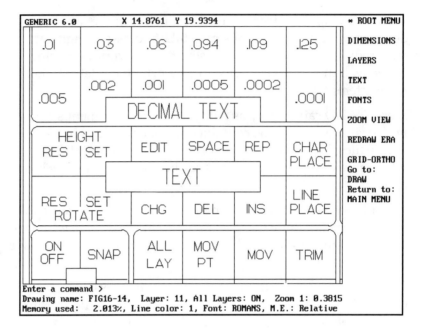

Figure 18.14:

Sample digitizer overlay.

The numbering of the overlay squares must not only coincide with the menu file but also include all the menus enabled in the environmental file. Menu 1, for example, may have 286 squares numbered from 1 to 286. Menu 2 may have 90 squares numbered from 287 to 376. Menu 3 may have 75 squares numbered from 377 to 451, and menu 4 may have 60 squares numbered from 452 to 511. The user must keep all the active menus in mind when laying out the overlay.

Another important overlay feature to consider is the active area. The smaller the active area, the faster the cursor moves on-screen. A good ratio to use for the active area is about 75 percent of the screen's drawing area; this gives the user good control for eye-hand coordination.

After the digitizer menu file and overlay are completed, a series of steps still must be taken before Generic CADD can use the overlay. The user must enable the digitizer menu in CADD. This is accomplished by the Select Digitizer command. Type **LD** and then select the Setup option. Follow the prompts for each menu area of the overlay. Then type **AA** to select the active area of the overlay, and follow the prompts. Finally, the environment must be updated. Type **EN** and press Enter. This final step saves the digitizer setup.

What do you do when the list of commands is greater than the number of squares available? You may not need to start over. Remember the second button on most calculators? Using the second calculator button, you can add a second function to the 1 key. The following example uses this second-button principle.

Suppose, for example, that 8 squares are left on the overlay and you have 14 commands left—all of the same type. In the normal area of the digitizer file and overlay, place the first 7 commands plus a macro that toggles to a new menu. Then, at the end of the menu file, place the next 7 commands plus another macro that toggles back to the original commands (see example). Because the last 8 commands in the menu file belong to a new menu, you must tell Generic CADD that a new menu is in the file. To do this, type **DM** and then **S**. Then follow the prompts and type **EN** (Environment Save).

The macros for toggling the menus follow:

```
Menu toggle macro; line no.,DM,E,4,5,#;
Toggle back macro; line no.,DM,E,5,4,#;
```

Remember that when a new menu is enabled over another, the original menu no longer functions. Also, make sure that the two toggle macros are placed on the same square.

If you are a new user or are under pressure to get work out, consider purchasing one of the industry-specific digitizer menus. They can save an enormous amount of time because editing purchased menus and overlays to suit your work is much faster than writing a custom menu from scratch.

Linking Menus

The loading of menus in a multimenu environment can be controlled in two ways. Either load several small menus, one at a time, or swap one menu for another. Both approaches are outlined in the following sections.

Adding Menus

When one menu is loaded on top of another, Generic CADD appends the second menu to the first. This is known as *linking* menus. One of the drawbacks of using this method is that it generates several small menu files that must then be maintained. Generic CADD's sidebar feature solves the problem of remembering the file names, but unless the file names of the menus indicate their functions, you still won't know what each file does. Therefore, give each menu file a name that serves as a reminder of its function.

Chaining Menus

Chaining menus is an alternative to linking menus. *Chaining* enables you to replace one menu with another. This is useful because special-purpose menus, such as component library menus, can be quite large (a component menu may need more than 39K). The larger the menu, the longer it takes to create and maintain. When menus exceed the amount of RAM allocated by CADD, the overflow is stored in a memory buffer on the hard drive. A large menu, used with a large drawing, can slow system performance.

The Component menu (see fig. 18.15) is a menu for inserting clamps into a drawing. You can see the differences between the item choices and the chaining macros on the page shown. The chaining macros erase the current menu and replace it with another. The next menu can be chained to the first or to the last (fourth) menu. Only one menu is in memory at any given time.

The macros that chain or swap menus are as follows:

```
item name,VX,LV,new menu;
line no.,LV,Y,new menu;
item name,VX,LV,old menu;
item name,LD,Y,old menu;
```

Chaining in menus saves keystrokes, memory, and time. What's more, the procedure is done correctly every time.

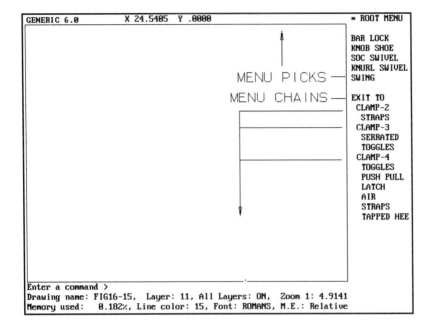

```
GENERIC 6.0          X 24.5405  Y .0000                    * ROOT MENU

                                                           BAR LOCK
                                                           KNOB SHOE
                                                           SOC SWIVEL
                                                           KNURL SWIVEL
                            MENU PICKS ─                   SWING

                            MENU CHAINS ─                  EXIT TO
                                                            CLAMP-2
                                                            STRAPS
                                                           CLAMP-3
                                                            SERRATED
                                                            TOGGLES
                                                           CLAMP-4
                                                            TOGGLES
                                                            PUSH PULL
                                                            LATCH
                                                            AIR
                                                            STRAPS
                                                            TAPPED HEE





Enter a command >
Drawing name: FIG16-15,  Layer: 11, All Layers: ON,  Zoom 1: 4.9141
Memory used:   0.182%, Line color: 15, Font: ROMANS, M.E.: Relative
```

Figure 18.15:

Component menu with chain macros.

Customizing Menus

Custom menus can encompass any type of menu for any purpose; they adapt Generic CADD's menu structure to meet your needs. Figures 18.5 through 18.16 illustrate a variety of custom menus. Custom menus can be used to access components, automate drafting, and for such special purposes as inserting standardized text.

Making Menus for Component Libraries

If you have just a few components, you can get by without a special system for keeping track of them. The sidebar, for example, enables you to view a list of the components in the database and to access the hard disk on the default path. This approach works adequately with a limited number of components, but with hundreds or thousands of component names to choose from, the process slows considerably. The Custom menu offers the best path to speedy access.

The Custom menu can be as simple as a list of component file names that begins with the command CP and ends with a semicolon, as follows:

```
item or line no.,CP,comp;
```

This is not as effective as a menu that controls rotation, scale, explosion layer, snaps, images, and insertion point, while also placing the component. But a menu controlling all these features would be quite large.

One way to reduce the size of such a menu file would be to place the modifying commands at the beginning of every page, like this:

```
Rotation,CR;
Scale,CZ;
Snaps,GC;
Image on,CI,++;
   off,CI,--;
Exp Lay,XY,P;            C or O also can be used
Insert pt.,IP;
```

This list would take seven lines. These same menu items could all be included in the string to yield about 1/3 more component placements per page:

```
menu name,CR,A,@,@,CZ,~,~,GC,++,CI,--,
XY,P,CP,name,IP,@,@,@;
```

Either method works just fine, as will any combination of the two (see fig. 18.16 and fig. 18.17).

Using Menus for Automated Drafting

Automated drafting menus can access macros, batch files, and standard component files to perform drafting tasks.

Macros on a Menu

Macros can be used to draw small symbols for placement in a drawing file. This lends speed, and there are no disk files to contend with. Menued macros produce the same results every time they are used. Figure 18.18 shows a menu page of detail balloons drawn by macros.

```
101:  ** KNOB
102:  SELECT,
103:      LAYER,YC,~;
104:      SCALE,CZ,~,~;
105:      ROTAT,CR,A,@,@;
106:      EXP-LAY,XY,C,!;
107:
108:  38BAR 131S P,CP,CL0014P;
109:  38BAR 131S S,CP,CL0014S;
110:  38BAR 231S P,CP,CL0015P;
111:  38BAR 231S S,CP,CL0015S;
112:  38BAR 331S P,CP,CL0016P;
113:  38BAR 331S S,CP,CL0016S;
114:  50BAR 162S P,CP,CL0017P;
115:  50BAR 162S S,CP,CL0017S;
116:  50BAR 262S P,CP,CL0018P;
117:  50BAR 262S S,CP,CL0018S;
118:  50BAR 462S P,CP,CL0019P;
119:  50BAR 462S S,CP,CL0019S;
120:
121:  Prev,PG,0;
122:  NEXT,PG,KN2;
123:  * KN2
124:
```

Figure 18.16:

From a Component menu.

```
190:  190,A4;
191:  191,PO;
192:  192,RP;
193:  193,EP;
194:  194,CZ,~,~,CR,A,@,@,XY,C,CP,HEXBOLTP;
195:  195,CZ,~,~,CR,A,@,@,XY,C,CP,HEXBOLIZ,IP,@,@,@;
196:  196,CZ,~,~,CR,A,@,@,XY,C,CP,HEXBOLTS,IP,@,@,@;
197:  197,CZ,1,1,CR,A,@,@,XY,C,CP,TBALLS;
198:  198,CZ,1,1,XY,C,CP,TBALLP;
199:  199,CZ,~,~,CR,A,@,@,XY,C,CP,SPRINGS,IP,@,@,@;
200:  200,CZ,~,~,CR,A,@,@,XY,C,CP,PLUGS;
201:  201,CZ,~,~,CR,A,@,@,XY,C,CP,PLUGP;
202:  202,CZ,~,~,CR,A,@,@,XY,C,CP,PHSS;
203:  203,CZ,~,~,XY,C,CP,PHSP;
204:  204,ZL;
205:  205,ZA;
206:  206,ZI;
207:  207,ZM;
208:  208,ZU;
209:  209,GS,~,~;
210:  210,GO;
211:  211,CO;
212:  212,MI;
213:  213,RC;
```

Figure 18.17:

From a Digitizer menu.

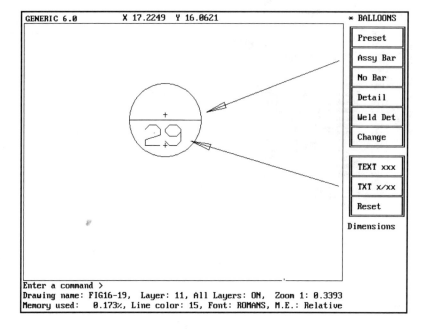

Figure 18.18:

Menu page of macros.

Standard Components on a Menu

Standard components can be placed quickly into a drawing file. The process is fast, and there are no disk files to remember. When using menu components (as when using a menu with macros), the user can expect the same results every time. Figure 18.19 shows a menu page of dimension symbols that can be inserted as components.

Submenus can be used as selective branches their parent menu. A toggle clamp, for example, has several variations: solid or open bar, straight or tee handle, vertical or horizontal bases. By creating a tree menu that has submenus for each successively smaller clamp, the path can be narrowed to a single list of choices.

Standard Drawings on a Menu

After you have used Generic CADD only a short time, your collection of drawing files will grow. These files soak up disk space with no way to access the data efficiently. Some of these drawings may be used repeatedly as standard items. Other drawings can be used as templates on which minor changes can be made. To access these important drawings, build a menu and reap huge benefits. Such a menu enables you to cut and paste drawings, thus reducing the huge blocks of time needed for drawing tasks. The standard drawings obtained from the menu and used in figure 18.20 reduced a 4-hour drawing task to 15 minutes.

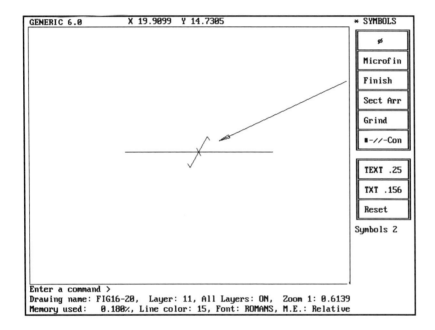

Figure 18.19:

Menu page of industry standard components.

Complete drawings can be stored as drawings or text (batch) files, called up with a menu, and placed into a drawing. Figure 18.21 demonstrates how this approach can be used.

Creating Menus for Special Needs

Special needs menus are determined by the user; they are whatever the user needs. One such need could be a menu to place standardized text into a drawing. Because text placement by macro increases the speed of text input by a factor of 15, a text-placement menu certainly fills the bill. Because fewer keystrokes are involved when you use a text-placement macro, you can expect more accuracy and less fatigue.

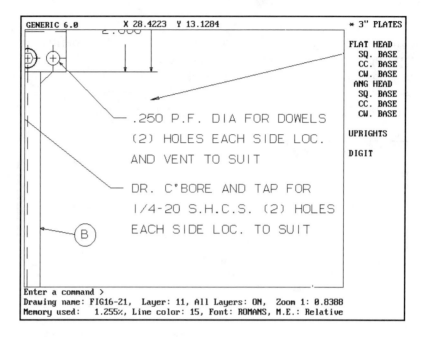

Figure 18.20:

Menu page of standard drawings.

One submenu could include key words that pertain to all text on a floor plan; another could refer to foundations; and the next could deal with elevations. As figure 18.21 demonstrates, just page to the proper submenu to add text to a drawing.

Summary

This chapter explains how Generic CADD's menu system works. The menu supplied with the program is all that some users need. Others users need a little more, however; still others, a lot more. Whatever your requirements, the capability to edit or write custom menus easily really sets this software apart from the others.

This chapter has shown you how to edit, what to edit, how to write, and what to write. As you gain experience in editing and writing menus, more ideas occur to you. Editing is a continuing, always improving process.

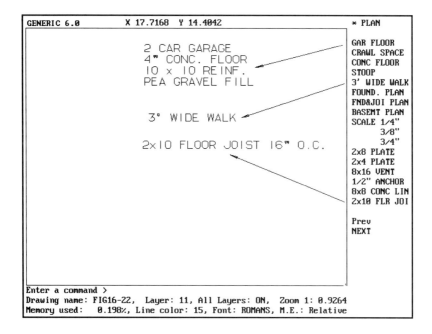

Figure 18.21:
Placing text.

Growing data files cause users to write, link, and swap menus for efficient use of data. Menus are Generic CADD's way to keep track of user files.

As a final note, it is strongly recommended that you read all the material supplied by Generic CADD concerning custom menus. Referring simultaneously to this chapter and the Generic CADD manuals is a helpful practice.

The next chapter introduces the use of longer macros which are stored on disk rather than in a menu or on a function key. The power available to automate your drafting work is about to increase again.

Batch Files, Formulas, and Variables

A batch file is a series of CADD commands, parameters, and special functions that execute automatically when you use the Load (LO) command's Batch option. A batch file is essentially a script, written in the language of two-letter commands and other special syntax, that Generic CADD follows to perform a task. Use batch files to automate drawing tasks or act as an interface between Generic CADD and another program.

Now batch files, which gained many new capabilities with the release of version 6.0, are often called *macro files* in the program's documentation. The two terms are used interchangeably here.

Generic CADD batch files use the ASCII text format to create and store information, which makes it possible to write Generic CADD batch files from scratch, using a word processor or text editor. The ASCII format also makes it possible to "borrow" information from other sources, provided that the information is in ASCII format. The ASCII nature of CADD batch files makes it possible for data from a variety of sources to be used to create objects in CADD.

The structure of batch files in Generic CADD is similar to that of other macros, except that batch files can consist of an unlimited number of lines. The other forms are limited to one line.

This chapter covers the fundamentals of creating, running, and editing batch files as macros. Chapter 20 explores the many new batch-file features added to Generic CADD with the release of version 6.0, including the use of variables and a macro programming language.

Using Tools for Editing Batch Files

Viewing and editing batch files is done with either a word processor or a text editor. Most utility packages, such as PC-Tools, Norton Utilities, and Mace Utilities, include an editor program. MS-DOS 5 has the MS-DOS Editor, which is excellent for writing and editing batch files.

If you do not have an editor, you can use a word processing program. Most shareware word processors can save text in the ASCII format and are thus well-suited to editing Generic CADD batch files. Commercial word processing programs usually save files in a document format with special formatting codes. Because these formatting codes "choke" Generic CADD when it attempts to load the batch file, learn how to save your text files in simple ASCII text format. This process sometimes is called "saving without formatting" or "saving as text." You can use EDLIN, a DOS program that enables you to edit files one line at a time. Because this program is very awkward to use, however, it is recommended only as a last resort.

Your editing program, regardless of its type, is referred to generically as an *editor* in this chapter.

An editor should be able to perform search-and-replace functions (particularly useful when using a batch file to edit a Generic CADD drawing). To complete the exercises in this chapter, you need to know how to load, use search-and-replace, and save files with your editor.

Saving a Drawing as a Batch File

Generic CADD enables you to save an entire drawing as a batch file, or you can save portions of a drawing, using the selection process.

When you save a drawing as a batch file, Generic CADD "reverse engineers" the drawing and creates a batch file of the commands necessary to re-create your drawing in its current form. The set of commands is not necessarily the same set you used to create the drawing. Although you may have drawn a rectangle using the Rectangle (RE) command, for example, the batch file will use four Line (LI) commands to re-create that same rectangle. Bézier curves are saved using the individual Bézier (BW) command.

Component definitions are not saved in the batch file. If your drawing contains components, the Component Place (CP) commands will be in the batch file. This is a problem only when you load the batch file. If the appropriate CMP files are not available in the current component directory, Component not found flashes on the screen and Generic CADD continues with the next command in the batch file. Generic CADD cannot reverse engineer fills or hatches, and these entities are not saved in batch files.

 Sometimes you can restore a corrupted drawing file by executing the Save Batch (SB), Drawing Remove (DX), and Load Batch (LO,B) commands, in order. You should first ensure that all components have been saved to disk so that they are not lost. Then use the Change and Filter commands to move all hatches and fills to an unused layer. Use the Layer Save (YS) command to save this layer as a separate file, which then can be reloaded after the Load Batch operation is complete.

Save Batch (SB)

You can save your entire drawing as a batch file with the Save Batch (SB) command. You can also save a batch file with the

Save (SA) command by choosing Batch (B) as the file to save. Generic CADD will prompt you for a name to use when saving the batch file and will suggest the name of the current drawing with the extension MCR. You can either press Enter to accept the suggested name, or enter a new name. You do not need to add the extension when entering a new name; Generic CADD does this automatically.

All previous versions of Generic CADD, through version 5, saved batch files with TXT as an extension; the MCR extension was introduced in version 6.0. If you have created batch files with previous versions of Generic CADD, you must either rename them with the .MCR extension, or type the complete name when requesting the file with the Load (LO,B) or Load Batch (LB) commands.

The following exercise shows you how to save a drawing as a batch file, using the Save Batch command. Later, you will load this batch file and watch Generic CADD re-create your drawing by executing the commands in the batch file.

In preparation for this exercise, start Generic CADD and load a drawing (it does not matter which one). Use the Zoom All (ZA) command so that the entire drawing is visible on-screen, then follow these steps:

Saving a Drawing as a Batch File

Prompt	Input	Description
Command	**SB**	Starts the Save Batch command
Save file as: >> C:\CADD6\MCR\ DRAWINGNAME.MCR	**BATCH1**	Renames and saves the batch file

That is all there is to it. You have just created your first batch file.

Selection Save Batch (BS)

The Selection Save Batch (BS) command enables you to save a portion of a drawing as a batch file. After entering the command, you use Generic CADD's selection process to choose what parts of your drawing to save as a batch file. After you press Enter to confirm your selections, Generic CADD prompts you for a name for the file. As with the Save Batch command, Generic CADD will suggest the name of the current drawing; press Enter to accept the suggested name or type in a different name.

The following exercise displays the Selection Save Batch command. Using Generic CADD's Selection interface, choose part of your drawing (about half of it is fine) to be saved as a batch file. Do not choose the whole drawing, because that would be no different from using the Save Batch command.

Saving a Portion of a Drawing as a Batch File

Prompt	Input	Description
Command	**BS**	Starts the Selection Save Batch command
Selection	Type **W** or **O** or **Y**, and so on	Uses one or more selection methods to select parts of the drawing to be saved as a batch file
Selection	Press Enter	Confirms selection
Save file as: >> C:\CADD6\MCR\ DRAWINGNAME.MCR	**BATCH2**	Renames and saves the batch file

The simplicity of the process is deceptive. You enter only a few commands and Generic CADD figures out which commands are needed to re-create your drawing. When you later look at the batch files you have just created, you will be amazed at everything Generic CADD takes into consideration when saving a drawing as a batch file.

Loading a Batch File

When you load a batch file, Generic CADD processes the commands in the file one by one, building the drawing with blinding speed right before your eyes. It's like watching Generic CADD run on autopilot. Watch closely—you will see the commands flash by.

Choose the Batch (B) option under the Load (LO) command to begin loading a batch file. Generic CADD prompts you for the name of the batch file to load. If the video menu is on, Generic CADD lists the available batch files in alphabetical order. You may select a batch file either by highlighting it with the menu bar and pressing the second button on your mouse, or by typing in the name and pressing Enter. As with all load commands, you may activate the file selector or use the side menu to look for files in other directories on your hard disk.

In the following exercise, you erase the drawing from the screen and then re-create it from the batch file. Because Generic CADD automatically executes the Zoom Limits command when you remove the entire drawing from memory, you use the Zoom Previous command to reset the screen, watching as Generic CADD loads the batch file.

Re-Creating a Drawing from a Batch File

Prompt	Input	Description
Command	DX	Starts the Drawing Remove command
Do you really want to remove the current drawing Y/N?	Y	Removes the drawing

Prompt	Input	Description
Command	**LO**	Starts the Load Command
Drawing Component Batch...	**B**	Selects batch file
Select file from side menu >>	Move menu bar to BATCH1 and click second mouse button	Selects BATCH1 as file to load

Generic CADD re-creates your drawing, piece by piece. Soon the drawing reappears, just as it was before you erased it. (You may have to do a ZA; sometimes you cannot see the drawing.) If you want to see Generic CADD load the second batch file you saved, repeat the preceding steps, selecting BATCH2 (rather than BATCH1) as the file to load.

Creating a Batch File

Creating a batch file to export data from a drawing is useful, and is discussed later in more detail. The primary use for batch files in Generic CADD, however, is to automate the drawing process. As mentioned earlier, a text editor ordinarily is used to create batch files. When you use an editor, though, you must remember some rules and guidelines about creating batch files, and learn the special functions some characters have when used in a batch file.

Rules and Guidelines for Batch Files

When creating batch files, remember the following rules:

- Anything typed after a semicolon is assumed to be a comment, not part of the command.

- The command portion of each line *must* not exceed 80 characters.

- The command portion of each line *must* end with a semicolon, even if no comments follow.

- Commands and parameters *must* be separated by a comma.

- Toggles (such as AL) *must* be turned off or on by using -- or ++ as parameters, respectively.

- If the first character on a line is a semicolon, the entire line is assumed to be a comment and is ignored.

Writing a batch file is like writing any program—instead of Pascal or C or BASIC, the language is Generic CADD. As with other programs, you can make your work easier by following some basic guidelines.

Comment Everything

Write frequent comments into your batch files; don't worry about overdoing it. The commands in a batch file may make sense to you when you first write them, but you might be confused by them later. When writing a batch file, assume that you will need to modify it sometime in the future and comment accordingly. If other people will use your batch files, remember the programmer's adage: "Comment unto others as you would have them comment unto you."

Use Structure for Clarity

You can put several commands on one line (up to 80 characters), but this can make your batch files look confusing. If several commands make sense together, group them on a line; otherwise it is best to limit each line to one command. Your batch file will be easier to understand and edit.

Extra spaces in a batch file are ignored. You can use extra spaces to your advantage by placing them between coordinate pairs on the same line to make successive X,Y coordinates easy to see.

To illustrate this point, consider the following structures of the same batch file.

Written this way, the file is difficult to understand:

```
TS,P,C,25,L,160,!,S,10,A,1.25,J,C,P,!,--,!;  Text Settings
```

This example, which includes comments, requires more time and space to write, but is much easier to understand:

```
TS;             Starts Text Settings command
P,C,25;         Sets sPacing between Characters to 25 percent
L,160,!;        Sets sPacing between Lines to 160 percent
S,10;           Sets slant to 10 degrees
A,1.25;         Sets Aspect ratio (>1=wide, <1=narrow)
J,C;            Sets Justification to Centered
P,P,--;         Turns off Proportional spacing
!;              Ends Text Settings command
```

Both versions perform the same function, but one is much easier to read and understand than the other.

Never Assume Anything

A batch file can be loaded at any time—never assume that any of Generic CADD's settings or toggles are set correctly. Just imagine what would happen if the units in your batch file were based on inches and Generic CADD was set for meters. If you are familiar with programming, think of adjusting settings and toggles as initializing all your variables. The following checklists cover most of the settings you need to consider when making batch files.

If your batch file draws new entities, remember to set:

- Manual entry mode (Origin, MO; Relative, MR; Basepoint MB)

- Units (UN)

- Line Color (LC)

- Line Type (LT)

- Line Width (LW)

- Current Layer (YC)

If your batch file uses double lines, remember to set:

- Double Line settings (DB)
- Auto Fillet (AF)
- Fillet Radius (FR)

If your batch file macro places text, remember to set:

- Text Color (CS,T)
- Font Selection (TS,F)
- Text Size (TS,Z)
- Text Rotation (TR)
- Other required Text Settings (TS)
- Text Rotation (TR)

If your batch file macro draws dimensions, remember to set:

- Font Select (US,F)
- Text Size (US,T,Z)
- Dimension Layer (UY or US,L)
- Dimension Color (CS,D or US,C)
- Dimension Direction (UD)
- Proximity Fixed (PF)
- Dimension Display (DD)
- Extension Settings (XS)
- Arrow Settings (AR)
- Dimension Text Settings (DT or US,T)

If your batch file edits the current drawing, remember to set:

- All Layers Edit (AL)
- All Layers Snap (SY)
- Chamfer Distances (CA)
- Fillet Radius (FR)

Some settings are not critical to the proper operation of batch files but can slow the execution of a batch file as it is loaded into Generic CADD. Make sure that these three settings are off:

- Rubber Banding (RB)

- Object Drag (OD)

- Highlighting (HI)

When Generic CADD creates a batch file from a drawing, it turns off these three settings. If you look at a batch file created by Generic CADD (the two you just made, for example), you can see that the first line in the batch file sets the units. The next line turns off the three settings and sets manual entry relative to the origin.

Because there are many text and dimension settings to worry about, you can enable CADD to take care of writing the commands that set text and dimension options. Simply make a drawing of a single text line or dimension. Adjust all the settings the way you like them and save that drawing as a batch file. Then you can simply clip out that portion of the batch file (created by CADD) and paste it into the batch file you are writing, or use it nested.

Special Characters in Batch Files

Batch files use the same special characters as macros. If you are not already familiar with the following symbols, you need to know their function:

- **Semicolon (;).** The semicolon marks the end of a line of commands. Generic CADD assumes that any text found on the same line after a semicolon is a comment, and ignores it.

- **Comma (,).** The comma separates commands and parameters. A comma following a parameter performs the same function as pressing Enter.

- **Plus signs (++).** Two plus signs following a toggle command turn on the toggle. Commands that are either on or off, and commands that have only two settings, such as Dimension Text Placement (DT,P), are considered toggles.

- **Minus signs (--).** Two minus signs turn off a toggle when they follow a toggle command, such as Ortho Snap (OR).

- **At sign (@).** The at sign is used in place of a coordinate pair. Generic CADD pauses and prompts for a point. You can enter the point using any of the normal methods (a mouse or digitizer, the arrow and Enter keys, or manual entry).

- **Tilde (~).** The tilde is used in place of a parameter other than a coordinate pair. It can be used any time Generic CADD expects a value or a name. As with the at sign, Generic CADD pauses and prompts for a parameter. You can respond by typing from the keyboard.

- **Number sign (#).** The number sign performs the same function as pressing Esc. It is useful for exiting commands like Text Line (TL) and Text Place (TP).

- **Exclamation mark (!).** The exclamation mark performs the same function as pressing Enter. It is useful for exiting selection functions or Text Settings (TS) commands.

- **Slashes (/).** Slash characters cause Generic CADD to treat the next character as if it were not a special character. Slashes are used primarily for placing characters such as # and ! in a text line without their activating the Escape or Enter functions. Two consecutive slash marks are required for the slash to function. Generic CADD version 6.0 also uses slashes to identify the new macro programming language (MPL) commands. The program analyzes the characters immediately following a slash. If they match one of the MPL commands, the function is called. If the characters do not match, the next character is ignored.

Although batch files may seem complicated because of all the rules and guidelines that accompany them, do not be intimidated by them. Use the guidelines as a checklist while making your own batch files or as a troubleshooting guide when they do not work properly. You do not need to be a programmer to write a batch file. If you can use the two-letter commands to run Generic CADD, you can write a batch file.

Writing a Simple Batch File

In the next section, you will write a simple batch file that draws a square. Activate your editor and create a new file named DISK.MCR in your C:\CADD6\MCR directory (the default directory for batch files, unless you have identified a different directory). Type the following lines into your editor. (You do not have to type the comments that appear after the semicolon on each line.)

```
UN,I;                   Sets units to inches
OD,--,RB,--,OR,--;      Turns off Object Drag, Rubber Band, and Ortho
MO;                     Sets manual entry relative to origin
YC,0;                   Sets current layer to 0
LC,11;                  Selects line color 11
LT,0;                   Selects line type 0
LW,0;                   Selects line width 0
RE;                     Draws 5.25" square
0,0;
5.25,5.25;
ZA;                     Performs the Zoom All command
```

Check your input carefully for typographical errors, such as omitting semicolons, and then save what you have typed. If you are using a word processor, save the file in ASCII text format. Then start Generic CADD. When you are at the drawing screen, start the Load (LO) command and select Batch file (B). You should see DISK listed on the side menu; select it with the second button of your mouse and watch your batch file in action. (If you do not see DISK listed on the side menu, use the File Path command to check the path for batch files and make sure that the File Path is set to the same directory in which you saved the DISK.MCR file.)

The batch file you just typed and saved draws a centered rectangle on your screen, as shown in figure 19.1. If this is not what you see, exit Generic CADD and use your editor to check your batch file again. Most batch file problems are caused by a simple error, such as a missing semicolon or a comma instead of a period. After making any necessary corrections, load the batch file into Generic CADD and try again.

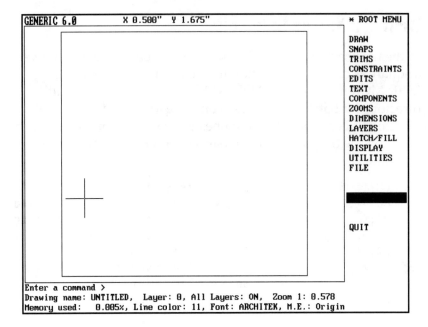

Figure 19.1:

Centered rectangle created by batch file.

The following batch file creates a more complicated figure than a rectangle. Exit Generic CADD without saving the drawing, and start your editor again. Load the file DISK.MCR and add the following lines to the end of the file (after the Zoom All command):

```
C2;                    Draws a 1.5" diameter circle
2.625,2.625;
3.375,2.625;
LI;                    Draws three connected lines
5.25,4.0625;
5.125,4.0625;
5.125,3.8125;
5.25,3.8125;
OB,5.25,3;             Breaks side of rectangle
5.25,4.0625;
5.25,3.8125;
C2;                    Draws a 1/4" diameter circle
3.625,2.375;
3.75,2.375;
L1;                    Draws a single line
2.375,1.25;
```

```
2.375,0.375;
L1;                     Draws a single line
2.875,1.25;
2.875,0.375;
A3;                     Draws a 3-point arc
2.375,1.25;
2.625,1.5;
2.875,1.25;
A3;                     Draws a 3-point arc
2.375,0.375;
2.625,0.125;
2.875,0.375;
RB,++,OD,++;            Turns on Rubber Band and Object Drag
```

Save this file after checking your work for accuracy. Then start
Generic CADD and run the Load (LO) command again, choosing
B for Batch file. Choose DISK from the side menu, as before.

The result should look like figure 19.2. Again, if the drawing does
not appear as it should, use your editor to examine the batch file
for mistakes.

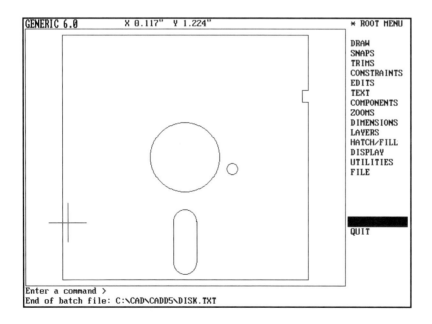

Figure 19.2:

*Screen after loading
DISK.TXT.*

The preceding batch file was written with one point per line. You can condense the batch file somewhat by entering all points for a given command on the same line, separating the X,Y pairs with spaces to make it easier to read.

What follows is the same batch file in a more condensed format with generalized comments. The comments for sections of the batch file that draw objects precede the draw commands on a separate line. Both methods work equally well—use the one you prefer.

```
UN,I,OD,--,RB,--,OR,--,MO;           Performs standard setup
YC,0,LC,11,LT,0,LW,0;                Sets layer and line parameters
;                                    Ends setup
;                                    5.25" square (disk outline)
RE, 0,0, 5.25,5.25;
ZA;                                  Starts the Zoom All command
;                                    1.5" diameter circle (center
                                     hole)
C2, 2.625,2.625, 3.375,2.625;
;                                    3 lines and break right side
;                                    at lines (write protect notch)
LI, 5.25,4.0625,  5.125,4.0625,  5.125,3.8125, 5.25,3.8125;
OB, 5.25,3,  5.25,4.0625,  5.25,3.8125;
;                                    1/4" diameter circle (timing
                                     hole)
C2, 3.625,2.375,  3.75,2.375;
;                                    lines and arcs (R/W head slot)
L1, 2.375,1.25,  2.375,0.375;
L1, 2.875,1.25,  2.875,0.375;
A3, 2.375,1.25,  2.625,1.5, 2.875,1.25;
A3, 2.375,0.375,  2.625,0.125, 2.875,0.375;
RB,++,OD,++;                         Turns on Rubber Band and
                                     Object Drag
```

Writing an Interactive Batch File

So far, you have worked with batch files that are totally automatic. You often need to interact with a batch file, however, to have more control over the drawing process. In the next section, you create a batch file that pauses and prompts you for input.

The following example shows you how to automate the method for making pie charts, shown in Chapter 4. This batch file pauses for you to enter the center of the pie chart. After it draws the basic pie chart, the batch file prompts you to label each section, using a leader. You use a basepoint as the center of the pie chart, and all coordinates are entered relative to that basepoint. You will learn about the different lines as you go through the batch file, so that you better understand what each line in the batch file does.

Use your editor to create a file called PIE.MCR in your batch file directory (usually C:\CADD6\MCR). The first thing you should do in any batch file is to make your basic settings, such as the current layer, line type, and so on. The following lines do this. (The first several lines are identical to those at the beginning of DISK.MCR. You can "borrow" them from that file to save time.)

```
UN,I;                    Sets units to inches
OD,--,RB,--,OR,--;       Turns off Object Drag, Rubber Band, and Ortho
MO;                      Sets manual entry relative to origin
YC,0;                    Sets current layer
LC,11;                   Sets line color
LT,0;                    Sets line type
LW,2;                    Sets line width
```

This is a fairly standard beginning for a batch file. If you want to use a color other than 11 (bright cyan), simply substitute a different value. You may want to save this setup and use it as a beginning for all your batch files, changing the values when needed. Notice that the line width is set to 2; this is purely a matter of preference for the first several objects to be drawn in the batch file.

Because you will be using leaders to label the pie's different wedges, you need to change some text and dimension settings also:

```
TR,0,TS,P,C,30,L,150,!,S,0,A,1,J,L,P,P,++,!;   Text Settings
```

The preceding line sets the Text Rotation (TR) command to 0 degrees. It then invokes the Text Settings (TS) command to set the between-character spacing (C) to 30 percent, the between-line spacing (L) to 150 percent, the slant (S) to 0 degrees, the aspect ratio (A) to 1:1, and the justification (J) to left. Finally, it turns on proportional spacing (P). If you were placing text, you would want to select a text font, size, and color. Those commands are not included here because only leaders are being used.

The following lines adjust the dimension settings that affect leaders:

```
UY,0;                           Sets dimension or leader layer
US,F,NAME,T,Z,.25,!,A,T,N,A,25,L,.5,!,!;
                                Sets font and text size for
                                dimensions; sets arrows
LL,.25;                         Sets leader shoulder length
DT,P,++,O,I,.25,!;              Sets text inline offset
```

The preceding lines govern the setting that affect leaders. If you were placing dimensions, you would need to write commands for more settings. The Arrow Settings (AR) command sets the arrow type (T) to filled notched (N), the angle (A) to 25 degrees, and the length (L) to one half inch. Again, an exclamation mark is used to end the Text Size and Arrow Settings commands. The inline offset determines the offset between the shoulder line and the leader text.

The final step in the settings portion of the batch file is to set the limits and issue the Zoom Limits command. This is not always necessary, but in this case it ensures that the screen will be an appropriate size for the pie chart. A "blank" line consisting only of a semicolon is an easy-to-see marker that denotes the end of the settings portion of the batch file.

```
LS,12,12,ZL;  Sets limits, starts Zoom Limits command
;             Ends setting portion
```

To draw the pie chart, you need to draw a number of objects based on a single location. The next two lines of the batch file prompt you for a basepoint and turn on manual entry relative to the basepoint:

```
BP,@;   Prompts user for basepoint location
MB;     Starts manual entry relative to basepoint
```

The at sign (@) pauses Generic CADD and prompts you for the X,Y coordinates needed for the basepoint command. Unless you learn to take advantage of Generic CADD's advanced programming features (described in Chapter 20), this will be the only type of variable available in your batch files. It enables you to enter a point and then have the batch file draw objects or carry out operations relative to the basepoint. For this technique to work, you must change manual entry mode to be relative to the basepoint (MB) rather than to the origin (MO) or last point (MR).

The following command draws a circle with a two-inch radius centered on the basepoint. If you want a larger circle, you need only alter the X value of the second coordinate (which is on the circumference of the circle):

```
C2, 0,0,  2,0;          Draws 4" diameter circle
```

You then need to draw the lines necessary to divide the circle into four wedges. Each command starts the line at the center of the circle and uses a Snap Percentage (SR) command to end the line at the appropriate point on the circle's circumference. Because the percentage is always measured from the same point on the circle, the percentage for each wedge must equal the total for all wedges up to that point. Draw the first line (which is at 0 percent or 100 percent, depending upon your point of view) last so that the line does not cause Generic CADD to find two objects when you use the Snap Percentage command. The following commands draw the lines:

```
L1, 0,0, SR,2,0, 40;         Marks 40% wedge
L1, 0,0, SR,2,0, 70;         Marks 30% wedge
L1, 0,0, SR,2,0, 90;         Marks 20% wedge
L1, 0,0, 2,0;                Marks last wedge (10%)
```

If you adjust the diameter of the circle, you must also adjust the X value of the second coordinate pair for each line. You can also adjust the percentages to make differently numbered or sized wedges.

The following two commands set a finer line width and turn on the Rubber Band command so that you can position the leaders:

```
LW,0;                    Sets line width
RB,++;                   Turns on Rubber Band command
```

You need four leader commands to label each section of your pie:

```
LE,40% ~,@,@,@;
LE,30% ~,@,@,@;
LE,20% ~,@,@,@;
LE,10% ~,@,@,@;
```

The tildes pause Generic CADD while you edit the leader text. In each case, you have "preloaded" the leader text with the percentage of the wedge to be labeled. You can add to this percentage, or even backspace over it when the tilde transfers control of the leader text line to you. The three at signs pause Generic CADD and prompt you to type or pick the three points needed to draw the leader (start, end, and shoulder direction).

Finish the batch file by turning on any options you may have turned off. The following is a standard line for the end of a batch file; it ensures that you are not dragging a line from some point, and that both the Rubber Band and Object Drag commands are turned on after the batch file finishes. (The RB command in this example is redundant because you just turned it on, but turning it on again doesn't hurt anything.)

```
PU,OD,++,RB,++;      Turns on the Object Drag command
```

Here is the entire batch file as it should appear on your editor's screen:

```
UN,I;                          Sets units to inches
OD,--,RB,--,OR,--;             Turns off Object Drag, Rubberband,
                               and Ortho
MO;                            Sets manual entry to Relative
YC,0;                          Sets current layer
LC,11;                         Sets line color
LT,0;                          Sets line type
LW,2;                          Sets line width
TR,0,TS,P,C,30,L,150,!,S,0,A,1,J,L,P,P,++,!;
                               Text Settings
UY,0;                          Sets dimension/leader layer
US,F,ENGINEER,T,Z,.25,!,A,T,N,A,25,L,.5,!,!;
                               Sets font and text size for
                               dimensions; arrow settings
LL,.25;                        Sets leader shoulder length
DT,P,++,O,I,.25,!;             Sets text inline offset
LS,12,12,ZL;                   Sets limits and starts Zoom Limits
                               command
;                              Ends settings portion of batch file
BP,@;                          Prompts for basepoint location
MB;                            Sets manual entry to Basepoint
C2,0,0,2,0;                    Draws 4" diameter circle
L1, 0,0, SR,2,0, 40;           Marks 40% wedge
L1, 0,0, SR,2,0, 70;           Marks 30% wedge (40+30=70)
L1, 0,0, SR,2,0, 90;           Marks 20% wedge (70+20=90)
L1, 0,0,  2,0;                 Marks last wedge (10%)
```

```
LW,0;                        Sets line width
RB,++;                       Turns on Rubber Band command
LE,40% ~,@,@,@;              Labels section of pie chart
LE,30% ~,@,@,@;              Labels section of pie chart
LE,20% ~,@,@,@;              Labels section of pie chart
LE,10% ~,@,@,@;              Labels section of pie chart
PU,OD,++,RB,++;              Turns on Object Drag command
```

After checking your batch file for mistakes, save it and exit your editor. Then start Generic CADD and follow these steps:

Testing the Pie Chart Batch File

Prompt	Input	Description
Command	**LO**	Starts the Load command
Drawing Component Batch file....	**B**	Selects batch file as type of file to load
Select file from side menu >>	Type **PIE** or select from side menu with second mouse button	Selects file to load
Set a new basepoint (X,Y)	Enter a point near center of screen	Centers pie chart and draws circle with four wedges (see fig. 19.3)
Enter string> 40%	Enter a label for the first wedge	Identifies wedge
Enter leader starting point	Click on circle near first wedge	Positions arrowhead of the leader
Enter leader terminal point	Point end of arrow at circle and click	Positions other end of arrow
Enter a point indicating shoulder direction	Move the cursor to left or right and click	Positions text left or right of leader arrow

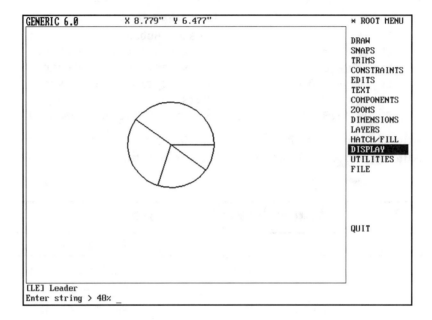

Figure 19.3:

The basic pie chart before leaders are inserted.

Repeat these steps for the remaining three leaders, pointing to each wedge of the pie chart in turn. When you are finished, your results should look like figure 19.4.

Using Shell to Executable

The capability of Generic CADD to shell out to other programs greatly expands the use of batch files. *Shell out* means that you leave the Generic CADD program and run another program. This is not like quitting Generic CADD, because Generic CADD is still loaded in memory when you shell out.

Many programs simply remain loaded and enable you to use the available remaining memory, often 100K or less of free RAM. Because Generic CADD uses all available memory, it needs to perform a few tricks to shell out. Generic CADD writes your entire drawing and all but a very small portion of itself out to disk in a shell file, leaving most of the computer's RAM available in the shell. Unfortunately, you cannot load any software that remains resident in memory (such as TSR programs) and expect to return to Generic CADD.

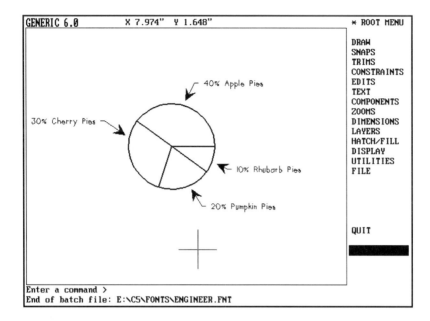

```
GENERIC 6.0        X 7.974"   Y 1.648"           * ROOT MENU

                                                  DRAW
                                                  SNAPS
                                                  TRIMS
                                                  CONSTRAINTS
                         40% Apple Pies           EDITS
                                                  TEXT
                                                  COMPONENTS
                                                  ZOOMS
  30% Cherry Pies                                 DIMENSIONS
                                                  LAYERS
                                                  HATCH/FILL
                                                  DISPLAY
                                  10% Rhubarb Pies UTILITIES
                                                  FILE

              20% Pumpkin Pies


                                                  QUIT


Enter a command >
End of batch file: E:\C5\FONTS\ENGINEER.FNT
```

Figure 19.4:

The completed pie chart.

Because you can shell out to a nearly unlimited number of programs, this function can be used in a nearly unlimited number of ways. You can use the Shell to Executable (SH) command to help write and debug batch files, or to run an editor to make a text file that is then loaded using Generic CADD's Load ASCII (LA) command. You can even shell to a program that writes another batch file.

Generic CADD can be used to edit text that has been placed in a drawing, but you may find that editing large blocks of comments can be done more easily with a word processor or text editor. Use CADD's Shell to Executable (SH) and Load ASCII (LA) commands, along with a text editor, to create large blocks of text. The following batch file, for example, shells out to the PC-Write editor (ED.EXE) and edits a file called TEMP.DOC. The batch file invokes Generic CADD's Load ASCII command to load the file and then prompts the user for the placement in the drawing.

```
SH,ED.EXE,TEMP.DOC;
LA,TEMP.DOC,@;
```

You can use the SH command also to shell to a program that writes another batch file, then load that batch file when you return to Generic CADD. Shelling to a program can be used for what is sometimes called *parametric design*, where the drawing process is automated by another program and Generic CADD serves mostly as a graphics engine programmed with batch files.

The Shell to Executable command is perhaps best used for shelling to your editor program to edit and debug batch files. Because a single misplaced comma or semicolon can cause a batch file to fail, batch files often fail on the first several attempts. Debugging a batch file may mean loading your editor, modifying the batch file, exiting the editor, running Generic CADD, testing the batch file, exiting Generic CADD, loading the editor again, and so on. It is a tedious process at best.

As an alternative to that tedious process, use the Shell to Executable command to shell out of Generic CADD and run your editor. When you finish editing the batch file, you exit the editor and automatically return to Generic CADD. You can make this even easier by putting the shell command on a macro. The following macro, for example, shells out to the PC-Write editor (ED) and edits a batch file called WORK.TXT:

```
SH,ED.EXE,WORK.TXT
```

Using Batch Files To Modify a Drawing

Batch files provide a way to alter a drawing when Generic CADD's editing and change commands fall short. A batch file created by the Save Batch (SB) command not only gives you access to all the commands required to construct a drawing, it also enables you to alter those commands.

Say, for example, that you have a drawing with a great deal of dimensioning in it and you want to change the arrowhead style of all the dimensions. If you are working with Generic CADD 6.0, you can use standard selection to change dimensions. If you are still using version 5.0, Generic CADD enables you to change individual dimensions with the Dimension Change (UG) command but does not provide a way to change more than one dimension at a time. (Changing all the dimensions in an entire drawing is a rather tedious task, even if you make a macro that only requires you to point at the dimension text.)

An alternative approach (with Generic CADD 5.0) is to start by using the Selection Save Batch (BS) and the Filter commands to save all the dimensions in the drawing as a batch file. Then shell out to your editor (or quit Generic CADD and run your editor) and call up the batch file. Use your editor to search for AR (the Arrow Settings command) and make the appropriate changes to alter the arrowhead style. The AR command shows up in the batch file only where dimensions or leaders were placed using a different arrowhead style. Thus, although the AR command may show up several times in a batch file, it is almost certain to appear less often than the number of dimensions and leaders in the drawing.

After making the changes to the batch file, return to Generic CADD 5.0. Use the Erase and Filter commands to erase all the dimensions in the drawing. (If you have shelled out to your editor instead of quitting Generic CADD, you can select the last selection [L], which will be the same dimensions that were saved as a batch file earlier.) Then use the Load Batch (LB) command to load the batch file you just edited. The batch file will re-create all your dimensions, this time drawing them with the new style of arrows according to the changes you made to the batch file.

Using Batch Files To Extract Data from a Drawing

Because batch files are saved in ASCII format, they are an ideal medium for extracting data from your drawing. Extracting data is useful primarily for programs that do not support formats—such as DXF (Drawing Interchange Format)—designed specifically for the interchange of drawing data between Generic CADD and CADD-related programs.

A batch file contains the exact coordinate data for every entity in a drawing—the end points of every line, a point in the center or on the circumference of every circle, and so on. It contains other useful information also, such as the name and location of every component in the drawing.

If you look at the batch files you saved earlier using Generic CADD's Save Batch (SB) and Selection Save Batch (BS) commands, you will see that they are highly ordered. Generic CADD places one command to a line and one pair of points to a line when it saves a batch file. Thus, writing a program that parses through a batch file for the information you wish to extract is fairly easy.

You need some experience with a programming language to write a program that reads and processes an ASCII file such as a Generic CADD batch file, but you don't need to be a wizard. Many users have been able to use batch files for a variety of tasks with languages such as Quick Basic and Turbo Pascal.

You could, for example, search a batch file for CP (Component Place) commands and note the name of each component. From this information you could construct a bill of materials list. Or, you could read in a batch file and reorder the entities and points to create a "cut path" to be used by a machine. The possibilities are limited only by your imagination and programming ability.

Linking CADD to Other Software with Batch Files

One of the more powerful uses of batch files is as a link to other programs. When software does not support more traditional methods of exchanging drawing data, batch files provide an effective way to create a drawing from other information. Generally, using a data exchange format specifically designed for Generic CADD data, such as DXF (Drawing Interchange Format), is the best plan. If another program supports reading and writing DXF files, you can use Generic's AutoConvert program to translate DXF files to and from Generic's proprietary DWG and CMP formats.

Information from a number of sources can be imported into Generic CADD through batch files. If you have data in coordinates (X,Y) format, for example, translating it into batch file format and creating a drawing based on that data is relatively easy to do. Ideally, another program (such as a spreadsheet) can be made to save data to disk in a Generic CADD batch file. This enables you to highly automate the drawing process and engage in *parametric design*, where an entire drawing is created from a few parameters.

Massaging Raw Data into Batch File Format

Generic CADD is an excellent tool for plotting coordinate-based information such as statistical data. The challenge is to transpose the data from raw form into a format that means something to Generic CADD. In this process, which is known as *massaging*, the material is put into a different form but the content is not altered.

Ordinarily, an editor or word processor (preferably one with macro capability) is used for this task, although a special program can be written. You should have to resort to writing a special program, however, only if the information is particularly diverse or esoteric.

Most statistical data takes a fairly regular form and can be edited with a word processor and a simple macro. Say, for example, you have information in X,Y format that represents measurements of three groups, and you want to create a graph to see how the groups relate to one another.

You do not need to worry about the size or scope of the numbers involved. X may range from 1 to 4, and Y from 200 to 20,000. When massaging data into a batch file, *never* alter the values of the original data. Make your alterations by placing the raw data in a formula inside the batch file. The formula can be easily modified with the search-and-replace function, leaving the original data intact.

The following example assumes that the data is listed one point to a line:

```
pppp g xx.xxxx yy,yyy.y
```

In this example, pppp is a point number, g is the group the point belongs to, xx.xxxx is one value, and yy,yyy.y is another value. As an additional twist, assume that the X and Y ranges are disparate, with X running from 0 to 100 and Y ranging from 0 to 100,000.

Assume that you want to place a symbol at each point location which identifies the group to which that point belongs. You also want to be able to look at any point and get the point number so that you can look up other data related to that point. You can do this in Generic CADD by making three components, one to identify each group. Attach to each component an attribute, perhaps called "point," which contains a field for the point number. (The attribute could contain all the preceding information, but massaging the data would be a little more difficult.)

You should follow these steps before you process the batch file:

1. Create an attribute named "point" which contains one field named "point #" with a default value of nothing (just press Enter).

2. Create three components to be used as symbols for the three groups: such as a triangle filled with green, a circle filled with blue, and a rectangle filled with red. The name of each component should be the same as the name for each group; this could even be a number such as 1, 2, or 3. You probably want the reference point to be in the center of each symbol.

3. Attach the "point" attribute to each component as it is created. Determine a default location for the attribute and leave the default value for "point #" blank. Set the display default to off. (You probably do not want the drawing cluttered with all the attribute text.)

4. Experiment with placing a few of the components manually. Pick a few points at random and place several symbols at the appropriate X,Y locations. This will enable you to experiment with component scales, text sizes, and so on to get a feel for what works well. You may determine, for example, that you

want to divide all Y values by 100 to make the graph more readable.

Always try a few dry runs manually to get a feel for how things will work when designing a batch file. Make notes along the way to determine what commands need to be issued and what information needs to be supplied to perform those commands. In this example, testing and taking notes would help you see that the following sequence is needed to place one point of data:

1. Issue the CP (Component Place) command.

2. Supply the name of the component (the "group," in this case).

3. Enter the X and Y coordinates to place the component.

4. Enter the "point #" for the attribute.

Be sure to note which settings make things work properly, such as setting Attribute Settings to prompt you to edit field values at placement, and turning on Autoplacement.

Consider the format of the original data and how you want the resulting batch file line to appear. In this example you are starting with data in the following format:

```
pppp g xx.xxxx yy,yyy.y
```

You want the resulting batch file line to look like this:

```
CP,g,x.xxxx,yyyyy.y/100,pppp;
```

The first step is to purge the comma in the middle of the Y value. You need to insert CP at the beginning of each line and a semicolon at the end of each line. You also need to insert /100 after the Y value, and change (to commas) the spaces that separate all the elements. Perhaps the most difficult step will be moving the point number to the end of the line, with a space between it and the Y value. You may be able to combine several of these steps into a macro, or you can tackle them one at a time.

Stripping the comma from the middle of the Y value can be done with a simple search (for a comma) and replace (with nothing). If you can arrange the data so that everything is separated with spaces (`CP g x.xxxx yyyyy.y/100 pppp;`), another search-and-replace can easily place commas where they are needed.

If you can make a macro to take care of the other steps, massaging the data into a batch file will be easy. If your editor's macro facility supports self-repeating (or looping) macros, the process will be almost painless.

A macro for the word processor PC-Write follows. It uses simple commands that most editors or word processors support. The general function for each command is noted so that you can follow the process, or create a similar macro for using your favorite editor or word processor.

With Insert mode turned on and the cursor at the end of the first line of data, type the macro as follows:

Writing a Macro in a Word Processor

Input	Description
Ctrl-@	Starts recording a macro
/100	Inserts /100 after Y value
Space bar	Inserts a space after /100
Home	Moves cursor to beginning of line
CP	Inserts CP at beginning of line
F6	Begins marking text to be moved
Ctrl-Right arrow	Moves cursor right one word
Left arrow	Moves cursor left one space
F6	Ends marking text to be moved
End	Moves cursor to end of line
F6	Moves marked text to cursor
F5	Turns off marking
End	Moves cursor to end of line
;	Inserts a semicolon at end of line
Down arrow	Moves cursor down one line
End	Moves cursor to end of line
*	Stops recording macro; makes a repeating macro

In PC-Write, the asterisk key (the one by the keypad, not Shift-8) is the macro key. By pressing it when you are recording a macro, you automatically stop recording and create a self-repeating macro. Macro languages vary, but nearly all of them can create a macro that repeats until it reaches the end of the file.

Some word processors move text by using the preceding mark-move-unmark sequence; others use a mark-cut-paste sequence. Nearly all editors or word processors have commands that move the cursor to the beginning or end of the line, or to the first character of the word to the left or right. You do not have to depend on all values in data being the same length when you use such functions. The preceding macro would work, for example, if the point number is two digits or five digits, but pressing the left arrow would work only for four-digit numbers.

You may need to experiment to discover how your editor treats a series of numbers, such as 12.34 567.89. PC-Write, for example, treats 12.34 as one word. If the cursor were at the 1 in this nine-number sequence, pressing Ctrl and the right-arrow key would move the cursor to the 5. Microsoft Word works differently, however; pressing Ctrl and the right-arrow key would move the cursor to the period, then to the 3, then to the 5. Learn to anticipate your editor's characteristics when creating macros.

Having massaged the data into a batch file, you need to insert a section only at the top of the file to account for any settings. In the batch file described earlier (using data from another program to place components), for example, you need to concern yourself with the following items:

- Component Scale (CS)

- Font Select for Attributes (AS,F)

- Text Size for Attributes (AS,Z)

- Attribute Settings (AS)
  Auto Placement on (A,++)
  Edit Fields at Placement (P,++)

After loading the batch file, you may discover that you want to make some adjustments—the components may be too large, for example, or the Y scale may need to be compressed to give the graph a more favorable appearance. You just need to edit the batch file. The job may be as simple as changing one line, or you may need to use the search-and-replace function (replacing /100 with /200, for example). After making the changes, return to Generic CADD and load the batch file again.

Parametric Design

Perhaps the most exciting use for batch files is as a link with another program (such as a spreadsheet) to create a highly automated drafting and design environment. Many drawings can be reduced to a generic design which can be compiled into formulas that describe the basic geometric relationships between its objects. Nearly anything can be drawn this way, from a camshaft in an engine to the cutting diagram for a cardboard box. This technique is called *parametric design*.

The formulas for a drawing can be placed into a program that calculates the coordinates for every point needed to create a batch file for Generic CADD. Spreadsheet programs are well-suited to this task because they are designed to work with many values and formulas. The spreadsheet normally is divided into three parts: a data-entry section, a formulas section containing the formulas for each point, and a portion that is printed to disk to create a Generic CADD batch file.

A new design can be generated by simply changing a few variables that recalculate the spreadsheet, and creating a new batch file. The final step is to load the batch file into Generic CADD to view the basic design. This enables you to rapidly perform what-if experiments with your designs. In more advanced parametric designs, some values can be allowed to float, whereas other values determine the design.

Consider the pattern for a cardboard box shown in figure 19.5. Every point needed to draw the lines for this pattern can be determined from four values: the height (H), width (W), depth (D), and the gap (G) needed between the flaps (a factor of the thickness of the cardboard). Making a list of the lines needed to draw this pattern and the formula for the end points of each line is relatively simple.

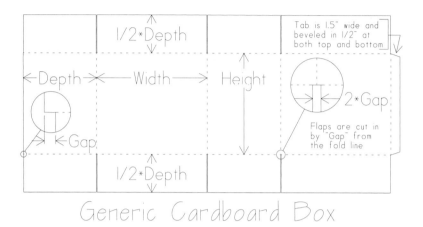

1/2*Depth

Tab is 1.5" wide and beveled in 1/2" at both top and bottom

←Depth—✕—Width—→ Height

2*Gap

Flaps are cut in by "Gap" from the fold line

←Gap

1/2*Depth

Generic Cardboard Box

Figure 19.5:

Basic pattern for a cardboard box.

The data-entry portion of the spreadsheet contains areas for entering the height, width, depth, and gap parameters from which the rest of the design is derived. The formulas section would contain the formula for each point needed to create the drawing. The batch-file section contains the Generic CADD commands and references to the formulas section needed to create the batch file. The batch file is created by printing the batch-file section to a disk file.

Figure 19.6 shows the left half of the box with the formulas for several of the points indicated. The lower left corner is duplicated at the right with four points (labeled 1, 2, 3, and 4) and three lines (A, B, and C).

Examine the three parts of the spreadsheet needed to draw the three lines. The data-entry section would look something like this:

	A	B
1	Height	12
2	Width	16
3	Depth	8
4	Gap	0.0625

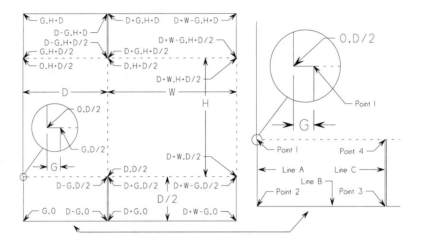

Figure 19.6:

Box Outline with formulas.

Column A contains the labels; column B holds the values from which the rest of the spreadsheet is calculated. If your spreadsheet program enables you to name cells, rename cells B1 through B4 as H, W, D and G, respectively. This not only makes filling in formulas much easier but also, and more important, it makes reading and editing the formulas easier if you need to change your drawing template later.

A logical place to put the formulas section is to use columns X and Y in the spreadsheet to hold the formulas for the X and Y coordinates for each point. Using columns X and Y offers a very intuitive layout where the formulas for the X and Y values for point 1 are in cells X1 and Y1, point 2 in cells X2, Y2, and so on. Most spreadsheet programs require you to begin a formula with a number or a plus or minus sign so that the spreadsheet does not think you are entering text. Set your spreadsheet to display the formulas for this section (as opposed to the values) to make reading and editing easier.

The formulas section for points 1 through 4 might look like this:

	X	*Y*
1	+B4	+B3/2
2	+B4	0
3	+B3-B4	0
4	+B3-B4	+B3/2

The section of the spreadsheet you print to disk to make a batch file consists not only of cells that contain text for the Generic CADD commands needed to draw objects, but also of cells for X and Y coordinates that refer to cells in the formulas section. While creating the spreadsheet, set the display to show "formulas." The section will look like this:

	D	E	F	G	H	I	J	K	L	M
1	Line A	LI,	+X1	,	+Y1	,	+X2	,	+Y2	;
2	Line B	LI,	+X2	,	+Y2	,	+X3	,	+Y3	;
3	Line C	LI,	+X3	,	+Y3	,	+X4	,	+Y4	;

The following is the same section with values displayed as they would appear prior to printing to disk:

	D	E	F	G	H	I	J	K	L	M
1	Line A	LI,	0.0625	,	4	,	0.0625	,	0	;
2	Line B	LI,	0.0625	,	0	,	7.9375	,	0	;
3	Line C	LI,	7.9375	,	0	,	7.9375	,	4	;

The D column of cells is for your reference and to make editing easier. It takes slightly more time to type them in, but if you have to make changes several weeks later, you will be glad you did. Columns G, I, K, and M are set to a width of 1 because they contain single characters only. Setting the width to one character makes viewing the spreadsheet easier. Remember, Generic CADD does not care about extra spaces in batch file lines; limiting column width needs to be done only if the lines may exceed the 80-character limit.

To create the batch file, configure your spreadsheet for the simplest printer allowed (usually labeled something like "text printer"). Select DISK FILE as the destination for the printed output, and be sure to use MCR as the file-name extension. Then simply select the range of cells to be printed (in this case, columns E through M), and print them to a disk file. That file can then be loaded into Generic CADD to create the basic drawing. You can add finishing touches such as comments, title blocks, and so on.

The template for the cardboard box you have worked with could be called simple parametrics. In more advanced parametric designs, values often are interrelated. Some of them can be set to float, others are fixed; the formulas are then solved for the floating values.

The procedure that automatically generates a staircase in the GenCADD Architectural module (an add-on product for Generic CADD) is an example of a more advanced parametric design. A number of variables—the height and length of the staircase, the number of steps, and the tread and rise of each step—determine the finished design of a staircase. These variables are interrelated; the number of steps is related to the height of the staircase and the rise of each step, for example. One of these values can always be found, based on the other two.

Summary

Batch files are one of Generic CADD's most powerful and versatile features. They enable you to automate your drafting and design tasks by writing a script of commands to perform any number of functions, from creating an entire drawing to selectively editing portions of a drawing.

You can use batch files also to create charts and graphs, simply by altering the values in a standard batch file.

Batch files provide a link to import data from other programs. Statistics and other information can be taken in raw form and massaged into a batch file to represent the data in graphic form. You can automate the design process and delve into parametric design by using a spreadsheet to create batch files that convert the numbers into a nearly finished drawing.

This chapter introduced the capabilities of macro programming with larger files. The next chapter continues by introducing more elaborate programming capabilities, including Generic CADD's new macro programming language (MPL). Your ability to automate your design and drafting tasks is about to take another quantum leap forward.

Macro Programming Language Fundamentals

This chapter starts with a little review. The last three chapters have introduced, bit by bit, the various ways Generic CADD can be customized. Chapter 17 introduced keyboard macros—short groups of Generic CADD two-letter commands accessed by pressing a function key. Expanding on the concept of writing macros, Chapter 18 introduced menu customization, explaining that macros can be added to the on-screen menu as well as being accessed by function keys. Chapter 19 went beyond menu customization to introduce the use of entire files—*batch files*—devoted to the execution of Generic CADD commands.

Function-key macros and individual lines in a menu are limited in length, and menus have a practical size limit—they can be confusing if too long. Batch files offer the advantage of unlimited size. When a batch file is operated from inside Generic CADD, the commands stream into CADD, line after line, directly from disk.

But as presented in Chapter 19, batch files are essentially just overgrown macros. Macros, menus, and batch files all use the same commands in the same way.

The inventive Generic CADD user who makes full use of macros, menus, and batch files eventually reaches a point where the power seems to have diminished. Like moving from an XT to a 486-based computer, yesterday's more-than-adequate system is today's limitation. When you feel you have reached the limit in customizing Generic CADD with macros, menus, and batch files, you are ready for the information in this chapter—material that is to function-key macros what a 486 is to an XT.

A variety of new programming features are available for the first time in Generic CADD version 6.0. A few of the features in this chapter were available but undocumented in version 5.0, publicly explained only in the first edition of this book. But now Autodesk Retail Products (formerly Generic Software) has not only taken the wraps off such existing features as math functions and variables, but also added 30 new functions which make up the essentials of a programming language for Generic CADD.

If you have never used programming languages such as BASIC or Pascal, the resources described in this chapter may seem a bit foreign, and perhaps a little intimidating. Because the new programming features are so different in application from the rest of Generic CADD, Autodesk Retail Products includes with version 6.0 a separate manual just for the macro programming language. The new manual (called the *Customization Guide*) does a fine job of presenting a technical explanation of each new command. If you lack a programming background, however, the *Customization Guide* may seem overwhelming. This chapter takes a softer approach, introducing these powerful new features in a way the less technical CADD user can appreciate. The goal of this chapter is to prepare you to take full advantage of the *Customization Guide*. The only previous programming experience assumed is that you have worked through the exercises in the previous three chapters. After all, writing a 30-character keyboard macro also is programming.

Examining Macros Supplied with Generic CADD 6.0

Of the 20 batch files (also known as *macros*) included with Generic CADD 6.0, only 12 are documented in the *Customization Guide*. To see the list of batch files in the menu (see fig. 20.1), use the batch file option of the Load (LOB) command.

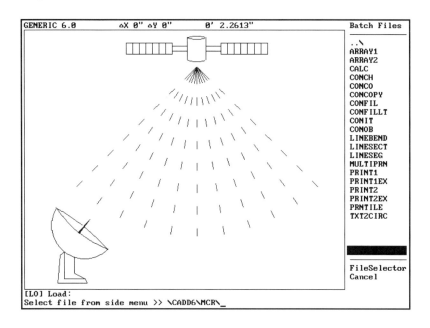

Figure 20.1:

Batch files shipped with Generic CADD 6.0.

All 20 macros are written using the CADD macro programming language (MPL). The macros are included with the product for two reasons: to offer you new editing and printing routines and to provide you with examples of the new macro programming language. These 20 macros automate such tasks as repetitive copying, printing multiple copies of drawings, and tiling a drawing over several sheets of paper. Many of these new batch files include comments that help to explain each line in the file. CADD users who want to learn MPL can not only run the batch files, but also study how each was written.

Later in the chapter, one of the batch files that ships with Generic CADD is analyzed line by line. But first the available macros, organized by type, are reviewed. Those not documented in the *Customization Guide* are explained in greater detail. To use any of these commands, type **LO** for Load, **B** for Batch file, and then type the name of the macro and press Enter.

Macros for Copying

ARRAY1.MCR (documented) is used to copy objects in an array of columns and rows. First the macro prompts the user to identify the objects to be copied (using a selection window). Next the macro requests a reference point, just as the regular copy commands do. Then the macro asks the user to identify a horizontal offset and a vertical offset, to show the horizontal and vertical distances between the original and the first copy. Finally, the macro asks the user for the number of copies, and creates the array.

ARRAY2.MCR (documented) take a more manual approach to creating a array than ARRAY1. After the user identifies the objects to be copied, the macro asks for the number of columns to be made, and then the number of rows. The macro then asks the user to identify an offset; copies are made to equal the number of columns requested. Finally, the macro asks the user to identify another offset, for the distance from the original to the first row to be copied. The macro then creates copies equal to the number of rows requested.

CONCO.MCR (documented) and CONCOPY.MCR (undocumented) enable you to continuously copy selected objects. The macros prompt the user to place a window around the objects to be copied, then prompt for a reference point, similar to the Copy (CO) or Window Copy (WC) commands. The macros then repeatedly ask the user to identify a location for a new copy, until the user presses Esc to end the command (see fig. 20.2).

Both CONCO and CONCOPY use Component Place and Component Image to create the new copies. The macros create a temporary component out of the objects identified by the user. Every time a copy is placed in the drawing (using Component Place), Component Image makes sure that individual objects, not a component, go into the drawing.

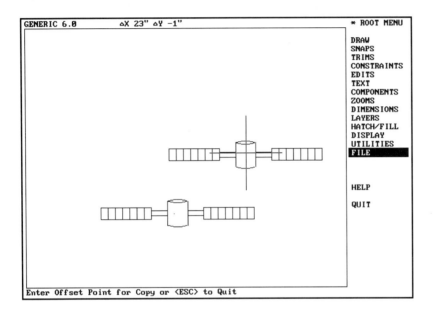

Figure 20.2:

Using CONCO or CONCOPY to copy objects.

The difference between these two batch files is that CONCO examines the current status of the Component Rotation (CR) and Component Scale (CZ) commands, saves the value of each command, and temporarily sets Component Rotation to zero degrees and Component Scale to 1 for both the vertical and horizontal scale. This ensures that the copies are identical to the original. (CONCO restores the original settings of Component Rotation or Component Scale when the command is finished.) CONCOPY also uses Component Place and Component Image, but does not modify the settings of Component Rotation and Component Scale. If Component Rotation is set to 45 when CONCOPY is used, for example, all copies placed using the macro are rotated 45 degrees counterclockwise.

Macros for Line Editing

CONFIL.MCR (documented) and CONFILLT.MCR (undocumented) enable you to use the Fillet (FI) command repeatedly. CONFIL prompts the user to identify both lines for the fillet, then executes the filleting and asks the user to identify two more lines for filleting. CONFILLT provides a separate prompt for each line in the pair to be filleted, then fillets the two lines and starts the process again. Both macros use the existing setting of the Fillet Radius (FR) command.

CONCH.MCR (documented) enables you to repeatedly use the Chamfer (CH) command. This macro uses the existing setting in Chamfer Distances (CA). The user chooses two lines and the macro chamfers them. The macro then prompts the user to identify two more lines, and the process is repeated until the user presses Esc.

CONOB.MCR (documented) enables you to repeatedly use the Object Break (OB) command. The macro prompts the user to select a line and then the two break locations. The break is inserted, and the macro repeats the cycle until the user presses Esc.

CONIT.MCR (documented) enables you to repeatedly use the Intersection Trim (IT) command. If you have drawn the walls for an entire floor plan with Double Line (L2), you can use this macro to trim all the intersections in one sequence. The macro prompts the user to select a point in the center of an intersection and another point that identifies the direction of the trim (just as usual for Intersection Trim). When the trim is completed, the user is prompted for another intersection and the process continues until the user presses Esc.

LINEBEND.MCR (documented) is used to replace a straight line with two new lines that meet at an angle. Figure 20.3 shows the results of a before-and-after sequence. This macro combines the use of Object Break (OB) and Move Point (MP), in essence creating a new command.

LINESECT.MCR (documented) and LINESEG.MCR (undocumented) divide one straight line into several smaller lines of equal

length. (The user specifies how many.) There is no visible difference in operation between these two macros. The difference is in
how they were written. Comparing LINESECT with LINESEG
gives the aspiring MPL writer an opportunity to see that there is
usually more than one way to write a macro.

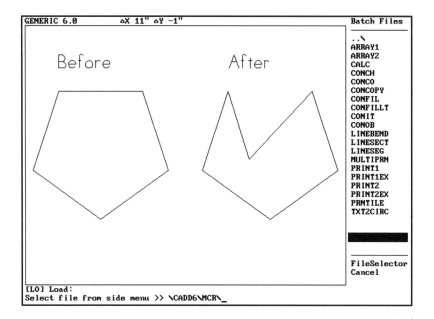

Figure 20.3:

*Before and
after using
LINEBEND.MCR.*

Macro for Placing Text

TXT2CIRC.MCR (undocumented) is the only text macro that
ships with Generic CADD 6.0. It was a last-minute replacement
for the two macros mentioned in the *Customization Guide*
(NEWTCIRC.MCR and TL2CIRC.MCR). The swap is mentioned
in the READ.ME file that ships with Generic CADD 6.0. This
macro makes it possible to place text along a circle. The macro
asks for the circle to be identified, then the user is asked whether
the text is already in the drawing or will be typed in as new text.
Figure 20.4 shows an example of both options provided by
TXT2CIRC.

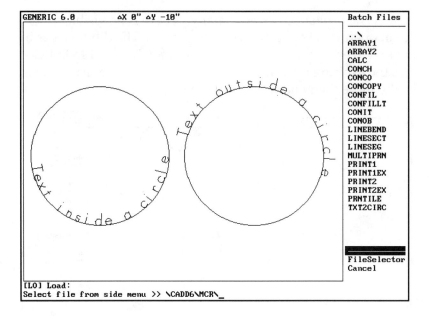

Figure 20.4:

Placing text with TXT2CIRC.

Macros for Printing

PRNTILE.MCR (documented), PRINT1.MCR (undocumented), and PRINT1EX.MCR (undocumented) all do the exact same thing—make it possible for a drawing to be printed in sections on dot-matrix and laser printers, providing a way to obtain output larger than one physical page. The documentation provided in the *Customization Guide* for PRNTILE applies equally to PRINT1.MCR and PRINT1EX.MCR.

All three macros prompt the user for printer type (dot-matrix, laser, PostScript), sheet size, and drawing scale (as a ratio of real to print size). Next, each macro asks how much overlap you want from tile to tile. Printing with an overlap makes matching the tiles together easier because you can overlay lines to achieve a perfect match. Each macro then examines the size of the drawing and displays a suggested print tiling grid. Each block in the grid represents one piece of paper (see fig. 20.5). If you are satisfied with the grid, type **A** for Accept. Each macro prints the drawing onto as many pieces of paper as are shown on-screen. If you want to change the scale of the printout, or move the tiles to prevent a split at a crucial place in the drawing, type **R** for Rescale or **C** for Change. To exit without printing, type **Q** for Quit.

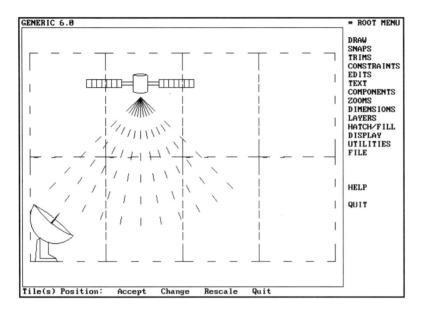

Figure 20.5:

Using PRNTILE to print a drawing.

Comment lines are not included in the PRNTILE and PRINT1 batch files; PRINT1EX does provide comment lines for the curious.

PRINT2.MCR (undocumented) and PRINT2EX.MCR (undocumented) automate the first few steps involved in printing a drawing. Both macros use the existing print settings (printer, resolution, page size, and so on). Both macros bring up the Page Setup screen and then end, leaving the user to set the scale and rotation manually, and then to print the drawing. The only difference between the two batch files is that PRINT2EX.MCR has comment lines included.

MULTIPRN.MCR (undocumented) will make many experienced Generic CADD users happy. It is used to set up a print queue of CADD drawings. The macro prompts the user to enter the name of a drawing to be printed, continuing to ask until Esc is pressed. Then the macro prints each drawing selected. To print multiple copies of one drawing, select the drawing as many times as the number of copies you need printed.

One word of warning: MULTIPRN.MCR uses all existing printer settings. If you have just used PRNTILE.MCR, the page size may be set to an unusual size. To be safe, check the printer settings menu before using MULTIPRN.MCR.

Macro for Calculating

CALC.MCR (documented) provides digitizer users with a useful on-screen calculator. The main reason it is included with Generic CADD is to present the aspiring macro programmer with examples of unusual and interesting ways to use CADD's MPL. The *Customization Guide* presents three calculation macros: A video menu (VCALC.MNU), a digitizer menu (DCALC.MNU), and the on-screen calculator (CALC.MCR). Working through the exercises in the *Customization Guide* that explain the creation and use of these macros would be a good next step after completing this chapter.

Understanding the Elements of the Macro Programming Language

To put it simply, the purpose of any programming language is to provide a way to tell the computer what to do. Like any language, programming languages have vocabulary and grammar. If you save the statement CR,90 as a keyboard macro, you have written a program. CR (which translates into English as Component Rotate) is part of MPL vocabulary; 90 is part of the vocabulary also (MPL understands numbers and mathematical expressions). This particular program tells Generic CADD to rotate a component 90 degrees counterclockwise before placing it in a drawing. Until you issue new instructions, every component placed will be rotated in this way.

The grammar of Generic CADD's MPL is precise. If instead of saving CR,90 you saved the statement 90,CR as a keyboard macro,

Generic CADD would be unable to process your request, because the statement makes no sense to the program. To say that MPL is precise does not mean that MPL is also rigid and limited in its forms of expression. The macro CR,(45+45) means the same thing as CR,90; so does CR,$SQT(8100);. This last statement translates into English as "Component Rotate using the value of the square root of 8,100 as the degrees of rotation." This last statement may be impractical, but it works.

The vocabulary and grammar of MPL are designed to organize and interpret information for a specific purpose: the creation of graphic images that represent coordinate locations and vectors. Math functions are a part of the grammar of MPL; numbers and logical relationships are part of the vocabulary. Because the program must be capable of seeking instructions from the programmer, the grammar of MPL also allows for the storage and use of written messages. MPL does not understand these messages, it simply knows how to store them, display them, and execute a task based on the response to the messages.

MPL is able to organize the different types of information it must use. Messages and other nonmath expressions are known as *strings*, numbers are assigned to *variables*, variables are placed in memory using *indices* (the plural of *index*). Strings, variables, and indices can be stored in files. Files are given identification numbers known as *handles* while being used by a macro. MPL can create new files to store data, it can read the contents of existing files, and it can add data to existing files.

The various elements of Generic CADD's MPL are described in further detail in the sections that follow.

Formulas and Variables

Generic CADD is, in essence, a way to express geometry. Because geometry is a branch of mathematics, it follows that CADD's MPL understands the language of mathematics. Specifically, MPL understands a variety of math functions and can process two kinds of variables. Variables created during the normal use of Generic CADD are called *system variables*; those defined by a macro are known as *assigned variables*.

Mathematical Functions

The earlier sample macro CR, (45+45) is a simple example of Generic CADD's capability to use mathematical expressions as well as numbers. If you have ever entered fractional values in CADD, you have used this capability. A fraction is really a simple division operation. For example, 1/4 is the same as 1 divided by 4.

The following mathematical functions can be used in macros:

- Addition (+)
- Subtraction (–)
- Multiplication (*)
- Division (/)
- $SQR(X) The square of X.
- $SQT(X) The square root of X.
- $ABS(X) The absolute value of X. Absolute value returns the positive value of a number, as if it were multiplied by –1. For example, the absolute value of –3.14 is 3.14.
- $SIN(X) The sine of angle X.
- $COS(X) The cosine of angle X.
- $ATN(X) The arctangent of value X. This function provides an angle whose tangent is the value X.
- $LN(X) The natural or *base e* logarithm of X. Usually referred to as the *natural log of X* (*e* is an indeterminate constant similar to pi).
- $EXP(X) *e* to the X power, sometimes expressed as *e*^X.

The following rules apply to these mathematical functions:

- X may be any real number or mathematical formula, and may include system variables (defined shortly).
- X must be enclosed in parentheses. The function $SIN32 will not work, whereas $SIN(32) will.

- Numbers must be expressed in decimal form. Degrees must be in decimal, not D:M:S (Degrees:Minutes:Seconds).

- Avoid mixed dimensions, such as 2'3".

- Spaces may be added for clarity; they are ignored when Generic CADD evaluates the expression.

- X to the Y power (X^Y) can be derived by using the "natural log" and "*e* to the X" functions, using the following formula: X^Y = $EXP (Y*$LN(X)).

When Generic CADD solves mathematical expressions, it does so in the following order:

1. Anything enclosed in parentheses. Deepest nested parentheses are evaluated first.

2. The previously described $ functions, such as $SQR.

3. Multiplication and division.

4. Addition and subtraction.

Here are some examples of how the equations are formatted in Generic CADD:

```
4 + 5 * 8 - 6       =   4 + 40 - 6  =   38      =   38
(4 + 5) * 8 - 6     =   9 * 8 - 6   =   72 - 6  =   66
4 + 5 * (8 - 6)     =   4 + 5 * 2   =   4 + 10  =   14
(4 + 5) * (8 - 6)   =   9 * 2       =   18      =   18
```

System Variables

When the statement CR,90; is provided to Generic CADD, the program must store the value *90*. When a coordinate location is identified, the two numbers that represent the location must be stored also. Coordinates and values are stored in the CADD Environment, as described in Chapter 1. The newest values and coordinates are stored temporarily as system variables. When the macro CR,90; is executed, *90* is stored in a system variable. If another macro, CZ,2; is then executed, *90* is bumped out of the variable and replaced by *2*. Strings and error notices also have temporary dwellings. Each is described in the following sections.

The $VAL Variable

The $VAL variable is updated whenever a single value is entered. Whenever you use a CADD command that requires one number (such as Line Color or Component Rotation), $VAL is updated to whatever value you enter. You can set $VAL to the current value of any setting by activating the proper command and accepting the default (current) value for that setting. For example, if you issue the Component Rotation command and press Enter without typing a number, no change is made to the component rotation setting, but $VAL is updated to reflect the current Component Rotation value.

Being able to place a number in $VAL enables you to increment or alter any setting, based on the current setting. For example, the following line in a macro will alter Component Rotation by 90 degrees:

```
CR,!,CR,$VAL + 90; Sets CR to CR+90 degrees
```

In the preceding macro, CR stands for Component Rotation (as if you did not already know). The exclamation mark in a macro represents the Enter key. Thus, CR,!, acts as if Enter had been pressed to accept the current value of Component Rotation, leaving CR unchanged and setting $VAL to the current component rotation. The Component Rotation command is issued again, followed by the phrase $VAL + 90, which adds 90 degrees to the current value (held in $VAL) of Component Rotation.

You can also take advantage of $VAL to set one value equal to another. Say, for example, that you want the line color to be changed to match the layer number whenever you change the current layer, so that objects with color 1 are on Layer 1, those with color 2 are on Layer 2, and so on. You could set the current layer manually (with Layer Current, YC), or you could use the following macro:

```
YC,~,LC,$VAL; Sets current layer; color = layer number
```

In this macro, YC starts the Layer Current command, and the tilde pauses so that you can select the layer. LC sets the Line Color to $VAL, which was updated to reflect the layer number just selected.

The $PNTX and $PNTY Variables

Translated into English, $PNTX is the Point X variable and $PNTY is the Point Y variable. $PNTX and $PNTY work as a pair. Both are updated whenever you set a value that uses a pair of settings, as for Component Scale (CZ) or Grid Size (GS). These variables are updated also whenever you use a Snap command, such as Snap to Nearest Point (NP or third mouse button) or Snap Intersection (SI). Note that only points entered by using CADD commands update these variables; points entered manually or by clicking do not change the variables.

One way to use these two variables is to make a pair of macros that either double or halve the current component scale. Consider the following examples:

```
CZ,!!,CZ,$PNTX * 2,$PNTY * 2;      Doubles component scale
CZ,!!,CZ,$PNTX * .5,$PNTY * .5;    Halves component scale
CZ,!!,CZ,$PNTX * 2,$PNTY;          Doubles X component scale
                                   only
CZ,!!,CZ,$PNTX,$PNTY * 2;          Doubles Y component scale
                                   only
```

You may want to "store" one of these system variables on occasion. The easiest way to do this is to use a setting you rarely (if ever) use as a holding place for the value. Some people use the Line Scale (LZ) command as a holding place for $VAL, for example. Because the basepoint takes a pair of values and is seldom used, some people use it as a holding place for $PNTX and $PNTY. The procedure is as follows:

```
LZ,$VAL;           Puts $VAL into LZ
LZ,!;              Gets $VAL from LZ
BP,$PNTX,$PNTY;    Puts $PNTX and $PNTY into BP
BP,!!;             Gets $PNTX and $PNTY from BP
```

The $STR Variable

Some of the information Generic CADD uses is in the form of words, expressions that cannot be used in a math equation. For example, the macro DN,FIDO; renames the current drawing to FIDO. After changing the name of the drawing to FIDO, Generic

CADD places the word *FIDO* into a variable called $STR (the string variable). Another macro can then be written to take advantage of the contents of $STR:

```
DN,!,TL,@,$STR;
```

In the preceding macro, the Drawing Name (DN) command is followed by the Enter key; this makes no change to the name of the drawing, but places the name into $STR. Next, the Text Line (TL) command prompts the user for a coordinate location (@) and writes the contents of $STR at the specified location. This macro could be part of a larger macro that creates a title block, inserting the name of the drawing at a user-specified location.

The $DERR and $FERR Variables

Sometimes a user responds to a command not with a number or a name (or other string), but with a keystroke that indicates "no input received." Enter and Esc are the two keys that can generate such a response. CADD assigns a code number to each response, and stores the most recent response in a variable known as $DERR. The Enter key generates a –1; the Esc key generates a –2. The preceding macro, DN,!,TL,@,$STR;, placed the current drawing name into $STR and also placed the code number –1 into $DERR (because of the DN,! sequence).

If a file-access command goes wrong, an error message is generated. For example, if you tried to load a drawing from drive A, but the door of the floppy drive was open, the error message Disk Not Ready would be generated. The variable $FERR stores a code number that identifies the last result of a file-access command. $FERR will contain a zero if the last file access was successful. If the last access was not successful, $FERR will contain a code number, as listed in the *Customization Guide*.

In complicated macros, it is important for the macro to know the status of an action. By checking the values of $DERR or $FERR and acting on the results found, you can write a macro that can continue to operate no matter what the results of a previous action may be.

Assigned Variables

The variables discussed so far are generated as a by-product of other operations. But it is also possible to create variables and assign values to them. Variable types are available for the following types of data:

- *Integers:* Limited to whole numbers between –32768 and 32767

- *Real numbers:* Decimal numbers with 7 to 8 significant digits in either direction, such as 34454.3, 1.123456, and 1200000

- *Points:* Pairs of real numbers, used to store X and Y values

- *Strings:* Sequences of up to 20 or 80 characters of text, depending on the type of variable used

Each assigned variable created in a macro is assigned an *index*, a code number that identifies the variable in memory. Index numbers are assigned starting with zero; the number of index names matches the number of variables created.

Several commands listed in the following sections are used to assign and read these variables.

Programming Commands

The macros presented to this point use two-letter commands, system variables, and a few shorthand characters (such as ! for Enter, and @ for a coordinate location). But the real power in writing Generic CADD macros comes from the 30 new programming commands, which expand the vocabulary of the MPL. As with human language, a larger vocabulary opens the door to more eloquent expression.

These new programming commands can be used in all macros, whether called by a function key, added to a menu, or called as part of a batch file. The new commands follow the same rules as other parts of the MPL vocabulary, except that they must be preceded by a slash (/). Each command has a long name and a three-character abbreviation; either name may be used in a macro.

(A few of the commands have very short names, which is why the same name is repeated in parentheses.)

Instead of competing with the *Customization Guide* (and leaving the nontechnical reader behind), the following descriptions of MPL commands are for readers who are unfamiliar with programming and its common technical terms. The 30 MPL commands can be divided into the following categories:

- Display operations
- File operations
- Flow control
- Entity list operations
- Variable operations
- Utility operations

Each group, and the commands in it, are defined in the following sections.

Display Operations

Display operations are commands that provide control of Generic CADD's display. When a macro takes control of the screen, much of the information on-screen becomes clutter. These commands enable the programmer to control what is visible on-screen during the execution of a macro.

/CURSOR_HIDE (/CHD)

/CURSOR_HIDE, a toggle that controls the crosshairs (the drawing cursor), also controls the status of Drag Image. It does not affect the menu bar.

/MSUP (/MSP)

This message-supression command, a toggle, controls the display of messages in the prompt lines. This command can block out the normal CADD messages, enabling only special messages written by the programmer to appear at the bottom of the CADD screen.

/EXPERT_MODE (/XMD)

/EXPERT_MODE gives the macro total control of the CADD screen. The only keyboard input allowed is in response to specific requests from the macro.

/PROMPT (/PMT)

/PROMPT is used to display a message in the prompt area at the bottom of the screen. The text of the message can either accompany the command in the macro, or /PROMPT can read a message from a file on disk. Used with the /CHARIN command (described in the next section), /PROMPT can receive input from the user and direct the data to another command to continue the macro. It is also possible to create prompts that highlight a letter and accept mouse clicks, as the selection options do in commands like Copy (CO) and Entity Filter (EF).

/CHARIN (/CIN)

The /CHARIN command (for CHARacter IN) is used with /PROMPT to create special messages to which the macro user can reply. Macro operation is stopped until the user responds to the message created by /CHARIN.

Flow Control

Flow refers to the operation of a macro and the choices sometimes required during the execution of the macro. Flow-control commands act as gatekeepers. They look at the results of an earlier operation, and move the macro on in a specified direction.

/IF (/IF)

/IF directs the continued operation of the macro in response to an earlier action. For example, an /IF statement could read the value of the $DERR variable, which is either −1 (the Enter key) or −2 (the

Esc key), to determine how the user responded to an earlier prompt. An /IF statement looks for a true condition. If a true response is found, control of the program continues on that line. If a false response is found, the macro immediately quits reading the line and moves to the next line in the batch file. The macro MULTIPRN uses the /IF statement to read the value of $DERR, to see whether the user is finished selecting files to print, as follows:

```
/VIN,1,$DERR;
/IF,$I(1)[NE]0,/VIN,1,$I(0),/VIN,0,0,/GOTO,PRINT;
```

The English translation of the preceding lines (given that some of the commands have not been introduced yet) is "Create an integer variable (/VIN) called 1. Assign the value found in $DERR to this variable. If the value in Variable 1 is not equal to zero (/IF,$I(1)[NE]0,), reset Variable 1 to a value of zero (/VIN, 1,$I(0),), create another variable called Zero and give it a value of zero (/VIN,0,0,), and then transfer execution of this macro to a section called PRINT (/GOTO,PRINT;).

/GOTO (/GTO)

As mentioned in the discussion of /IF, /GOTO moves the execution of a macro to a specified location in the batch file. These locations are identified by a label defined in the /GOTO statement. In the portion of MULTIPRN printed in the preceding section, the phrase /GOTO,PRINT; appears at the end of the /IF line. If the /IF is true, /GOTO is executed and the macro searches for a portion of the batch file labeled .PRINT.

Variable Operations

Several commands create new variables, assign values to the variables, and read the contents of variables. Even a small macro can quickly make use of a variety of data types; the commands that control variables are among the most important in the MPL vocabulary.

/VARALLOC (/VLC)

Variables must be created before they can be put to use in a macro. /VARALLOC (for Variable Allocate) reserves space in memory for variables. /VARALLOC defines how many of each type of variable (Integer, Real, Point, String) is to be used by the macro. Index numbers are assigned automatically to the variables in numeric order, starting with zero (0).

/VINT (/VIN)

After variables have been created and given index numbers by /VARALLOC, they are ready to be assigned values. /VINT assigns values to Integer variables. Because not all variables are assigned values immediately, it is not uncommon to use the /VINT command several times in a macro.

/VREAL (/VRL)

/VREAL is used to assign a value to a Real variable. The value can be set by the macro, or provided as a result of user input.

/VPNT (/VPT)

/VPNT assigns point values, as in coordinate locations. This command always assigns values in pairs (you have $PNTX or Y if you need only one).

/VSTR (/VST)

/VSTR assigns text to a String variable. The maximum length of a String variable is 80 characters. As with other variables, the data assigned to a String variable can be specified by the macro or obtained through user input.

/STR (/STR)

Although mathematical functions cannot be performed on the contents of String variables created by /VSTR, other manipulations of the information in a String variable can be helpful. /STR performs these functions by using one of four available option letters along with the /STR command. /STR,S is used to extract characters from a String variable to create a substring; /STR,C is for concatenation of two Strings (combining their data to create a new string); /STR,L is used to calculate the length of a String variable; and /STR,U is used to convert the information in a String variable to all uppercase text.

/SETGLOBAL (/SGL)

The variables discussed so far are temporary. They are created and used during a Generic CADD session, and disappear when the session ends. If you need to extend the life of values being assigned to variables so that they can be used repeatedly in different applications, use the /SETGLOBAL command to transfer the values to permanent variables. Variables saved with the /SETGLOBAL command are saved with a drawing file. They can be accessed by MPL commands, just like values in temporary variables. The /SETGLOBAL command can save as many as 20 Integer variables, 20 Real number variables, 10 Point variables, and 8 Strings of no more than 20 characters each.

File Operations

Being able to work with files stored on disk provides a wealth of options for the creative MPL programmer. Reading information from files on disk makes it possible to use data created by other programs, including programs written by the user. The information must be in ASCII format to be read by the file-operations commands. Several commands are available to read and write to files. If you discover that the number of variables MPL allows is too limiting, file operations give you another way to store and process necessary information.

/FILEOPEN (/FOP)

To understand file operations, think of files as file cabinets, each quietly waiting to be used. Before the information in a file cabinet can be used, or before new information can be put into it, the file cabinet must be opened. /FILEOPEN selects a text file on disk and opens it for use by a macro. Because opening a file takes up memory, only five files can be open simultaneously.

When a file is opened, /FILEOPEN defines a reason for opening the file, using one of four control letters:

- **R** (Read). Information in the file will be read and used elsewhere by the macro.

- **W** (Write). New information will be placed in the file. A file designated as a Write file is either empty or contains expendable data, because writing to a file overwrites the existing data (except in an Append file).

- **A** (Append). Data will be added to an existing file without overwriting.

- **F** Identifies a file as being of Fixed length, available for both read and write operations. A file from a database, with many records all of the same length, is one example of a fixed-length file.

/FILEREAD (/FRD)

After a file has been opened by /FILEOPEN, other commands can take advantage of the information in the file. /FILEREAD reads a line from an open file and places it in the system variable $STR. From $STR, the data can be placed into an assigned variable. Moving the data out of $STR before using it is important, because CADD always uses $STR to store the most recent text used by the program, including the next line of data read from the open file.

/FILERESET (/RST)

When a line or two from an open file has been read, the program remembers where the reading stopped. If the file is read again, the process continues from where it stopped. /FILERESET tells a macro to start at the beginning with the read operation instead of remembering where it stopped.

/FILEWRITE (/FWR)

/FILEWRITE can take data from a macro and write it to a file that has been opened to receive data. This command makes it possible to save the results of calculations or other operations separate from a drawing file.

/FILECLOSE (/FCL)

Leaving a file cabinet open when you are through with it is sloppy filing; the same applies to open files in a macro. /FILECLOSE closes files previously opened with /FILEOPEN. Because there is a limit of five open files at any one time in a macro, closing a file as soon as it is no longer needed frees up memory for another file to be opened. To make sure that the file was closed properly, the system variable $FERR can be checked. If the value in $FERR is zero, the operation was a success. If the value in $FERR is not equal to zero, a problem occurred. The *Customization Guide* has a list of error code numbers and their meanings. (You can check $FERR to test the success of any file operation, not just /FILECLOSE.)

/MESSASSIGN (/MES)

The files discussed so far are for the storage of data to be processed by a macro. Messages used by a macro also can be stored in files. One file of messages can be shared by several macros, much as you can use components in a variety of drawings. The message files must be in ASCII format and follow a variety of simple rules (listed in the *Customization Guide*). Unlike data files, only one message file may be open at a time.

Entity List Operations

Every object in a drawing is fair game to become data for a macro. As discussed in previous chapters, Generic CADD stores a variety of data about each line, text character, component, attribute, and other object in the drawing. Entity list operations can examine these objects and use the results in a variety of ways. Generally, entity list operations are a two-step process with commands for each step. First entities are selected, then they are examined.

/CREATE_EEX_LIST (/CEL)

Before entities can be examined, they must be assembled into what is called an *entity list*. Because the items in the list are numbered sequentially, a macro can track the items on the list. /CREATE_EEX_LIST creates an entity list, using the selection methods you know from the editing commands (Window, Object, Layer, Drawing, Last Selection, Filter). As soon as /CREATE_EEX_LIST is used, the number of entities on the list is stored as a value in the $VAL system variable. Because this number is used by the macro to identify the objects, it is good practice to assign this value immediately to a separate variable (because $VAL will be overwritten by the next operation that generates a value).

/LASTENTITY (/LST)

If the only entity you need to track is the last one placed in the drawing, use /LASTENTITY to assign it to an entity list.

/DISPOSE_EEX_LIST (/DEL)

When you finish with an entity list, it should be removed from memory to make room for other operations. /DISPOSE_EEX_LIST removes an entity list from memory. You do not need to use /DISPOSE_EEX_LIST when you finish with one entity list only to create another. Both /LASTENTITY and /CREATE_EEX_LIST delete the previous entity list when starting a new one.

/EEX (/EEX)

/EEX (Examine Entity List) enables a macro to examine the contents of an entity list, searching for the information needed. A macro may need to match the color of a specific line or the rotation of a component in the list. A long list of code letters and numbers (listed in the *Customization Guide*) are used with /EEX to identify the data on the list. After the required information has been found, it can be assigned to the appropriate type of variable for further use. Every piece of information available about every type of object found in a CADD drawing, from the current between-character spacing of text to the type of arrowhead in use, can be read from an entity list and used in a macro.

Utility Operations

Utility operations are a mixed bag of commands primarily of interest to the experienced programmer. Commands in this group can access information from the DOS environment, locate specific geometry, count objects in a drawing, and allow for the operation of other programs written by the programmer.

/SYS (/SYS)

The /SYS command provides access to information found in the DOS environment. A series of codes are used to assign the information to either the $STR or $VAL variables. From there the information can be moved to an assigned variable for use in a macro. Information gleaned from the DOS environment can include the date and time, the settings of DOS variables (including ones set by AUTOEXEC.BAT and CONFIG.SYS when your computer starts up), and data created by other programs and stored by DOS.

/DEF (/DEF)

The /DEF (Definition) command can determine what components and attributes have been defined in a drawing. This is different from the function performed by the entity list command /EEX, which identifies the *placement* of components and attributes. /DEF finds both the number of definitions and the contents of each definition in the drawing, and makes the information available for storage in variables.

/SELECT (/SEL)

This command puts Generic CADD into selection mode, allowing continued selection of objects from a standard selection prompt (the same prompt used by commands like Copy [CO] or Erase [ER]). Using this command gives the MPL writer the flexibility of not having to know in advance how many objects are to be selected. As with all other commands that identify objects or data, the values found by /SELECT can be assigned to variables for further use.

/EXTENTS (/EXT)

Early in this book you were introduced to Zoom Limits and Zoom All, two commands that adjust the amount of data shown on-screen. The same data used by these two commands can be used to find out the current extent of what is displayed on-screen. /EXTENTS can calculate the current extents of the screen or of selected objects.

/GEOM (/GEO)

Many of the commands in CADD's MPL would be at home in other programming environments. /GEOM is an exception. It is used to identify specific intersections of lines and circles in a drawing. /GEOM reports the point location of the intersection, making the information available to be assigned to a point variable for further use.

/SHELL (/SHE)

/SHELL is the equivalent of the Generic CADD Shell to Executable (SH) command. It enables the execution of another program. The difference between SH and /SHELL is that /SHELL does not remove Generic CADD from the screen. The program being run by /SHELL, then, should not make use of the screen. This command is designed to run programs written specifically for use with macros. Professional developers can write programs for use with Generic CADD by using /SHELL, as well as the file operation commands, to link their programs with CADD macros.

Becoming More Familiar with the Macro Programming Commands

There are only two ways to become proficient at writing macros with MPL. The first is to study how others use MPL. The second is to get your hands dirty, so to speak, and start working with the commands to create your own applications. This chapter provides several ideas for using MPL commands and you should be able to come up with many more.

As explained in the previous chapter, macros may be written either directly in Generic CADD (if they are small and will be placed on a function key), or in any word processor or text editor that reads and writes ASCII text. All the MPL commands, functions, and variables introduced in this chapter may be used in any macro, not just in batch files stored on disk.

Before you start writing macros, using the new MPL commands, you may want to gain a little more familiarity with the commands. Why not try a method the *Customization Guide* forgot to mention? You can enter MPL commands directly from the CADD prompt.

Running Macro Commands from the CADD Prompt

Although the *Customization Guide* does not mention it, several of the MPL commands described in this chapter can be run from the CADD prompt. With a couple of exceptions, running MPL commands from the CADD prompt is of limited value, because these commands were designed to be used in a batch file format. But entering these commands at the CADD prompt, and replying to their requests for input, is a great way to become more familiar with the commands and how they operate. In more than one case, using an MPL command at the CADD prompt provides an unexpected (undocumented) bonus.

The following list of MPL commands can be used from the CADD prompt. With each command is an explanation of what happens or what additional input is required. To use a command, type either its full name or the three-letter shorthand version at the CADD prompt. Be sure to type the slash first. For a complete discussion of these commands, refer to the information earlier in the chapter and compare the information in this chapter with the documentation provided in the *Customization Guide*.

/VARALLOC (/VLC) replies with the prompt:

```
Change macro variable allocation, 148 bytes remaining
Integers (20)   Reals (20)   Points (20)   Strings (20)
```

By pressing one of the option letters, you can change the number of variables available for that data type.

/VINT (/VIN) replies with the prompt:

```
Enter number of integer variable to set >>
```

When a number (the index number) is provided, a new prompt reads:

```
Enter the integer value >>
```

/VREAL (/VRL) replies with a prompt:

```
Enter number of real variables to set >>
```

When a number (the index number) is provided, a new prompt reads:

```
Enter the real value >>
```

/VPNT (/VPT) replies with a prompt:

```
Enter number of point variable to set >>
```

When a number (the index number) is provided, a new prompt reads:

```
Enter the X,Y value >>
```

/VSTR (/VST) replies with a prompt:

```
Enter number of string variable to set >>
```

When a number (the index number) is provided, a new prompt reads:

```
Enter the string variable >>
```

/STR (/STR) replies with prompt:

```
Macro String Function
Substring  Concat  Length  Upcase
```

By pressing one of the option letters, you can manipulate data in a string. Consult the *Customization Guide* for complete details. Notice that the four highlighted command letters listed in the prompt for this command correspond to the four control functions documented in the *Customization Guide* for this command.

/SETGLOBAL (/SGL) replies with a prompt:

```
Set Global Macro Variable
Set Integers  Reals  Points  Strings
```

By pressing one of the option letters, you can enter values for the various global variables. First you enter the variable name (the index number), then CADD prompts you for a value to be assigned. Notice that the four highlighted command letters listed in the prompt for this command correspond to the four control functions documented in the *Customization Guide* for this command.

/CREATE_EEX_LIST (/CEL) replies with the selection prompt used by CADD's editing commands (see fig. 20.6). After selecting entities using the selection commands, press Enter to end; a prompt replies Entity list for Entity Examine created. The data selected can be examined using /EEX, the Entity Examine command, described in the next paragraph.

/EEX (/EEX) replies with a request for an entity number. Entity numbers are assigned to objects selected using the /CREATE_EEX_LIST (/CEL) command. In figure 20.6, the component of the satellite dish was assigned Entity Number 1 after all objects in the drawing were selected. When a number is typed in, a series of choices appear in the prompt line (see fig. 20.7).

These choices match the code letters and numbers listed in the *Customization Guide* (in the section describing /CREATE_EEX_LIST). /EEX could be used to make changes to objects in the database, although doing so would be more cumbersome than using the Change (CG) command. The trick would be to determine the entity numbers of the objects you wanted to change.

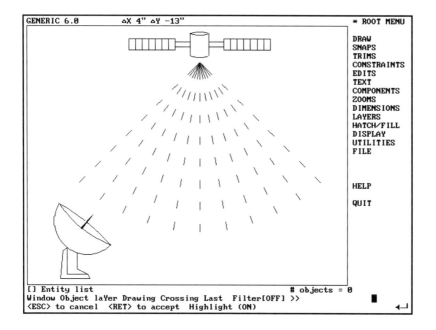

Figure 20.6:

/CREATE_EEX_LIST uses Selection options.

/SYS (/SYS) replies with a prompt showing four choices for accessing data from the operating system. Only the first three (**Date, Time, Environment**) are documented in the *Customization Guide* (page 65). The fourth, **Cadd**, is not. Figure 20.7 shows the first prompt after you type **/SYS** at the CADD prompt.

Compare the highlighted options with the list of parameters documented in the *Customization Guide*, and follow through to compare each initial selection (**Date, Time, Environment**) with the set of second parameters listed for each. Because **Cadd** is not documented, no second parameters are given in the *Customization Guide*. Figure 20.8 shows the set of second parameters for the Cadd option of /SYS.

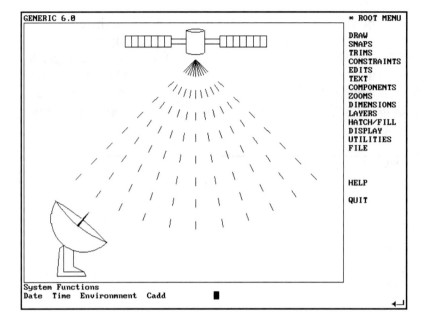

Figure 20.7:

Choices offered by /SYS.

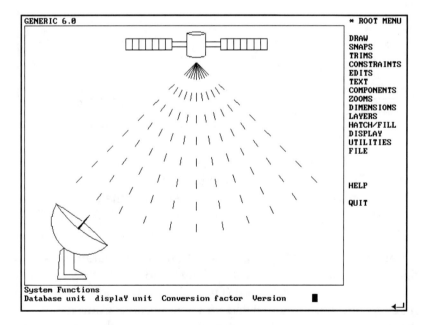

Figure 20.8:

Cadd environment options for /SYS.

Translating the Continuous Fillet Macro

The chapter closes with an examination of one of the macros that ships with Generic CADD 6.0. CONFIL.MCR, which enables for continuous filleting, is one of several macros that provide for continuous operation of an editing command.

Each line of CONFIL.MCR is followed by an explanation.

    /MSP,++,/XMD,++,OR,--,MO;

Message suppression is turned on (/MSP,++), Expert mode is turned on (/XMD,++), Ortho mode is turned off (OR,--), and manual entry is set to origin (MO;).

    /VLC,P,2,I,1,S,1,!;

Variables are allocated for the macro (/VLC,). There will be two Point variables (P,2,), one Integer variable (I,1,), and one String variable (S,1,!;).

    /SYS,C,Y,/VST,0,$STR;

The /SYS command identifies CADD display units (/SYS,C,Y,) and places them into a String variable called $S(0) (/VST,0,$STR;).

    /SYS,C,D,UN,$STR;

The /SYS command identifies CADD database units (/SYS,C,D,), places the contents into the system variable $STR, and sets the display units of the drawing to match (UN,$STR;).

    .FILLET;

This is the label of a subroutine. All the lines that follow, until the next label, are part of this subroutine.

    /PMT,1,'Select first line to fillet or <ESC> to finish',#;

A defined prompt-line statement is placed on the top CADD prompt line (/PMT,1,) with the message Select first line to fillet or <ESC> to finish.

    /VPNT,0,@;

A Point variable is assigned to store the location of the line identified in response to the previous prompt.

```
/CEL,O,$X(0),$Y(0),!;
```

An entity examine list is created. It will be scanned later to see whether an object was selected.

```
/IF,$VAL[EQ]0,/PMT,1,'Object not found: Press <ESC> to
finish or <ENTER> to continue',#,/CIN;
```

If the temporary system variable is empty [equal to zero] (/IF,$VAL[EQ]0,), display the following line in the top prompt line: Object not found: Press <ESC> to finish or <ENTER> to continue. Store the code number of the reply (–1 for Enter, –2 for Esc) as a system variable.

```
/IF,$VAL[EQ]-2,/GOTO,EXIT;
```

If the temporary system value equals –2, which means that Esc was pressed (/IF,$VAL[EQ]-2,), transfer execution of the program to the EXIT subroutine (/GOTO,EXIT;).

```
/IF,$VAL[EQ]-1,/GOTO,FILLET;
```

If the temporary system variable equals –1, which means that Enter was pressed or mouse button one clicked and a line identified (/IF,$VAL[EQ]-1,), transfer execution of the program to the FILLET subroutine, in effect looping back six steps (/GOTO,FILLET;).

```
/IF,$DERR[NE]0,/GOTO,EXIT;
```

If the value of the error variable $DERR is not equal to zero (/IF,$DERR[NE]0,) transfer execution of the program to the EXIT subroutine. (Remember, the codes for $DERR are –2=Esc, –1=Enter, 0 = OK.)

```
.FILLET2;
```

This is the label of a subroutine called FILLET2. All lines until the next label are part of this subroutine.

```
/PMT,1,'Select second line to fillet or <ESC> to finish',#;
```

In the top prompt line (/PMT,1,) the following prompt appears: Select second line to fillet or <ESC> to finish.

```
/VPNT,1,@;
```

A Point variable is assigned to store the location of the line identified in response to the previous prompt.

```
/CEL,O,$X(1),$Y(1),!;
```

An entity examine list is created to make sure that something is selected.

```
/IF,$VAL[EQ]0,/PMT,1,'Object not found: Press <ESC> to
finish or <ENTER> to continue',#,/CIN;
```

If the temporary system variable is empty [equal to zero] (/IF,$VAL[EQ]0,), display the following line in the top prompt line: Object not found: Press <ESC> to finish or <ENTER> to continue. Store the code number of the reply (–1 for Enter, –2 for Esc) as a system variable.

```
/IF,$VAL[EQ]-2,/GOTO,EXIT;
```

If the temporary system value equals –2, which means that Esc was pressed (/IF,$VAL[EQ]-2,), transfer execution of the program to the EXIT subroutine (/GOTO,EXIT;).

```
/IF,$VAL[EQ]-1,/GOTO,FILLET2;
```

If the temporary system variable equals –1, which means that Enter was pressed or mouse button one clicked and a line identified (/IF,$VAL[EQ]-1,), transfer execution of the program to the FILLET2 subroutine, in effect looping back six steps (/GOTO,FILLET2;).

```
/IF,$DERR[NE]0,/GOTO,EXIT;
```

If the value of the error variable $DERR is not equal to zero (/IF,$DERR[NE]0,) transfer execution of the program to the EXIT subroutine.

```
FI,$X(0),$Y(0),$X(1),$Y(1);
```

Fillet (FI) the two lines selected earlier; their locations were stored as X and Y 0 and X and Y 1 ($X(0),$Y(0),$X(1),$Y(1);).

```
/GOTO,FILLET;
```

Transfer execution of the macro to the subroutine FILLET, and begin again.

```
.EXIT;
```

This begins the EXIT subroutine.

```
/DEL;
```

Erase the Entity list created earlier.

```
UN,$S(0);
```

Reset display units to their original value.

```
/XMD,--,/MSP,--,PU;
```

Set Expert mode off (`/XMD,--,`) and set message suppress off (`/MSP,--,`). Issue a Pen Up command for good measure (`PSI;`).

Summary

Although not every Generic CADD user will take the time to write custom macros, there is plenty of power for even hard-core programmers to invent creative and innovative new applications for CADD. The 30 commands that make up the macro programming language (MPL) provide the power to access databases, manipulate data, and perform mathematical functions. Although the *Customization Guide* that comes with Generic CADD 6.0 is a thorough reference work for the many new programming features, it is a bit intimidating for the Generic CADD user not familiar with programming concepts and terms. Working through the examples in this chapter, experimenting with the new commands, and studying existing macros will help the average Generic CADD user become familiar enough with these new commands to take advantage of them regularly.

Using a Digitizer

G eneric CADD supports two types of pointing devices: relative-motion devices (mice and trackballs) and absolute-position devices (digitizers). The primary difference between these two classifications is the way they operate. Because a trackball is really just an upside-down mouse, this discussion refers to both devices as *mice*.

The mouse registers movement on the basis of a ball which rolls as the mouse is moved across a surface. The trackball uses the same principle but is stationary. Rolling the ball with your thumb or finger moves the cursor on-screen. Digitizers use a combination of a *tablet* and a pointing device, either a *stylus* or *puck* (sometimes called a *cursor*). A stylus looks like a pen, whereas a puck resembles a mouse with a clear lens containing a fine crosshairs cursor. This discussion refers to both styles of pointers as a puck.

The pointer senses its position relative to the tablet, often with a resolution as high as 1,000 parts per inch. The digitizer sends to CADD, in an X,Y format, a continuous stream of coordinates that indicate the position of the puck or stylus.

Mice are called *relative-motion devices* because they relay position information to CADD based on motion. A mouse does not know *where* it is on your desk. You can pick it up and move it without affecting the location of the cursor on your CADD drawing screen. Mice and trackballs take notice only when they are rolled or a button is pressed. They report this information to CADD, which keeps track of the location of the cursor, updating it when you move the mouse.

In addition, many mice now support a feature called *ballistics*, which means that the mouse is sensitive to how fast it is moved. When this feature is used, the mouse reports more or less movement to CADD depending on the rate at which it is moved. Ballistics enables you to move the cursor the entire width of the screen by making a small but rapid movement of the mouse. The primary advantages to a mouse are the small amount of space required to use it (consider the size of the average mouse pad) and its low cost.

Digitizers, on the other hand, report an *absolute position* to CADD based on the location of the puck. You can pick up the puck and wave it around as much as you want, but as soon as it is within sensing distance of the tablet, it reports its exact location relative to the tablet. In this sense the puck cannot get "lost." It always knows where it is relative to its tablet. Whatever the speed at which a puck is moved, it always reports the same X,Y coordinates for a given position on the tablet's surface.

Examining Digitizer Advantages

Because digitizers report an absolute position, they can be used for many tasks that would be difficult if not impossible for a mouse.

The most obvious use for a digitizer (from which its name stems) is for tracing or digitizing drawings. You can tape a drawing to the surface of the tablet and trace the drawing into CADD. This is possible because the puck always reports the same coordinates for a given position on the surface of the tablet. You can indicate to CADD, with an accuracy limited only by your ability to center the crosshairs on the point you want, the points needed to draw a line, circle, or other primitive.

The second advantage of a digitizer is that you can place a menu template on its surface. Thus, the digitizer can be used to enter CADD commands or macros by simply pointing to the appropriate command on the template and clicking the first puck button. This is more effective than using the screen menus because hundreds of commands can be placed on the surface of the tablet, whereas screen menus must be nested to save space. The use of a digitizer menu enables you to perform a wide range of commands in a *point-and-shoot* fashion.

If you are using a puck instead of a stylus, a third advantage to using a digitizer is that many digitizers come with multibutton pucks. Most digitizers can be ordered with a 12- or 16-button puck. Puck buttons, like the third mouse button or the computer's function keys, can be programmed for commands or macros. By placing on the puck buttons the commands you use frequently, you can greatly increase your productivity. Most digitizer users soon memorize which functions are on which puck buttons, and with one hand on the puck and eyes on the screen, they can draw and edit with amazing speed.

Installing a Digitizer

Installing a digitizer and configuring it for use with CADD is a fairly straightforward process. You configure the digitizer itself (if necessary), connect it to the computer, and use the CONFIG program to configure CADD to use the digitizer for your pointing device.

Appendix B of the *Generic CADD 6.0 Installation and Troubleshooting Guide* lists the configuration of most digitizers supported by Generic CADD. Refer to Appendix B to see whether any switches need to be set on the digitizer. These switches may be in the form of a physical switch (like a DIP switch) or in the form of *soft switches* accessed by using the digitizer's puck or stylus. Some digitizers may have no switches at all; they are controlled by setup codes established by Generic CADD. This practice is typical of digitizers that emulate the Summagraphics mm1201.

You may want to check also the file HARDWARE.DOC that comes with Generic CADD 6.0; it may contain information about digitizers that supplements the *Installation Guide*. If your digitizer is not listed in the manual, be sure to check the HARDWARE.DOC file before you panic.

If you do not see your digitizer listed, you may want to refer to the digitizer manual to see what emulations it supports. Two common emulations are Summagraphics Summasketch (model mm1201) and GTCO type 5. Most digitizers can be supported by CADD by emulating one of these two standards. Table A.1 summarizes some of the settings normally required for the digitizer to work properly with CADD in an emulation mode.

Table A.1
Digitizer Settings Used in Emulation Mode

Function	mm1201	GTCO type 5
Output Mode	"RUN"/"STREAM"	"RUN"/"STREAM"
Output Format	5-byte high resolution packed binary	6-byte high resolution packed binary
Resolution	500 lines per inch	1000 lines per inch
Report Rate	"Auto" or Maximum	"Auto" or Maximum
Baud Rate	9600 baud	9600 baud
Data bits	8	8
Stop bits	1	1
Parity	ODD	NONE

Although the nomenclature differs—some manuals refer to run mode and others to stream mode—the meaning is the same: a continuous stream of data whenever the puck or stylus is within sensing distance of the tablet.

When you are sure that the digitizer is properly configured, hook it up to your computer (usually through a serial port) and plug in any power sources that are required (refer to your digitizer manual for details). To properly configure CADD, you need to know what port your digitizer is connected to (normally a *serial port* identified as either COM1 or COM2). Most digitizers come with a cable to connect them to the computer. If a cable is not supplied, refer to the *Generic CADD 6.0 Installation and*

Troubleshooting Guide for cabling information compatible with your digitizer. Most digitizers use a standard cable, diagrammed in the *Installation Guide* at the beginning of the digitizer section in Appendix B.

Change to your CADD directory (usually C:\CADD6) and run the CONFIG program. Press Enter to get to the main configuration menu. Select Option 2, `Select a Pointing Device`, from the main configuration menu. CONFIG displays a list of pointing devices. If your digitizer is not listed on the first page, press Enter to see the next page. CADD currently supports about 65 pointing devices. Type the number representing your digitizer and press Enter.

If the type of digitizer you choose comes in more than one size, CONFIG displays a list of the available sizes. Type the number that represents the size of your digitizer and press Enter. CONFIG next asks you to identify which I/O (input/output) port your digitizer is connected to. Choose **1** for COM1 or **2** for COM2 and press Enter.

After you choose the COM port, CADD displays the default settings. Verify that the settings match those for your digitizer. If any of the settings appear to be different, change either the digitizer or CONFIG so that the settings match. Press Esc to exit from the serial port setup menu and return to the main CONFIG menu. Press Esc a second time to exit from CONFIG; answer **Yes** when CONFIG asks whether you want to save your changes.

Using a Digitizer as a Pointing Device

A digitizer may be used as an expensive but simple pointing device. The major difference between the digitizer and mouse is that the digitizer reports the absolute position of the puck on the tablet surface. Other than this, the digitizer's puck operates in all respects just like a mouse. The first button is used to point to the screen, and the second button is used to pick from the video menu (or as Pen Up). Any additional buttons may be assigned to commands or macros, using the Macro Assign (MA) command.

By default, CADD maps the entire surface of the digitizer to your drawing screen. Thus, if you want to point to the far upper right corner of the screen, you need to move the puck to the same corner on the digitizer. If you are accustomed to using a mouse, this may be rather frustrating. *Stroking* the mouse, a common mouse technique, is done by moving the mouse, picking it up and setting it down near its original location, and moving it again. Many digitizer users try to stroke their digitizer rather than reach across the entire surface. As you might guess, stroking a digitizer is futile.

When using a digitizer as a pointing device, you may want to reduce the digitizer's *active area* so that a much smaller portion of the digitizer's surface is mapped to the screen. Often, an active area three to five inches square is sufficient, reducing the need to reach all over the digitizer to enter points on the drawing screen.

To set up your digitizer with a reduced active area, type **AA** at the Command prompt. Then move the puck to a comfortable location on the digitizer and click first button. This point becomes the lower left corner of the digitizer's new active area. Ignore the cursor's location on-screen when you do this. Now move the puck approximately four inches above and to the right of the first point and click. This point becomes the upper right corner of the new active area. Again, ignore the cursor's location on-screen when you do this.

You have now redefined the active area of the digitizer. While you move the puck on the digitizer surface, notice that the drawing cursor *freezes* when the puck is outside the area you have defined. This is normal. Notice also that now a much smaller portion of the digitizer can be used to control the on-screen cursor. Although the active area can be set very small, it is not recommended; finding a small active area and controlling the cursor in a small active area can be difficult.

NOTE The upper right corner of the active area *must be* above and to the right of the lower left corner. If you define an invalid area (upper right corner either below or to the left of the lower left corner), CADD simply ignores all input from the digitizer until you use the AA command to define a valid active area.

Tracing Drawings with a Digitizer

One of the primary uses for a digitizer is to trace existing drawings in order to turn them into CADD drawings. You must take two steps when tracing a drawing. First, set up CADD and the digitizer for tracing. Second, trace the drawing by using CADD commands combined with coordinates input from the digitizer.

To trace a drawing accurately you must turn on Trace Mode (TM). When Trace Mode is off, CADD maps the active area of the digitizer to the drawing screen at all times. If necessary, it *stretches* the coordinates so that the corners of the active area correspond to the corners of the drawing area on the screen. This makes it impossible to trace accurately.

When Trace Mode is on, CADD maps the surface of the digitizer to a corresponding portion of the drawing area. To trace accurately, the coordinates are not stretched to fit the screen but are multiplied by a Trace Scale. You can see this effect clearly if you turn on Trace Mode (TM) and then Zoom Out (ZO). Notice that the cursor points only to part of the drawing area. When Trace Mode is on, any point you enter on the surface of the digitizer creates a point at the corresponding location in your drawing. This happens even if you are zoomed in and the cursor is not visible on-screen.

Setting Up for Tracing

The first step in setting up for tracing is to attach the original drawing to the digitizer surface in such a way that it does not shift or move—usually, by using tape. Some digitizers come equipped with a clear overlay for just this purpose. The drawing can be placed under the overlay, which reduces the risk of it moving. You may want to use a little tape also, just to make sure that the original does not shift in the middle of a tracing session.

Do not be overly concerned about making sure that the original is square to the digitizer surface. Because getting the original

100 percent aligned with horizontal and vertical is almost impossible, CADD provides a way to correct for any rotation of the original relative to the digitizer. You do not need to worry if the original is at an angle. Because CADD can correct for any rotation error, you can even place the original sideways to the digitizer surface if it fits better that way.

To verify the tracing scale and to correct for the rotation of the original, CADD needs at least two known points. These points can be anywhere on your drawing, but for the most accurate calculations, they should be as far apart as possible. You need to know the exact locations for these points. A good choice is to use the end points of a line of known length and angle, such as a property line or the long side of a building.

After choosing two points, enter them into CADD through Manual Entry. If the points are on a line, use the Line command. (The construction points on the ends of the line can be used to align the CADD drawing with the original.) Use the Zoom All (ZA) command, if necessary, so that both points can be seen on-screen.

If you are tracing artwork or a logo that does not have scale, you can use the corners of the paper to do the Draw Align command. Simply draw a rectangle in CADD to the exact size of the paper. Then you can align corners of the rectangle with the corners of the paper taped to the digitizer.

If you have reduced the Active Area (AA) of the digitizer in order to use a smaller area of the digitizer for pointing to the screen, the Active Area needs to be reset. (Refer to the "Using a Digitizer As a Pointing Device" section, earlier in this appendix.) You should use the AA command to reset the active area so that you can point to the entire original you are tracing.

Next you need to use the Drawing Align (DA) command to align the original on the digitizer surface. Even if you think you know the scale of the original, it is a good idea to let CADD calculate the scale to be sure it agrees with your information. When you enter points on the digitizer, hold the puck at the same angle to minimize any errors caused by the crosshairs being slightly off center.

For the next exercise, tape a standard 8.5"×11" piece of paper to
your digitizer so that the long edge of the paper runs side to side.
To demonstrate how CADD corrects for rotation angles, center the
paper under the digitizer, but place it at a slight angle. In this
exercise, you draw a rectangle to represent the paper and then
you align the drawing with the paper taped to the digitizer.

Tracing a Rectangle

Prompt	Input	Description
Command	**MO**	Sets Manual Entry mode relative to the Origin
Command	**UN I**	Sets display units to Inches
Command	**RE**	Sets Rectangle command
Enter one corner...	Type **0,0** and press Enter	Sets first corner of the rectangle at 0,0
Enter opposite corner	Type **11,8.5** and press Enter	Draws an 11"×8.5" rectangle
Command	**ZA**	Makes sure that you can see the whole rectangle
Command	**DA**	Establishes Drawing Align command
Is this the correct tracing scale? (Y/N)	**N**	Gives you the ability to have CADD calculate the scale
Do you know the scale ? (Y/N)	**N**	Calculates the scale

If you answer yes at the last prompt, CADD asks you for the proper scale.

You now use the NP command to enter any point on the screen. Move the cursor close to the lower left corner of the rectangle and type **NP**. You must snap to the point; otherwise, the alignment is not accurate. Next, center the puck crosshairs on the lower left corner of the paper taped to your digitizer and click the first puck button. Take great care entering this point to be sure you are exactly on the corner of the paper.

To enter a different point on-screen, use the NP command again. First, move the cursor close to the upper right corner of the rectangle and type **NP**. You must snap to the point for the alignment to be accurate. Now, center the puck crosshairs on the corresponding point on your original and click. Take great care entering this point to be sure it is exact.

CADD then displays the calculated trace scale (which should be close to 1:1) and the rotation angle (which it automatically corrects for). CADD's calculated scale factor may be slightly larger or smaller than the exact scale of the original. This may indicate an error in your original; more often, it may indicate a slight error when digitizing the points on the drawing.

For best results, note the calculated scale and rotation and repeat the process. It is recommended that you repeat the drawing alignment at least three times to get a statistical average for the scale factor. Repeat the command one last time, but answer yes when CADD asks whether you know the scale, and then type in the average of the calculated scales. Then continue the process to allow CADD to calculate the rotation angle.

After you complete the Drawing Align (DA) command, CADD automatically does several things for you. It sets the Trace Scale (RZ), begins correcting the coordinates coming in from the digitizer for the rotation angle, and turns on Trace Mode. In this sense, the Drawing Align (DA) command is a one-step process that sets up CADD for tracing.

If you are digitizing a copy of an original, you may expect the scale to be slightly off. It is not uncommon for photocopies to be approxi- mately 5 percent smaller than the original.

The information CADD uses in its digitizer configuration assumes that the CADD database is set for inches. If your database unit is other than inches, you can expect that the scale factor enlarges or reduces accordingly. For example, if your database unit is set for Feet, the scale is off by a factor of .083333 (1/12th), whereas if the database unit is set for Centimeters, the scale is off by a factor of 2.54. The traced drawing is still the proper size. Alternatively, you can contact the Autodesk Retail technical support department for instructions on how to edit the digitizer configuration file so that the scale factor is expressed correctly.

Tracing a Drawing

Note that tracing should be used only for elements in the drawing that are not of known position and size. If you have a dimen- sioned floor plan, it is usually easier to re-create the drawing in CADD using manual entry. Manual entry is not only faster but also more accurate. Often, however, only scale drawings are available. These drawings—especially maps and charts—are not completely or accurately dimensioned.

Learning to trace a drawing accurately takes time. You do not actually trace the drawing by dragging the crosshairs over the items to be digitized. This technique makes it entirely too easy to slip and create errors. In addition, the output is extremely difficult to edit.

The process of tracing (or more properly, *digitizing*) a drawing consists of using CADD commands combined with points from the digitizer which are used to define primitives. This is similar to drawing on-screen, except that you have the original drawing for reference.

To trace a line, for example, issue the LI command from the keyboard or with a puck button. Carefully center the crosshairs of the cursor over one end of the line and click, then do the same for the other end of the line. Arcs usually are traced using a 3-point arc (A3); circles usually are traced using a 3-point circle (C3).

Tracing curves takes a little practice. In sections where the curve is slight, you can usually get away with placing only a few points. On the other hand, in tight corners you may have to place several points to define the location of the curve before the corner, the shape of the corner, and the location of the curve after the corner. You can think of this process as a little like driving. On the straighter sections you can go faster, but on the corners you must slow down. Similarly, when tracing, you put the points farther apart in the straighter sections and put the points closer together at a curve.

Human error in positioning the puck is the primary factor contributing to poor-quality traced drawings. Fortunately, CADD provides several tools that reduce human error. In addition, some tricks are available to help you create more accurate digitized drawings.

Digitizing Tips

To get the best results from your digitizer and Generic CADD, take the following tips:

- Use a puck, not a stylus. The tip of a stylus tends to obscure what you are trying to trace, and the angle of the stylus can sometimes make a difference in the coordinates transmitted.

- Hold the puck at the same angle; do not spin it around. The crosshairs are rarely at the exact center of the sensing loop. If the puck is always held at the same angle, any error is consistent and thus has minimum effect on your final product.

- Set up an appropriately sized grid. Most objects created by people are sized in regular increments. By using snap to grid, you can ensure that the coordinates you trace are nice, even numbers.

- Use Ortho. People like right angles, and using Ortho ensures that if you trace 90-degree lines, the angle comes out that way.

- When using Ortho, use Snap Object (SO) to start lines attached to other lines or objects.

- When using Ortho, use Cursor Free (CF) or Snap Object (SO) to end lines at other lines or objects (so that you do not have to go back later and trim them to meet).

- Draw anything of known location and size, using manual entry. These objects can then be used as starting points or ending points of other objects. Think of them as landmarks.

- Use symmetry to your advantage. If something is symmetrical, draw half and then use a mirror command to create the other half.

- If you have a multibutton puck, consider putting commands such as LI, C3, A3, BV, CV, OR, CF, SO, NP, ZW, and ZP on the buttons. These are likely to be your most frequently used commands.

- Use Zoom Window to see an area in greater detail. The digitizer is usually more accurate than the screen. Trace mode is not affected by zooming. Use Zoom Previous to return to the previous view.

- When you are Zoomed In (ZI or ZW) on a section of your tracing, you can use Pan (PA) to look at another portion without zooming out first. Just issue the PA command and point using the puck to identify the center of the area you want to see.

Creating Digitizer Menus

Digitizers are excellent menu devices. Because the puck always knows where it is relative to the tablet surface, you can declare portions of that surface to function as a menu. This is done by placing a menu template on the surface of the digitizer and then configuring CADD to associate various commands or macros with the portions of the digitizer that correspond to the template. To accomplish this, you need two parts—the template itself and a menu file for CADD that contains the commands associated with the template. You can make your own template and menu or purchase a ready-made template that comes with a menu file.

The primary advantages of ready-made templates are convenience and quality. Someone else has already drawn the template, figured out the arrangement, and created the menu file. Also, ready-made templates are usually laminated or printed on sturdy plastic. Commercial templates are usually well illustrated with fairly intuitive icons that enable even a beginner to operate CADD with relative ease. "Autodesk Retail Software News," sent free to all registered users of Generic CADD, often contains advertisements for inexpensive digitizer templates. The templates come with instructions and all you need to get the digitizer set up and running.

Ready-made templates, being made for a large group of users, have the disadvantage of probably not being as well-suited to your individual needs as templates you make yourself. In addition, ready-made templates emphasize basic CADD commands more than macros. Experienced users customarily reserve the tablet menu for macros, pointing out that they can type two-letter commands from the keyboard as quickly as they can point to a command on a ready-made digitizer template.

Digitizer menus are used to quickly place symbols (components) on a drawing. You can place a miniature version of each symbol on the template and assign to that location a macro which places the appropriate component. Because component names often get rather cryptic, this visual reference menu enables you to select symbols visually instead of by name (as you must when picking the component off the side menu in CADD).

Whether you are a novice or advanced user, consider purchasing a ready-made digitizer template. Because a great deal of thought has gone into most existing templates, they are a good source of ideas for icons and layout when designing a personal template customized to your own needs.

The process of creating a digitizer template and menu file is discussed in Chapter 18. Chapter 18 also includes information on how to set up and configure Generic CADD so that the program will use a digitizer menu.

Generic CADD Commands

T his appendix lists all the Generic CADD commands. The first part of the appendix categorizes the commands by menu; the second part shows you which commands are covered in each chapter (as well as in Appendix A). Use these lists as a quick reference when you want to find a command in Generic CADD or in this book.

Commands Categorized by Menu

The following sections list Generic CADD's commands as they appear in the program's menus. The full command name is provided, along with its keyboard shortcut, generally a two-letter command. In this appendix, an asterisk (*) indicates commands that do not appear in the Generic CADD menu. Two asterisks (**) indicate commands that can be issued only from a digitizer.

DRAW Menu Commands

Full Command Name	Keyboard Shortcut
Point	PO
Line	LI

Full Command Name	Keyboard Shortcut
Individual Line	L1
Rectangle	RE
Regular Polygon	RP
Two-point Circle	C2
Three-point Circle	C3
Two-point Arc	A2
Three-point Arc	A3
Four-point Arc*	A4
Ellipse	EP
Bézier Curve	BV
Individual Bézier	BW
Complex Curve	CV
Double Lines	L2
Double Lines Settings	DB
Multidraw	MU
Multidraw Settings	MS

SNAPS Menu Commands

Full Command Name	Keyboard Shortcut
Snap Closest Point	SC
Snap Nearest Point*	NP
Snap Object	SO
Snap Midpoint	SM
Snap Percentage	SR

Full Command Name	Keyboard Shortcut
Snap Intersection	SI
Snap Parallel	SL
Snap Perpendicular	SP
Snap Tangent	ST
Snap Arc Center	SN
Snap to Grid	SG
Component Snaps	GC
Snap to All Layer	SY
Tolerance	TO
Quick Pick	QP

TRIMS Menu Commands

Full Command Name	Keyboard Shortcut
Trim	RM
Extend	XT
Fillet	FI
Fillet Radius	FR
Autofillet	AF
Chamfer	CH
Chamfer Distance	CA
Intersection Trim	IT
Multi-Trim	MT
Multi-Extend	MX
Quick Pick	QP

CONSTRAINTS Menu Commands

Full Command Name	Keyboard Shortcut
Ortho Mode	OR
Ortho Angle	OA
Tracking	TK
Cursor Free	CF
Grid Display	GR
Snap to Grid	SG
Grid Size	GS
Grid Origin	GO
Cursor Move	CM
Show Distance	SD
Manual Entry Origin	MO
Manual Entry Relative	MR
Manual Entry Basepoint	MB
Set basepoint	BP

EDITS Menu Commands

Full Command Name	Keyboard Shortcut
Move Point	MP
Move	MV
Copy	CO
Mirror Copy	MI
Radial Copy	RC
Rotate	RO
Scale	SZ

Full Command Name	Keyboard Shortcut
Change	CG
Object Break	OB
Stretch	SS
Bézier Edit	BE
Erase	ER
Erase Last	EL
UnErase	UE
Undo	OO
Redo	UU

SHORTCUTS Menu Commands

Full Command Name	Keyboard Shortcut
Object Copy	OC
Window Copy	WC
Object Erase	OE
Window Erase	WE
Object Move	OM
Window Move	WM
Window Stretch	WS
Window Rotate	WR
Drawing Rotate	DR
Window Scale	WZ
Drawing Scale	DZ
Object Change	OG
Window Change	WG
Drawing Change	DG

TEXT Menu Commands

Full Command Name	Keyboard Shortcut
Text Line Placement	TL
Text Change	TG
Text Line Edit	TE
Text Character Placement	TP
Text Insert	TI
Text Delete	TD
Text Replace	TX
Text Settings	TS
Font Select	TSF or FS
Text Rotation	TR
Window Create Text Font	WT
Load ASCII	LA
Text Append	TA
Match Parameters	MH

COMPONENTS Menu Commands

Full Command Name	Keyboard Shortcut
Component Place	CP
Component Create	CC
Window Component Create	CW
Component Scale	CZ
Component Rotation	CR
Component Explode	CE
Component Replace	CN

Full Command Name	Keyboard Shortcut
Component Remove	CX
Component Image	CI
Component Snap	GC
Explode Layer	XY
Save Components	SAC
Load Components	LOC
Comp Dump	CD

ATTRIBUTES Menu Commands

Full Command Name	Keyboard Shortcut
Attribute Create	AC
Attribute Attach	AT
Attribute Detach	DE
Load Attribute	LOT
Save Attribute	SAT
Export Attribute	XA
Display Attributes	AD
Edit Attribute	AE
Attribute Settings	AS

ZOOMS Menu Commands

Full Command Name	Keyboard Shortcut
Zoom All	ZA
Zoom Window	ZW
Zoom In	ZI

Full Command Name	Keyboard Shortcut
Zoom Out	ZO
Pan	PA
Zoom Previous View	ZP
Redraw Screen	RD
Backward Redraw	BR
Window Redraw	WD
Zoom Limits	ZL
Zoom Value	ZM
Zoom View	ZV
Name View	NV
Delete View	NX
Multiview	VP
Multiview Settings	VS

DIMENSIONS Menu Commands

Full Command Name	Keyboard Shortcut
Linear Dimension	LX
Angular Dimension	AX
Dimension Mode	UM
Dimension Direction	UD
Proximity	PF
Radial Dimension	RX
Diameter Dimension	IX
Leader	LE
Shoulder Length	LL

Full Command Name	Keyboard Shortcut
Dimension Move	UV
Dimension Change	UG
Dimension Settings	US

LAYERS Menu Commands

Full Command Name	Keyboard Shortcut
All Layer	AL
Layer Current	YC
Layer Display	YD
Layer Name	YN
Layer Hide	YH
Layer Erase	YE
Layer Rotate	YR
Layer Scale	YZ
Layer Change	YG
Dimension Layer	UL
Layer Load	YL
Layer Save	YS

HATCH/FILL Menu Commands

Full Command Name	Keyboard Shortcut
Window Hatch	WH
Object Hatch	OH
Fitted Hatch	FH
Boundary Hatch	BH

Full Command Name	Keyboard Shortcut
Hatch Setting	HS
Window Fill	WF
Object Fill	OF
Fitted Fill	FF
Boundary Fill	BF
Fill Color	FC

DISPLAY Menu Commands

Full Command Name	Keyboard Shortcut
Line Color	LC
Line Type	LT
Line Width	LW
Line Scale	LZ
Color Settings	CS
Fast Redraw	FA
Coordinate Display	DC
Numeric Format Display	NF
Units	UN
Display Screen	DI
Reference Points	PR
Construction Points	PC
Standard Points	PS
Redraw	RD
Object Drag	OD
Rubberband	RB
Highlight	HI

MENUS Menu Commands

Full Command Name	Keyboard Shortcut
Load Menu	LV
New Menu	VXLV
Remove Menu	VX
Display Menu	VM
Load Digitizer Menu**	LD
Select Digitizer Menu**	SD
Drawing Align**	DA
Active Area**	AA
Trace Mode**	TM
Trace Scale**	RZ

UTILITIES Menu Commands

Full Command Name	Keyboard Shortcut
Explode	EX
Measure	ME
Measure Distance*	MD
Macro Assign	MA
Screen Flip	SF
Entity Filter	EF
Selection	SE
Limits	LS
Match Parameters	MH
Shell to Executable File	SH
View Fast Text	TV
Drawing Origin	DO

Full Command Name	Keyboard Shortcut
Save Batch	SB
Select Batch	BS
Object Info	OI
Bill of Material	BI

FILE Menu Commands

Full Command Name	Keyboard Shortcut
Load	LO
Save	SA
Select Save	SV
Drawing Rename	DN
Drawing Remove	DX
File Path	FP
Load ASCII	LA
Plot	DP11
Print	DP12
PostScript	DP13
Select Plot	PL
Pack Data	PD
Definition Unload	DU
Update Environment	EN
Quit	QU

CONVERT Menu Commands

Full Command Name	Keyboard Shortcut
DWGIN	LOA
DXFIN	LOX
DXFOUT	SAX
Exchange Setup	XG

(The Update Environment command also is available during the Quit command. After you issue the Quit command, you can press **E** when Generic CADD prompts you to press **C** for Continue or **Q** for Quit.)

Commands Listed by Chapter

The following sections show you which Generic CADD commands are introduced in each chapter of this text. Use this list as a quick guide when you want to learn about any Generic CADD command.

Chapter 1

Full Command Name	Keyboard Shortcut
Rectangle	RE
Zoom All	ZA
Undo	OO
Redo	UU
Erase Last	EL
UnErase	UE
Save	SA
Drawing Save	DS

Full Command Name	Keyboard Shortcut
Selection Save Drawing	SV
Layer Save	YS
Load	LO
Drawing Load	DL
Layer Load	YL
Remove Drawing	DX
Drawing Rename	DN
Quit	QU

Chapter 2

Full Command Name	Keyboard Shortcut
Limits	LS
Current Layer	YC
All Layers Edit	AL
Name Layer	YN
Line Color	LC
Line Width	LW
Line Type	LT
Line Scale	LZ
Color Settings	CS
Screen Display	DI
Units	UN
Numeric Display Format	NF
Coordinate Display	DC
Reference Points	PR
Construction Points	PC

Full Command Name	Keyboard Shortcut
Standard Points	PS
Object Drag	OD
Rubberbanding	RB
Highlight	HI
Display Menu	VM
Remove Menu	VX
Environment Save	EN

Chapter 3

Full Command Name	Keyboard Shortcut
Line	LI
Individual Line	L1
Two-point Arc	A2
Three-point Arc	A3
Four-point Arc	A4
Two-point Circle	C2
Three-point Circle	C3
Ellipse	EP
Bézier Curve	BV
Individual Bézier	BW
Complex Curve	CV
Regular Polygon	RP
Double Line Settings	DB
Double Lines	L2
Multidraw	MU
Multidraw Settings	MS

Chapter 4

Full Command Name	Keyboard Shortcut
Grid Size	GS
Grid On/Off	GR
Snap to Grid	SG
Snap to Nearest Point	NP
Snap to Closest Point	SC
Snap to Midpoint	SM
Object Move	OM
Cursor Free	CF
Snap Percentage	SR
Snap Tangent	ST
Snap to Arc Center	SN
Snap Perpendicular	SP
Snap Intersection	SI
Snap Parallel	SL
Snap Object	SO
Component Snaps	GC
Snap To Non-Editable Layers	SY
Redraw	RD
Backward Redraw	BR
Window Redraw	WD
Fast Redraw	FA
Quick Pick	QP

Chapter 5

Full Command Name	Keyboard Shortcut
Manual Entry Relative	MR
Display Coordinate	DC
Manual Entry Basepoint	MB
Ortho Mode	OR
Ortho Angle	OA
Tracking	TK
Cursor Movement	CM

Chapter 6

Full Command Name	Keyboard Shortcut
Font Select	FS
Text Settings	TS
Between Character Space	TSPC
Between Line Space	TSL
Proportional Spacing	TSPP
Slant	TSS
Aspect	TSA
Justification	TSJ
Text Rotation	TSR
Text Color	TSC
Text Line Placement	TL
Text Character Placement	TP
Text Edit	TE
Text View	TV

Full Command Name	Keyboard Shortcut
Text Change	TG
Text Insert	TI
Text Replace	TX
Text Delete	TD
Load ASCII	LA
Window Create Text	WT

Chapter 7

Full Command Name	Keyboard Shortcut
Zoom All	ZA
Zoom Limits	ZL
Zoom Window	ZW
Zoom Previous	ZP
Zoom In	ZI or ZU
Zoom Out	ZO or ZB
Zoom Value	ZM
Name View	NV
Zoom View	ZV
Delete View	NX
Pan	PA
Layer Hide	YH
Layer Display	YD
Grid Re-Origin	GO
Drawing Re-Origin	DO
Multiview	VP
Multiview Settings	VS

Chapter 8

Full Command Name	Keyboard Shortcut
Drawing Plot	DP

Chapter 9

Full Command Name	Keyboard Shortcut
Object Copy	OC
Object Break	OB
Trim	RM
Extend	XT
Tracking	TK
Intersection Trim	IT
Fillet	FI
Chamfer	CH
Fillet Radius	FR
Autofillet	AF
Chamfer Distances	CA
Object Erase	OE
Object Change	OG
Object Move	OM
Move Point	MP
Bézier Edit	BE
The Like Option	=
Match Parameters	MH

Chapter 10

Full Command Name	Keyboard Shortcut
Selection	SE
Entity Filter	EF
Screen Flip	SF
Stretch	SS
Scale	SZ
Move	MV
Copy	CO
Change	CG
Rotate	RO
Mirror Copy	MI
Multi-Trim	MT
Radial Copy	RC
Multi-Extend	MX
Explode	EX
Window Copy	WC
Window Scale	WZ
Window Erase	WE
Window Move	WM
Window Rotate	WR
Drawing Rotate	DR
Drawing Change	DG
Layer Scale	YZ
Layer Erase	YE
Layer Rotate	YR
Layer Change	YG

Chapter 11

Full Command Name	Keyboard Shortcut
Component Create	CC
Window Create	CW
Component Place	CP
Component Scale	CZ
Component Rotation	CR
Component Insertion Point	IP
Component Image	CI
Component Explode	CE
Component Snaps	GC
Component Save	SAC
Component Load	LOC
Component Dump	CD
Component Replace	CN
Component Remove	CX

Chapter 12

Full Command Name	Keyboard Shortcut
Hatch Settings	HS
Window Hatch	WH
Object Hatch	OH
Fitted Hatch	FH
Boundary Hatch	BH
Window Fill	WF
Object Fill	OF
Fitted Fill	FF
Boundary Fill	BF

Chapter 13

Full Command Name	Keyboard Shortcut
Linear Dimension	LX
Angular Dimension	AX
Radial Dimension	RX
Diameter Dimension	IX
Leader Lines	LE
Dimensioning Mode	UM
Dimension Direction	UD
Proximity	PF
Dimension Display	USD
Dimension Extension	USE
Arrows	USA
Dimension Font Select	USF
Dimension Text Size	USTZ
Dimension Text	UST
Dimension Layer	USL
Dimension Colors	USC

Chapter 14

Full Command Name	Keyboard Shortcut
Attribute Create	AC
Attribute Attach	AT
Attribute Save	SAT
Attribute Load	LOT
Attribute Detach	DE
Attribute Edit	AE

Full Command Name	Keyboard Shortcut
Attribute Settings	AS
Attribute Display	AD
Attribute Export	XA

Chapter 15

Full Command Name	Keyboard Shortcut
Bill of Material	BI

Chapter 16

Full Command Name	Keyboard Shortcut
Load AutoCAD Drawing	LOA
Load DXF File	LOX
Exchange Setup	XG

Chapter 17

Full Command Name	Keyboard Shortcut
Macro Assign	MA
Screen Flip	SF

Chapter 18

Full Command Name	Keyboard Shortcut
Load Menu	LV
New Menu	VXLV
Remove Menu	VX
Display Menu	VM

Chapter 19

Full Command Name	Keyboard Shortcut
Save Batch	SB
Select Save Batch	BS
Shell To Executable	SH

Chapter 20

Full Command Name	Keyboard Shortcut
Load Batch	LOB

Appendix A

Full Command Name	Keyboard Shortcut
Load Digitizer Menu	LD
Select Digitizer Menu	SD
Drawing Align	DA
Active Area	AA
Trace Mode	TM
Trace Scale	RZ

How Generic CADD and Generic 3D Work Together

Generic 3D is a three-dimensional wireframe modeling and shading program that works in conjunction with Generic CADD. Generic 3D is a stand-alone program, which is designed to provide Generic CADD users with three-dimensional drafting capabilities. The great majority of people who use Generic 3D also own and use Generic CADD.

Generic 3D is closely modeled after Generic CADD. The two programs' interfaces do differ, however, because of the distinction between two-dimensional drafting and three-dimensional drafting. Generic CADD, as you recall, uses a double-axis drawing cursor. Each line of the cursor represents one of the two drawing planes (the X and Y planes). A triple-axis drawing cursor is in Generic 3D. Each line of this cursor represents one of the three drawing planes (X, Y, and Z).

The current version of Generic 3D, version 1.1, was released in 1989. As this book was going to press, Autodesk Retail Products had announced plans to release a new version of Generic 3D by the fall of 1992. There have been two major updates of Generic CADD since the last release of Generic 3D; an overhaul is overdue.

Reviewers have given Generic 3D high marks for the way it helps the user navigate the cursor through what appears to be three dimensions when the cursor really exists on the flat video monitor. Autodesk Retail Products (the new name of Generic Software) achieved this solution by developing two tools—Tracking and Cursor Free—especially for Generic 3D. These two commands, now part of Generic CADD, were originally created for Generic 3D. Tracking and Cursor Free are more valuable in a three-dimensional environment than in the two-dimensional environment (which is saying a great deal, because they are both very helpful in 2D drafting). These two tools enable the user to easily identify locations in the drawing. Other useful navigational features include the ability to limit the 3D cursor to two dimensions (XY, YZ, or XZ) and to rotate the cursor to realign the three planes represented by the cursor. This last feature is especially helpful when the user imports two-dimensional Generic CADD drawings into Generic 3D because Generic CADD drawings have only the X and Y axes. If Generic CADD had a third dimension (Z), it would lie at a right angle to the X,Y plane. By rotating the 3D cursor, you can position Generic CADD's 2D objects so that they lie at any rotation and angle in space in a Generic 3D drawing.

Using Generic CADD Files with Generic 3D

Generic 3D can read drawings created by Generic CADD, for the purposes of turning them into three-dimensional models, but Generic 3D was released when Level 3 was the current version of Generic CADD. The Generic file format changed with the introduction of the next version (version 5.0), and the extension name given to Generic CADD drawing files changed with the release of Generic CADD 6.0. Generic 3D, therefore, cannot read the drawing files created by either version 5.0 or 6.0 of Generic CADD.

It is possible, however, to import Generic CADD drawing files into Generic 3D. To save a Generic CADD drawing file so that it may be used by Generic 3D, use the Level 3 drawing option of the

Save (SA,L) command. This saves the drawing using the old Generic CADD DWG format, which Generic 3D can read. Figure C.1 shows the floor plan, drawn earlier in this book, about to be saved in Level 3 format for use with Generic 3D.

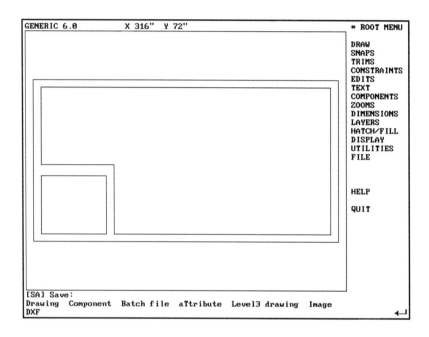

Figure C.1:

Using the Save as Level 3 Drawing option in Generic CADD 6.0.

You can save Generic 3D drawings in a flat, two-dimensional format that is directly readable by Generic CADD. No special conversion of the file is necessary because Generic CADD can read DWG files.

Using Generic 3D To Modify a 2D Drawing

When installed on the same computer, Generic CADD and Generic 3D exist independently of each other. By issuing the Shell To Executable (SH) command in Generic CADD, you can temporarily exit Generic CADD, use Generic 3D, and return to CADD. Generic 3D does not currently offer the Shell To Executable command.

You can use Generic 3D to create drawings from scratch, or you can start drawings in Generic CADD and turn them into three-dimensional drawings in Generic 3D. The 3D program's extrusion capabilities can give three-dimensional features to a two-dimensional drawing from Generic CADD.

The following paragraphs describe the steps involved in changing a two-dimensional drawing created in Generic CADD into a three-dimensional model in Generic 3D. Figure C.2 shows the house plan (from fig. C.1) after it has been imported into Generic 3D.

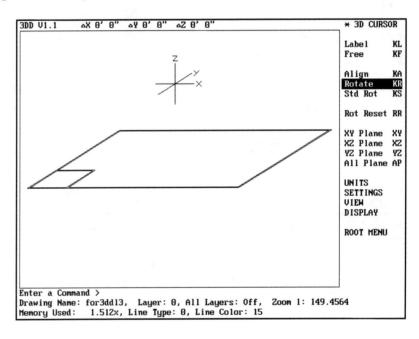

Figure C.2:

The house plan from fig. C.1 after being loaded into Generic 3D.

In this example, the Generic 3D cursor is rotated so that the Z axis points up and down. (By default, the cursor rotation is set so that the X and Y axes lie on the plane of the screen, whereas the Z axis projects outward.) By rotating the cursor in this manner before loading the drawing into Generic 3D, you can load the 2D drawing as shown in figure C.2. All two-dimensional drawings brought into Generic 3D line up with the cursor's X,Y heading.

Adding 3D Characteristics to 2D Objects

The two-dimensional floor plan is now a series of connected lines floating in space in Generic 3D. Before you can extrude the floor plan into a true three-dimensional object, you must convert the floor plan into polygons, a process that identifies a group of connecting lines as a single object. The next step is to extrude the polygons, as illustrated in figure C.3.

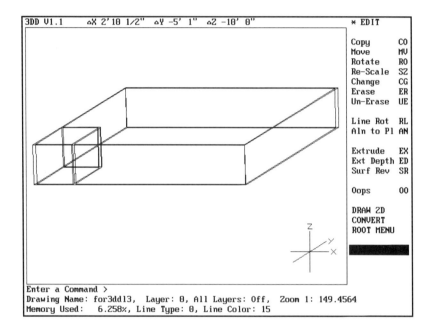

Figure C.3:

The floor plan after being extruded to create three-dimensional walls.

You also can create three-dimensional objects from a flat, two-dimensional object by spinning it about an axis. When you spin the object, Generic 3D considers each place where the object stops along the path of the spin to be a new piece of the object. This type of 3D object is known as a *surface of revolution*. Figure C.4 shows a flat, two-dimensional arc; figure C.5 shows the arc transformed into a hemisphere, after being treated by Generic 3D's surface-revolving feature.

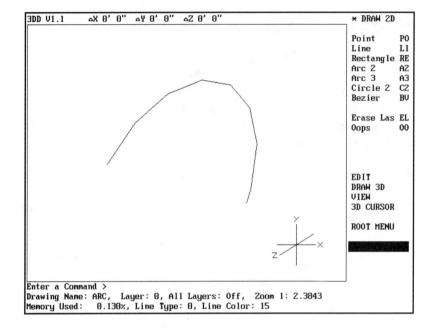

Figure C.4:

A flat arc created in Generic 3D.

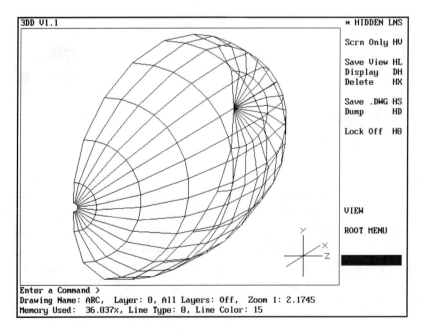

Figure C.5:

The arc after being spun about an axis to create a hemisphere.

Creating Views of 3D Objects

Generic 3D automates the process of creating perspective, isometric, and orthogonal views. From any view, you can remove the lines that would be hidden if the object were really a solid. Figure C.6 shows the hemisphere with the hidden lines removed.

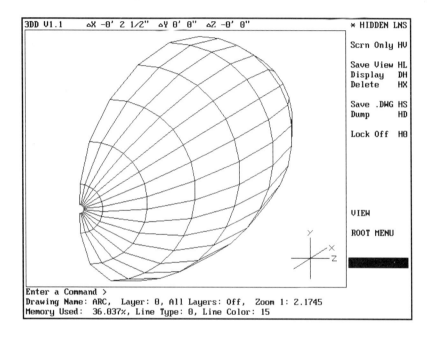

Figure C.6:

A view of the hemisphere with hidden lines removed.

Creating Renderings of 3D Objects

Generic 3D also can create renderings, making wireframe models appear as though they are solids. (Unlike AutoCAD or other more expensive three-dimensional CAD programs, however, Generic 3D does not recognize objects as solids with properties of density, weight, and so on.). Figure C.7 shows a wireframe box, drawn using the Generic 3D Box (BO) command. Figure C.8 shows a perspective view of the box, looking in from one end. Figure C.9 shows the same view, rendered to give the box the appearance of a solid. With the right video hardware, it is possible to create some very eye-appealing renderings with Generic 3D. The low-resolution black-and-white rendering in figure C.9 does not do justice to Generic 3D.

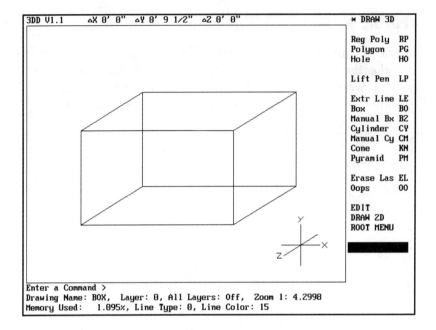

Figure C.7:

A simple box drawn in Generic 3D.

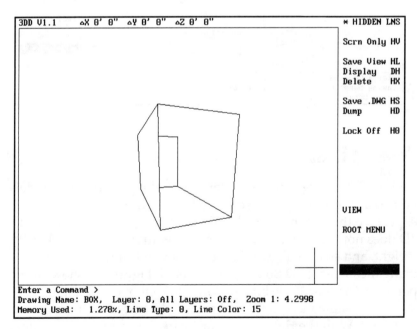

Figure C.8:

The box after being rotated to provide a perspective view.

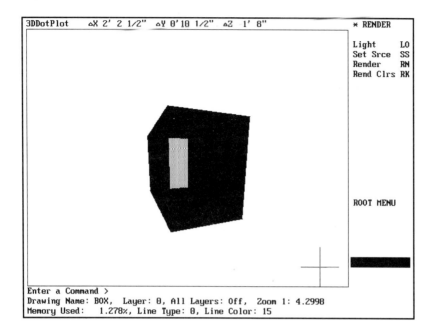

```
3DDotPlot    ΔX 2' 2 1/2"   ΔY 0' 10 1/2"   ΔZ  1' 8"         * RENDER

                                                             Light     LO
                                                             Set Srce  SS
                                                             Render    RN
                                                             Rend Clrs RK




                                                             ROOT MENU



Enter a Command >
Drawing Name: BOX,  Layer: 0, All Layers: Off,  Zoom 1: 4.2998
Memory Used:    1.278%, Line Type: 0, Line Color: 15
```

Figure C.9:

The box after rendering.

Other Generic 3D Features

Like Generic CADD, Generic 3D enables you to create and save components that you use often, to automate the repeated use of common objects. You also can purchase symbol libraries directly from Autodesk Retail Products.

Generic 3D cannot place text or dimensioning in a drawing. If you use Generic CADD, you can start a project in Generic CADD and then take the drawing into Generic 3D. There you can create the drawing's three-dimensional aspects, save special views of the drawing, and then take a final version of the file back into Generic CADD, where you can add text and dimensions.

Generic 3D is compatible with the same hardware as Generic CADD, which means that Generic 3D can be used on budget-level XT computers as well as on state-of-the-art 80486-based computers. Used together, the two programs are a cost-effective alternative to expensive three-dimensional CAD programs. Unlike Generic CADD, however, Generic 3D does not have virtual memory capabilities; thus, drawing size may be limited by the amount of available RAM (conventional or EMS) in your machine.

Generic 3D retails for $349 and is available from software retailers who sell Generic CADD. You can purchase Generic 3D directly by contacting the manufacturer at the following address:

Autodesk Retail Products
11911 North Creek Parkway South
Bothell, WA 98011
(800) 228-3601 (U.S. and Canada)
(206) 487-2233 elsewhere

Generic CADD, the DOS Path, and Local Area Networks

Until the release of version 6.0, Generic CADD was not recommended for use on a Local Area Network (LAN). The changes made to Generic CADD allow the program to operate successfully as part of a Local Area Network.

The key to successful use of Generic CADD 6.0 on a LAN is the capability of the program to be run from the DOS path. The path is a function of the operating system that allows programs to run in directories other than their own. Before the release of Generic CADD 6.0, for example, to start the program you had to go to the /CADD directory and type **CADD** at the DOS prompt of that directory. Typing CADD at any other directory caused DOS to reply FILE NOT FOUND. Now, if Generic CADD has been installed correctly, the program may be started from any directory recognized by the operating system.

The remainder of this appendix explains how to modify the installation of Generic CADD so that it can be used from any directory in a stand-alone computer and gives tips for installing Generic CADD on a LAN. Some of the specifics of LAN installation depend on the LAN software and the computer hardware in use. For additional information, consult the *Generic CADD 6.0 Installation and Troubleshooting Guide* as well as the documentation accompanying the LAN to be used.

Running Generic CADD from the DOS PATH

Preparing your computer to run Generic CADD from any directory is relatively easy, but the steps must be done in order.

1. Install Generic CADD as directed by the Installation program that accompanies Generic CADD. Make sure that Generic CADD runs correctly. If you have any problems running CADD, fix them before you attempt the following modifications.

2. Make a copy of your AUTOEXEC.BAT file, renaming it to something safe like AUTOEXEC.XXX. To do this using the DOS COPY command, type the following line at the DOS prompt of the root directory:

   ```
   COPY AUTOEXEC.BAT AUTOEXEC.XXX
   ```

3. Load AUTOEXEC.BAT into a word processor or text editor that can load and save files in ASCII format. EDIT, which ships with MS-DOS 5.0, is ideal, but most word processors and text editors can process ASCII text files.

4. If there is a PATH statement in the file, add the phrase

   ```
   C:\CADD6;
   ```

   to the line. There should be no spaces between characters. The assumption is made here that Generic CADD is located in the C:\CADD6 directory; modify the preceding line (and all the other similar lines in this set of instructions) if Generic

CADD 6.0 is in a different directory. If no PATH statement exists, add such a line. Type the phrase

```
PATH=C:\CADD6;
```

It is highly unlikely that no path statement exists in your AUTOEXEC.BAT. The lack of such a statement is a sure sign that the computer is not being used optimally. If this is true, do yourself a favor and buy a good introductory book on the use of DOS.

5. Create two new lines in AUTOEXEC.BAT by typing the following:

```
SET GCADD_FIL=C:\CADD6
SET GCADD_OVR=C:\CADD6
```

6. Save AUTOEXEC.BAT as an ASCII file and exit the text editor.

7. Reboot the computer. Either press Ctrl-Alt-Del simultaneously or press the computer's reset button. Never reboot a computer by shutting it off and turning it back on.

8. After the reboot is finished, test your work. Change to any directory on the hard drive except \CADD6 and type **CADD** at the DOS prompt. Generic CADD should load as usual. If it does not, review your work. Check your typing, and be sure that AUTOEXEC.BAT was saved as an ASCII file. If you have problems and want to abandon the modified version of AUTOEXEC.BAT, erase it and rename your original file to restore it as AUTOEXEC.BAT.

Running Generic CADD on a Local Area Network

The steps to preparing a Local Area Network to run Generic CADD are similar to preparing a single computer to run Generic CADD from any directory. The installation steps, which are detailed well in the *Generic CADD 6.0 Installation and Troubleshooting Guide*, are not repeated here. In brief, though, the steps are as follows:

1. Install Generic CADD on the shared device (the computer that controls the network).

2. Create a unique subdirectory for each person who will be using Generic CADD on local subdirectories. This is important, and is explained below. (*Local* refers to each computer attached to the network.)

3. Copy some files from the installation of CADD on the shared device to each of the unique subdirectories on the local devices. Be sure to include GCADD.OVR in this step—the manual mentions it, but the instructions could be interpreted as suggesting that GCADD.OVR is optional.

4. Edit each workstation's AUTOEXEC.BAT file, adding the same information suggested earlier for a single computer. Be sure to use the correct subdirectory name.

5. Reboot each local station.

6. From each local station, run CONFIG from the user's unique subdirectory. Modify the hardware listing for CONFIG to match the local settings. Be sure to modify the virtual memory and shell paths so that they access the local workstation's unique subdirectory for CADD.

7. Run CADD from each workstation. Modify the File Path (FP) settings so that the unique subdirectory is used to save drawing files, and the shared directory is referenced for fonts, components, macros, and so on.

8. If possible on your LAN, set the CADD program files to Read-Only status.

Caveat User

A few words of advice are in order. Local Area Networks are, to put it delicately, touchy. A LAN system must constantly juggle a myriad of operations, most of which were not designed to exist in a networked environment. Any modification to an existing LAN should be performed by the designated LAN administrator only.

Although it is possible to successfully run Generic CADD from a network, Generic CADD was not designed to be a "network-aware" piece of software. When CADD loads a drawing file, the entire file is loaded into RAM (and, if the file is large enough, hangs over into EMS, XMS, and virtual memory). To a LAN, this means that there is no file locking in Generic CADD. If two users load the same drawing file from the shared drive, both are able to make changes to the file. Both can save the file to the shared drive, but, as LAN technicians like to say, "the one who saves last wins." When the second user saves the drawing file, the save overwrites the work of the first user. To prevent this, users should be encouraged (or required) to use a local drive to save files.

It was mentioned earlier that the unique subdirectory created for each CADD user must be a local subdirectory. Placing these subdirectories on the shared drive degrades the performance of both Generic CADD and the entire network. If you are planning to create the unique subdirectory on the shared drive because your potential CADD users have workstations without floppy disk drives or computers without a local hard drive, you should not install Generic CADD on the network. Either upgrade your workstations or limit CADD to users who can be given a proper installation.

When adjusting the CONFIG for each workstation, the hardware assignments must be unique to each workstation. If users try to access the same virtual memory or shell paths at the same time, they are likely to lose data.

 Autodesk has a separate staff devoted to locating unauthorized installations of their products. If you intend to install Generic CADD on a Local Area Network to avoid the cost of buying a copy of the product for every user, you are in violation of federal law as well as your purchase agreement.

Index

719

Add to Your New Riders Library Today
with the Best Books for the Best Software

Yes, please send me the productivity-boosting material I have checked below. Make check payable to New Riders Publishing.

❏ **Check enclosed.**

Charge to my credit card:

❏ **VISA**   ❏ **MasterCard**

Card # _____

Expiration date: _____

Signature: _____

Name: _____

Company: _____

Address: _____

City: _____

State: _____ ZIP: _____

Phone: _____

The easiest way to order is to pick up the phone and call 1-800-541-6789 between 9:00 a.m. and 5:00 p.m., EST. Please have your credit card available, and your order can be placed in a snap!

Quantity	Description of Item	Unit Cost	Total Cost
	Inside CorelDRAW!, 2nd Edition	$29.95	
	AutoCAD 3D Design & Presentation*	$29.95	
	Maximizing Windows 3 (Book-and-Disk set)	$39.95	
	Inside AutoCAD, Special Edition (for Releases 10 and 11)*	$34.95	
	Maximizing AutoCAD: Volume I (Book-and-Disk set) Customizing AutoCAD with Macros and Menus	$34.95	
	AutoCAD for Beginners	$19.95	
	Inside Autodesk Animator*	$29.95	
	Maximizing AutoCAD: Volume II (Book-and-Disk set) Inside AutoLISP	$34.95	
	Inside AutoSketch, 2nd Edition*	$24.95	
	AutoCAD Reference Guide, 2nd Edition	$14.95	
	AutoCAD Reference Guide on Disk, 2nd Edition	$14.95	
	Inside CompuServe (Book-and-Disk set)	$29.95	
	Managing and Networking AutoCAD*	$29.95	
	Inside AutoCAD, Release 11, Metric Ed. (Book-and-Disk set)	$34.95	
	Maximizing MS-DOS 5 (Book-and-Disk set)	$34.95	
	Inside Generic CADD*	$29.95	
	Inside Windows	$29.95	
	AutoCAD Bible	$39.95	
	*Companion Disk available for these books	$14.95 ea.	

❏ **3½″ disk**

❏ **5¼″ disk**

Shipping and Handling: See information below.	
TOTAL	

Shipping and Handling: $4.00 for the first book and $1.75 for each additional book. Floppy disk: add $1.75 for shipping and handling. If you need to have it NOW, we can ship product to you in 24 to 48 hours for an additional charge, and you will receive your item overnight or in two days. Add $20.00 per book and $8.00 for up to three disks overseas. Prices subject to change. Call for availability and pricing information on latest editions.

New Riders Publishing • 11711 N. College Avenue • P.O. Box 90 • Carmel, Indiana 46032
1-800-541-6789   **1-800-448-3804**
Orders/Customer Service   **FAX**

To order: Fill in the reverse side, fold, and mail

NO POSTAGE
NECESSARY IF
MAILED IN THE
UNITED STATES